Menu Magic

BOOKS BY ARLYN HACKETT

Health Smart Gourmet Cooking: American Regional Cuisine (1991)
Health Smart Gourmet Cooking (1992)
The Slim Chef (1987)
Can You Trust a Slim Santa Claus? (1986)

CONTRIBUTOR TO

The L.A. Diet

ARLYN HACKETT'S MENU MAGIC

Health-Wise Cuisine

LOW-FAT, LOW-CHOLESTEROL, LOW-SALT, LOW-SUGAR

HASTINGS HOUSE
Book Publishers
Mamaroneck, NY

Library of Congress Catalog Card Number 93-078852

ISBN 0-8038-9355-8

Printed in the United States of America

2   4   6   8   10   9   7   5   3   1

This book is dedicated to Bill and Hillary Clinton,
who enhanced the health of America
by introducing low-fat cooking to the White House kitchen.

Acknowledgments

This book would not have been possible without the trust, encouragement and patience of some wonderful friends and colleagues. I owe a giant thank-you to Hy Steirman, Gary Goldberg, Brett Kelly, Trent Smith, David Dartt, Garrett Dettling, Carol Ohmart, Fantasia Archbach, Renee Roff, and especially Rick Sulisky.

Contents

MENUS MAINLY VEGETARIAN

Pyramid Magic

I LOVE eating and cooking and just about everything concerning food except washing dishes. I also love good health. For me, the joys of eating, cooking and health are inseparable, but I know that not everyone feels the same way. Some people love to eat, but hate to cook. Others doubt that great-tasting dishes and healthy food can be the same thing. And, alas, there are even people who wish they could get through life without eating. This book is for people who have enthusiasm for good food and good health. For any skeptics, I hope that *Menu Magic* will bring a discovery that healthy food can taste delicious and cooking can be more fun than ever dreamed.

Menu Magic, as the name implies, is a collection of imaginative, low-fat menus for both entertaining and family dining. The "magic" of these menus is that every recipe is limited in fat, meaning that you can mix and match recipes between menus without worrying about having too much fat!

PYRAMID MAGIC

Are you tired of hearing about what you shouldn't eat? Are you beginning to wonder if there's anything left that's safe and delicious? Do you feel as if you need a Ph.D. in nutrition to know what to fix for dinner? My father used to say, "Too much of anything is bad, especially religion and politics." I suspect that if he were here today, he might add "nutrition" to the list. So much has been made of what not to eat, some people feel like saying, "What the hell, there's nothing left to eat and we're all gonna die sooner or later. Pass the French fries!" So much commotion about nutrition seems to be driving some eaters to care less about their diets.

My father's homespun philosophy is, however, what the crux of good nutrition is all about. "Too much of anything is bad," describes how we come to have dietary health problems. Too much fat, meat, salt, oil, fried food, sugar, refined products or celery can cause health problems. Did I really say celery? Yes! If you eat too much celery, it can kill you. If all you ate was celery, you would eventually die because you would be missing out on vital nutrients that are only contained in other foods. There is no one perfect food. To be healthy, we need to eat a balance of foods. Foods need to be eaten in proportion to each other. There are no such things as bad foods; there are bad proportions. The issue is having too much of some things and not enough of others. In nutrition, as in a lot of other things in life, balance is what is important.

What is a balanced diet? The U.S. Department of Agriculture and Department of Health and Human Services have begun an educational campaign to help Americans gain a better understanding of a balanced diet. The primary educational tool is the Food Guide Pyramid. The Pyramid visually portrays a balanced diet by depicting the varying food groups in proportion to one another. The foundation of the Pyramid is the grain group, composed of bread, cereal, pasta, rice and other grains. The recommendation is for you to have 6 to 11 servings from this group each day. With the grain category having the most servings, the Pyramid shows that the bulk of the diet should be complex carbohydrates. The second tier of the Pyramid is devoted to vegetables and fruits. Here the recommendation is for 3 to 5 servings of vegetables and 2 to 4 servings of fruit. As the Pyramid rises, the tiers narrow. The third tier is devoted to animal products and high-protein items. In the dairy section, including milk, cheese and yogurt, the suggestion is for 2 to 3 servings. The other half of the tier includes meats, poultry, fish, seafood, legumes (beans), tofu, eggs and nuts and again suggests 2 to 3 servings. At the very top of the Pyramid, the narrowest area is given to fats, oils and sweets, items that are to be used only sparingly.

Health campaigns usually are designed for the widest appeal and sometimes leave gaps that need clarification. For several years, we have heard the American Heart Association's recommendation that your fat intake should not exceed 30% of the total calories consumed and saturated fat should be no more than 10% of caloric intake. What most people have missed is that this is a guide only for healthy people. Persons with heart disease or who are overweight are encouraged to follow stricter standards. We may be inclined to think that we needn't worry about the standard for "sick persons," but, remember, heart disease and being overweight affect more than half of the population of America! The Food Guide Pyramid also needs some clarification. In the vegetable and fruit categories, you can choose just about any vegetables and fruits you want and provided each serving is a different product, you will have a reasonably healthy diet. Most vegetables and fruits do not have dramatic differences in fat content. However, in the dairy and meat categories, your options present enormous differences in fat content. Low-fat products are routinely a superior choice. High-fat dairy and meat products should be reserved for special occasions. For *Menu Magic,* I've slightly modified the Food Guide Pyramid to reflect food choices with optimal opportunities for good health.

THE *MENU MAGIC* FOOD PYRAMID

The *Menu Magic* Food Pyramid is about what you can eat. The purpose of the Pyramid is to advocate eating categories of foods in proportion to one another. Grains are the foundation of the diet, followed by vegetables and fruits. Proportionately, dairy and high-protein products are eaten in smaller amounts. The *Menu Magic* Food Pyramid has been adjusted to focus primarily on foods that you can eat unconditionally. Dairy and high-protein products have been restricted to those options that are low in fat.

GRAINS (6 TO 11 SERVINGS)

Grains are the foundation of our diet. The grain category comprises all products made with flour, including breads and pastas. It also includes cereals, tortillas, corn, rice, barley, bulgur and other grains. This is the group of foods we should use to fill up on. Active, athletic persons will definitely want a full regimen of 10 to 11 servings. Persons wanting to lose weight may elect to reduce grains to as few as 6 servings, while increasing their intake of vegetables. Whole grain products are best, although a few servings from refined products are definitely acceptable.

A serving of grain includes:

1 slice (1 ounce) bread	1/2 cup cooked cereal
1/2 muffin or bagel	1/2 cup dry, ready-to-eat cereal
1/2 cup cooked rice or other grain	1 six-inch tortilla
	4 rye crisps or other low-fat cracker
1/2 cup cooked pasta (1 ounce dry pasta)	1 small ear corn on the cob

**U.S. DEPARTMENT OF AGRICULTURE AND
U.S. DEPARTMENT OF HEALTH AND HUMAN SERVICES
RECOMMENDED DAILY SERVINGS FOR AGES 6 AND UP**

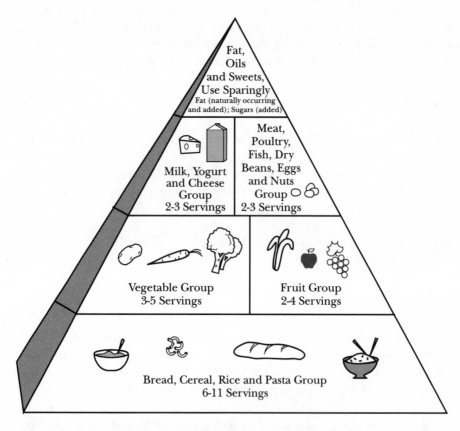

Food Guide Pyramid: *A Guide to Daily Food Choices*

MODIFIED PYRAMID FOOD PLAN
SUGGESTED BY CHEF ARLYN HACKETT

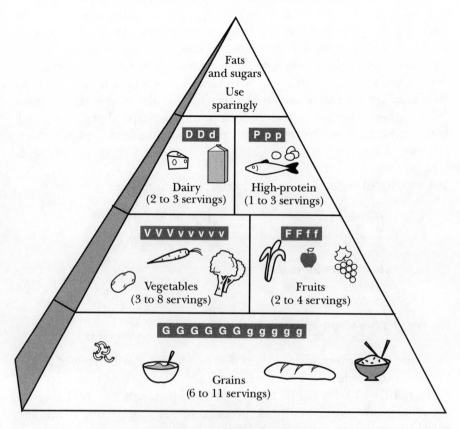

The *Menu Magic* Food Pyramid

Symbols in the shaded bars (capital letters) represent the minimum number of servings for each category. Lower-case symbols represent additional servings that may help you meet your calorie requirements and fulfill specific nutrient needs. What constitutes a serving is listed in the commentary that follows. In the dairy and high-protein categories, only those choices that are low in fat are noted.

VEGETABLES (3 TO 8 SERVINGS)

Vegetables are a vitamin and mineral bonanza. Eat a variety of vegetables, including fresh, raw and cooked vegetables. Consume no less than 3 servings per day, but 5 servings is a wiser choice. An ideal vegetable intake includes at least 2 servings of green vegetables and at least 1 serving of red, yellow or orange vegetables. It's hard to eat too many vegetables. Persons wanting to lose weight often find it beneficial to increase their vegetable intake to 8 servings per day, and in turn refrain from high-fat dairy or meat products and perhaps slightly reduced grain consumption. Persons who cannot or choose not to eat dairy products should definitely consider eating at least 5 servings of vegetables per day.

A serving of vegetables can be generally defined as:

½ cup cooked vegetables
1 to 2 cups raw leafy vegetables
½ cup raw (nonleafy) chopped vegetables
1 small baked potato
¾ cup vegetable juice

FRUITS (2 TO 4 SERVINGS)

Fruits are the ready-made sweets of the food world. Eat a variety of fruits. Ideally, you should use 2 to 4 servings, although persons who are not overweight and who fulfill their other food groups can feel free to consume more fruit. Fruit, like vegetables, is hugely important for supplying vitamins, minerals and fiber.

A serving of fruit includes:

½ papaya, mango or grapefruit
1 medium apple, pear, orange, banana, peach or cherimoya
2 plums or figs
3 apricots
½ cup berries or cherries
½ cup grapes
½ cup cubed fresh fruit, including melon and pineapple
½ cup cooked or canned fruit
1 large kiwi, star fruit or guava
¼ cup dried fruit
½ cup fruit juice

DAIRY (2 TO 3 SERVINGS)

A large part of the world's population do not drink milk as adults and do not seem to suffer from calcium deficiencies. Why then is it a problem for some people? It appears that healthy populations that do not drink milk eat a large amount of calcium-rich vegetables and usually eat a limited amount of animal proteins. If you don't drink milk, vegetable consumption is very important, particularly green vegetables. Of course, eating plenty of vegetables is important even if you do drink milk! Current recommendations for adults are for 2 servings of dairy per day. Nonfat dairy products are a far superior choice. Pregnant women, children and youth should consider 3 daily servings. Nonfat milk products are the order of the day. Whole milk, and even low-fat milk products, should be used sparingly.

For *Menu Magic,* a serving of dairy is defined as:

1 cup nonfat milk	*2 ounces nonfat firm cheese*
⅓ cup nonfat dry milk powder	*1½ ounces low-fat firm cheese*
½ cup nonfat yogurt, nonfat cottage cheese, nonfat ricotta cheese or evaporated milk	*1 ounce traditional firm cheese (occasional use)*

HIGH-PROTEIN PRODUCTS (1 TO 3 SERVINGS)

Most Americans worry too much about protein. Protein deficiency is extremely rare in the United States. Meats, including beef, lamb, pork, poultry, fish and seafood represent high concentrations of protein. Vegetables, grains, legumes and dairy products also contain protein, but in lower amounts. However, when you begin to add up all of the protein you might eat in a given day, it's amazing how much vegetable and dairy sources provide.

Some people are concerned that vegetable proteins are incomplete. However, if you eat both grains and legumes, or if you include dairy products or a small amount of animal protein, the vegetable proteins become complete. When I began the computer analysis of the menus in this book, I discovered that if one eats 2 servings of dairy, 5 servings of vegetables, and 8 to 10 servings of grains, it is likely that 1 serving of a high-protein product will be adequate, even if it comes from a vegetarian source. Several of my dietitian friends strongly recommend limiting the consumption of animal proteins to 1 serving a day. Additional protein should come from beans, tofu or egg whites. Another suggestion is to focus more on fish and seafood. Red meats should be viewed as a treasure that we have every now and then. Of course, protein isn't the only important nutrient that animal products provide. Animal products are a vital source of many minerals, including iron. If one doesn't eat any kind of meat, it becomes doubly important to consume a wide variety of vitamin-rich vegetables.

For *Menu Magic,* a serving of a high-protein product is defined as:

1 cup cooked dry beans or lentils

2½ to 3½ ounces cooked fish (any species)

2½ to 3½ ounces cooked seafood (any species)

2½ to 3½ ounces cooked turkey breast without skin

2½ to 3½ ounces cooked chicken breast without skin

2½ to 3½ ounces cooked top round or flank steak of beef, bison or venison

2½ to 3½ ounces cooked pork tenderloin

2½ to 3½ ounces cooked leg of lamb

3 egg whites

½ cup egg substitute

3 ounces tofu

The animal products listed above are noteworthy because they are low in fat, particularly saturated fat. Before using other animal products, consider their fat content (especially saturated fat). Nuts offer substantial protein, but also contain a high amount of fat. On the other hand, most nuts, except for coconut, are low in saturated fat. I take the position that nuts in small quantities are fine, but to rely on them as a source of protein is questionable.

EXTRAS (USE SPARINGLY)

"Extras" are products with a high concentration of fat and/or refined sugar that contribute very little nutritionally, except calories. Fried chips, candies, chocolate, pastries, sodas and many dessert items are likely to fall in the category of "extras." I think of "extras" to be enjoyed every now and then, but certainly not as a daily routine. In this book, you will find very few recipes that are noted with an "extra." Because of sugar content, I have given that designation to a few dessert and beverage recipes. However, even these recipes contribute nutrient values beyond just calories. Those watching their intake of refined sugars can easily substitute other desserts found in this book.

"Extras" are not always easy to define. What about foods that offer some nutrient value, in addition to calories, but have a high amount of added fat or sugar? How much oil can be used in preparing dishes before we consider it an "extra"? For a person who requires 2,400 calories per day (a fairly typical amount), 1 tablespoon of oil represents 120 calories, or 5% of the day's calories. A serving of 20 French fries contains a tablespoon of oil. Nearly half of the calories in a French fry comes from oil. Should French fries be labeled a vegetable, an "extra" or both? If those 20 French fries were the only food you had in a day with added oil, you could easily have a total diet that is low in fat. But what about the oil that's in the morning bran muffin? The fat in the lunch salad dressing? The fat in the margarine spread that was used to sauté the vegetables? And the oil used in the marinade for the broiled fish that you thought would be fat free? The amount of fat in products considered singularly does not seem like very much, but in a total day, the added fats can add up very fast. Compare this to a second diner who eats all day only products that are made without any refined oil or fat. This conscientious diner doesn't even eat any meat, cheese or eggs. But at the end of the day, this diner indulges in a chocolate blackout cake. The cake is clearly an "extra" and contributes a lot of fat. However, in terms of the whole day, this diner ends up consuming less fat. Does this mean any added oil should be considered an "extra"?

MENU MAGIC AND PLANNING A HEALTHY DIET

In creating this book, I wanted you to have recipes and menus that would make it easy for you to maintain a daily diet of 20% fat or less. To do this, I found that if one does not use more than 1 tablespoon of refined oil per day, a balanced diet of 20% fat could be easily achieved. Of course, this means that the majority of recipes don't contain oil. Those that do rarely exceed ¾ teaspoon per serving. You will not find any recipes that have an "extra" because of added fat. Since all of the recipes are low in fat, you can mix and match recipes between menus without concern for excessive fat. Almost any logical combination of recipes will result in a complete menu that is well under 30% fat and will likely be less than 20%. More than two-thirds of the recipes presented in this book are less than 15% fat.

If you want a higher-fat diet, remember to keep the focus on monoun-saturated fats, avoiding saturated fats and hydrogenated fats. Animal products are the most common source of saturated fat. Butter substitutes and other "solid fats" are a good example of a hydrogenated fat. Oils such as olive, canola, almond and hazelnut are the richest source of monounsaturated fats. In my profession as a light-style chef, I'm far more accustomed to taking fat out of cooking than putting it in. However, if I were to add fat to a diet, I would suggest including olives, avocado and dry roasted nuts. These are high-fat products (with most of the fat being monounsaturated), but they also contain many other nutrients.

The menus and recipes in this book are designed for flexibility. I am not trying to advocate a specific diet. Persons who want high-fat foods and lots of animal products can use this book. However, I know it is not always easy for people to find recipes that will allow them to have animal products and stay below 100 milligrams of cholesterol per day, or under 2,000 milligrams of sodium or less than 20% of calories from fat. This cookbook will enable you to do that.

Included with each menu and recipe is the following nutrient infor-mation:

- Number of calories per serving
- Percentage of total calories attributed to fat, carbohydrates, protein and alcohol
- Number of grams of carbohydrates, protein and fiber
- Number of milligrams of sodium
- Number of milligrams of cholesterol
- Number of grams of total fat
- Number of grams of saturated fat and monounsaturated fat
- Pyramid equivalencies

The nutrient information is provided to help you plan and maintain a healthy diet. Remember, the basic goal is to eat a high percentage of unrefined carbohydrates and a low percentage of fat every day. The Pyramid equivalencies, listed at the end of each recipe and menu, are there to help you plan balanced dining. The Pyramid equivalencies show how that dish fulfills the servings for each category of the Pyramid. Most dishes represent more than just one category. Because all of the dishes in *Menu Magic* are prepared with very little or no refined fats, you can freely substitute dishes from other menus to fulfill the serving guidelines. That's the magic of low-fat cookery.

Are you ready to change? Changing what we eat is frequently tied to making other changes as well. The most important change usually has to do with how much time you will make for food. Are you willing to spend more time preparing food instead of relying on packaged foods or fast foods? Are you willing to take the time to plan ahead, to think about what you are going to have for dinner so that you can make a more balanced decision about what to eat for lunch? Are you going to take time for healthy, in-between-meal snacks? And are you ready to eat more food? Yes, eat more food! A more balanced diet often means eating fewer fatty items, but eating more vegetables and grain products. This usually results in actually eating a greater volume of food but consuming fewer calories. Finally, are you ready to make time for an exercise program? Diet and exercise are inseparable. We need a wide variety of nutrients that comes from a robust diet and in turn we need regular physical activity to efficiently burn the calories in the food.

The last thing I ever want to do is have a miserable time trying to be healthy. Good health is a process. The goal of *Menu Magic* is to offer you menus and recipes that are enjoyable to prepare, a delight to eat and satisfying to your health and well-being. Are you ready to have a good time?

Measurement Conversions

Measurements are approximate. They have been rounded off to the nearest convenient measure.

Temperature

Throughout this book, Fahrenheit will be the standard temperature.

FAHRENHEIT	CENTIGRADE	FAHRENHEIT	CENTIGRADE	FAHRENHEIT	CENTIGRADE
212	= 100	325	= 163	450	= 232
225	= 107	350	= 177	475	= 246
250	= 121	375	= 191	500	= 260
275	= 135	400	= 204		
300	= 149	425	= 218		

Volume

1 teaspoon = 5 milliliters
1 tablespoon = 3 teaspoons or ½ ounce = 15 milliliters
1 cup = 16 tablespoons or 8 ounces = 236 milliliters/about ¼ liter
1 quart = 4 cups = 1 scant liter

Weight

1 ounce = 28.4 grams
1 pound = 16 ounces= 454 grams
2.2 pounds = 1,000 grams = 35 ounces = 1 kilogram

Length

1 inch = 2½ centimeters
1 foot = 12 inches = 30 centimeters

Selected Measures

Some ingredients weigh more than others: please use correct measure for each one.

FLOUR, CORNSTARCH, BAKING POWDER, BAKING SODA, GROUND SPICES
1 teaspoon = 3 grams
1 tablespoon = 9 grams
1 cup = 120 grams

BROWN SUGAR, TIGHTLY PACKED
1 tablespoon = 14 grams
1 cup = 224 grams

FRESH MINCED HERBS
1 teaspoon = 4 grams
1 tablespoon = 12 grams
1 cup = 192 grams

DRY MILK POWDER
1 tablespoon = 4 grams
1 cup = 64 grams

CHOPPED LETTUCE
1 cup = 55 grams

DICED ONION
1 cup = 160 grams

UNCOOKED BROWN RICE
1 cup = 160 grams

DRY BEANS
1 cup = 200 grams

PLAIN NONFAT YOGURT
1 cup = 228 grams

Menu Magic Menus

1 FOUR SEASONS CHICKEN DINNER, 3

Chilled Carrot Soup
Jeweled Apricot Chicken
Millet-Almond Pilaf
Mixed Summer Squash with Lemon Herbs
Chestnut Cake with Honey Glazed Chestnuts and Raspberry Coulis
Herbal-Flavored Mineral Water

2 TROPICAL HEAT WAVE, 13

Chayote Salad with Mustard Dressing
Pineapple Rice or Tropical Rice Salad
West Indian Plantain
Okra in Spicy Tomato Sauce
Grilled Jerk Chicken
Desert Island Punch
Baked Tropical Fruit Pudding with Pineapple Creme

Additional Recipe: Jerk Marinade

3 CHERRIES JUBILATION, 25

Summer Menu
Cherries Jubilation Salad with Cherry Barbecued Chicken
Garden Bread with Apple Cheese
Iced Mocha Royale

Winter Menu
Cherries Jubilation Salad
Cherry Barbecued Chicken
Red Rice
Garden Bread with Apple Cheese
Hot Mocha Royale

Additional Recipes: Cherry Salad Dressing, Cherry Barbecue Sauce, Red Beans and Red Rice

Autumn Vegetable Medley
Nisei Yams and Persimmons
Old Town Pumpkin Flan

Additional Recipes: Orange-Chile Paste, Turkey Consommé, Light Waldorf Vinaigrette

8 FARM FRESH, 91

Tomato and Cucumber Salad with Summer Marinade
Twice-Cooked Salmon with Sesame Crust
Corn on the Cob with Fresh Herbs
Natural Candied Carrots
Peaches and Creme

Additional Recipes: Light Summer Marinade, Apricot Glaze, Fruit Sweet, Honey Yogurt Creme, Yogurt Crème Fraîche

9 TAPAS PARTY, 102

Marinated Olives
Cucumber and Olive Salad
Radishes with Citrus Vinegar
Toasted Bread Rounds
Roasted Pepper and Anchovy Spread
Sardines and Spanish Sauce
Steamed Mussels with Tomato-Wine Broth
Spicy Braised Shrimp
Crab-Stuffed Eggs
Spanish Potato Salad
Herbed Asparagus
Fruit Wedges with Honey Dip
Madeira Spritzer

Additional Recipes: Spanish Sauce, Mustard Yogurt Spread, Spanish Potato Salad with Tuna

10 CALIFORNIA MEDITERRANIA, 120

Pacific Rim Gazpacho
Green Apple Tabouli
Garlicky Artichokes with Lemon-Herb Dipping Sauce
Golden Salad Niçoise with Golden State Vinaigrette
Pale Passion
Berry Almond Tea

Additional Recipe: Alternative Green Apple Tabouli

Mashed Potatoes with Herbs and Parmesan
Pumpkin Gingerbread with Fancy Warm Preserves

Southeast Asian Fondue with Assorted Dipping Sauces
Vietnamese Vegetable Platter
Braised Bananas

Additional Recipes: Asian Poaching Broth, New Saigon Dipping Sauce, Buddhist
Dipping Sauce, Fragrant Dipping Sauce

21 SPICY GARDEN, 246

Spinach and Red Bean Salad with Spicy Mint Vinaigrette
Spaghetti Squash with Broccoli, Peanuts and Fresh Ginger Sauce
Cornbread with Onion and Jalapeño and Orange-Chile Marmalade
Banana Yogurt Creme

Additional Recipes: Spicy Mint-Yogurt Dressing, Basic Yogurt Cheese

22 RIVIERA PICNIC, 256

Cucumber Soup with Tomato Caviar
Open-Face Artichoke Sandwich with Roasted Vegetable Spread
Potato Salad with Two Dressings
Almond Cake with Golden Fruit Mélange

Additional Recipes: Whole Wheat Pasta with Roasted Vegetable Spread, Mustard
Vinaigrette, Creamy Pimento Dressing, Passover Almond Cake

23 SOUP KITCHEN BUFFET, 268

Green and Gold Vegetable Soup
Black Bean and Shiitake Mushroom Soup
Peruvian Chicken Soup
Rainbow Crudités
Cheese and Herb Scones with Yogurt Cheese Dollops
Melba Ice

Additional Recipes: Green and White Vegetable Soup, White Bean and Mushroom Soup, Mexican Chicken Soup

24 SICILIAN THREE PASTA SUPPER, 281

Whole Wheat Spaghetti with Broccoli and Tomatoes
Fusilli with Anchovy and Red Pepper Sauce
Penne with Mushrooms, Artichoke Hearts and Dried Tomatoes
Fennel Salad with Lemon-Garlic Dressing
Whole Wheat Bread Sticks
Strawberries Balsamic

Menu Magic

1

Four Seasons Chicken Dinner

FOUR SEASONS Chicken Dinner is an elegant menu that is a blaze of seasonal color. With shipments of fresh produce from all over the world, American supermarkets have turned aside the seasons. In most major cities, you can get asparagus and strawberries all year long. Apricots are just as likely to appear in December as July. I often find that out-of-season produce is lacking in flavor and may have a strange texture. Nonetheless, I confess that sometimes I just can't resist having strawberries in January. This menu is a mix of products that in North America would rarely be in season at the same time, but with international shipping, the items are available most of the year.

FOUR SEASONS CHICKEN DINNER (MENU FOR 4)

Chilled Carrot Soup
Jeweled Apricot Chicken
Millet-Almond Pilaf
Mixed Summer Squash with Lemon Herbs
Chestnut Cake with Honey Glazed Chestnuts and Raspberry Coulis
Herbal-Flavored Mineral Water

The Chilled Carrot Soup does not have to be served cold. If you prefer hot soup, then by all means heat it up. However, be gentle in the heating. Do not boil the soup or it will curdle. There are major pluses in serving the soup cold. Chilled Carrot Soup can be made in advance and be completely ready to serve right from the refrigerator. Heating the yogurt destroys the acidophilus, one of yogurt's major health attributes. But hot or cold, you can enjoy the delicious flavor and reap the benefits of a rich dose of beta-carotene.

Jeweled Apricot Chicken has a rich glaze that many diners will assume has butter, but it is, in fact, fat free. Simple, easy techniques turn this version of apricot chicken into an elegant company dish. Many diners have never experienced the sweet, delicate flavor of millet. The Millet-Almond Pilaf is a satisfying complement to the more assertive flavor of the Jeweled Apricot Chicken. Making a special trip to a health food store to buy millet is definitely worth the effort.

Mixed Summer Squash with Lemon Herbs hopefully will inspire cooks to grow some of the less common herbs in their window gardens. Lemon herbs enliven the squash with a subtle wild taste that also has accents of citrus. Steaming the vegetables in vermouth creates a perfumelike flavor, again eliminating the need for oil or butter.

The Chestnut Cake with Honey Glazed Chestnuts and Raspberry Coulis is an extravagant delight that beautifully contrasts a mix of sweet, delicate flavors. The cake requires chestnut flour, a product usually found in Italian markets or gourmet shops. The flour has a sweet, delicate flavor. Because of its natural sweetness, you do not need to add much sugar.

A dry but fruity white wine is a pleasing complement to this meal. Herbal-Flavored Mineral Water is also a pleasant choice.

Four Seasons Chicken Dinner is a menu of subtle flavors, presented in a boldly colorful manner—a definite company pleaser! In addition to taste and presentation, your guests should be thrilled with the meal's nutritional attributes.

NUTRIENT INFORMATION FOR FOUR SEASONS CHICKEN DINNER

Persons wanting a heartier meal may elect to include a salad or bread with the meal. Nutrient information includes a single serving each of Chilled Carrot Soup, Jeweled Apricot Chicken, Millet-Almond Pilaf,

Mixed Summer Squash with Lemon Herbs and Chestnut Cake with Honey Glazed Chestnuts and Raspberry Coulis.

CALORIES
For total meal: 729
Fat: 14%
Carbohydrates: 62%
Protein: 24%

CARBOHYDRATES: 113.3 GM
PROTEIN: 45.1 GM
DIETARY FIBER: 8.0 GM
SODIUM: 504 MG
CHOLESTEROL: 76 MG

TOTAL FAT: 11.9 GM
Saturated fat: 1.9 GM
Monounsaturated fat: 5.7 GM

Pyramid equivalencies: 2 grains, 3 vegetables, 1¼ fruits, 1 protein, 1 dairy

Chilled Carrot Soup

I like to serve this in a clear glass bowl or goblet. Although it seems like summertime fare, I find it quite delicious in winter as well.

5 large carrots, peeled and trimmed
2 cups water
½ teaspoon ground cumin
¼ teaspoon ground cinnamon
⅛ teaspoon cayenne pepper
1½ cups plain nonfat yogurt

2 cups nonfat milk
2 tablespoons frozen orange juice concentrate
2 teaspoons low-sodium soy sauce
8 small sprigs fresh cilantro or mint

Grate enough carrot to yield ½ cup. Set it aside.

Slice the remaining carrots in rounds, ½ inch thick. Combine the carrot rounds, water and spices in a saucepan. Cover and simmer at a low temperature for 30 minutes. Slow cooking helps bring out the natural sweetness of the carrots. Chill the carrots and cooking liquid.

Place the carrots and cooking liquid in a blender and puree until smooth. Transfer the carrot puree to a bowl and whisk in the yogurt, nonfat milk, orange juice concentrate and soy sauce. Chill at least 1 hour before serving.

To serve, pour the cold soup in individual bowls or goblets. Sprinkle the grated carrot over each bowl and garnish with cilantro or mint.

YIELD: 8 servings

CALORIES
Per serving: 76
Fat: 4%
Carbohydrates: 67%
Protein: 29%

CARBOHYDRATES: 13.0 GM
PROTEIN: 5.6 GM
DIETARY FIBER: 1.5 GM
SODIUM: 208 MG
CHOLESTEROL: 2 MG

TOTAL FAT: .3 GM
Saturated fat: .2 GM
Monounsaturated fat: .1 GM

Pyramid equivalencies: 1 vegetable, ⅔ dairy

Jeweled Apricot Chicken

Use fresh apricots when available. Otherwise, use dried or canned apricots.

⅓ cup fruit-sweetened apricot preserves
⅓ cup water
¼ cup dry sherry
1 tablespoon unsalted Dijon-style mustard
2 teaspoons low-sodium soy sauce

3 thin slices fresh ginger
2 small fresh apricots or canned or dried apricot halves
4 single chicken breasts, boned, skinned and fat removed

Whisk together the apricot preserves, water, dry sherry, mustard and soy sauce. Add the ginger slices and set aside.

Cut the apricots in wedges ⅜ inch wide. You will need 16 wedges. Two apricots should yield more than enough wedges.

Make four evenly spaced slits on each chicken breast. Each slit should be slightly greater than the length of an apricot wedge. Gently insert an apricot wedge into each slit.

Lightly coat the bottom of a nonstick pan with the preserve mixture. Add the chicken breasts and coat with the remaining sauce. Simmer at medium temperature for 4 minutes, covered. Remove the cover and spoon some of the sauce over the breasts. Continue cooking at medium temperature, uncovered, for 5 minutes. If necessary, add more liquid.

Discard the ginger slices. Serve hot with sauce spooned over each breast. Serve with Millet-Almond Pilaf or other pilaf. A brightly colored steamed vegetable makes a beautiful visual accompaniment.

YIELD: 4 servings

CALORIES	CARBOHYDRATES: 19.4 GM	TOTAL FAT: 3.3 GM
Per serving: 214	PROTEIN: 27.0 GM	Saturated fat: .9 GM
Fat: 14%	DIETARY FIBER: .3 GM	Monounsaturated fat: 1.1 GM
Carbohydrates: 35%	SODIUM: 149 MG	
Protein: 51%	CHOLESTEROL: 73 MG	

Pyramid equivalencies: ¼ fruit, 1 protein

Millet-Almond Pilaf

Millet is a slightly sweet grain that when cooked has an appearance similar to bulgur or couscous. In fact, either will make an excellent substitute if you can't get millet.

2 cups unsalted, defatted chicken broth, or water
1 cup millet

2 teaspoons low-sodium soy sauce
2 tablespoons sliced almonds

Bring the broth to a boil. Add the millet and soy sauce. Stir and cover with a tight-fitting lid.

Reduce the heat to very low and cook for 30 minutes or until the broth is absorbed. Stir in the almonds and serve immediately.

YIELD: 4 servings

CALORIES	CARBOHYDRATES: 24.0 GM	TOTAL FAT: 2.7 GM
Per serving: 133	PROTEIN: 5.1 GM	Saturated fat: .2 GM
Fat: 17%	DIETARY FIBER: .3 GM	Monounsaturated fat: 1.2 GM
Carbohydrates: 69%	SODIUM: 88 MG	
Protein: 14%	CHOLESTEROL: 0 MG	

Pyramid equivalencies: 1 grain

Mixed Summer Squash with Lemon Herbs

Nurseries carry a variety of lemon-flavored herbs. Basil, mint and geranium are just a few of the choices that come in lemon flavor. Lemongrass can also be used. If you are unable to find lemon herbs, substitute 1 tablespoon finely grated lemon peel mixed with 1 tablespoon finely minced fresh parsley.

1½ cups green zucchini, sliced in rounds	1 teaspoon extra-virgin olive oil
1½ cups yellow zucchini or yellow crookneck squash, sliced in rounds	4 teaspoons finely minced lemon-flavored herbs
1 clove garlic, finely minced	4 sprigs lemon herb or parsley for garnish
1 cup extra-dry vermouth	4 slices fresh lemon

Combine the two colors of summer squash and mix with the garlic. Place on a steamer rack. Steam using vermouth instead of water. If necessary, add enough water to the pan to create a depth of ¼ inch. Steam 3 to 4 minutes, covered, or until the squash is tender but crisp.

Mix 2 tablespoons of the vermouth steaming liquid with the olive oil. Toss the cooked squash with the mixture. Add the lemon herbs and toss again. Reserve the remaining cooked vermouth for use in soups, sauces or for poaching fish.

Garnish with the sprigs of fresh herb and lemon slices.

YIELD: 4 servings

CALORIES	CARBOHYDRATES: 3.7 GM	TOTAL FAT: 1.3 GM
Per serving: 28	PROTEIN: 1.2 GM	Saturated fat: .2 GM
Fat: 48%	DIETARY FIBER: 1.6 GM	Monounsaturated fat: .8 GM
Carbohydrates: 37%	SODIUM: 5 MG	
Protein: 15%	CHOLESTEROL: 0 MG	

Pyramid equivalencies: 1 vegetable

Chestnut Cake with Honey Glazed Chestnuts and Raspberry Coulis

This cake is both simple and extravagant. Although it may be eaten plain, I believe the cake is more exciting when served on a pool of Raspberry Coulis and topped with Honey Glazed Chestnuts.

⅔ *cup white flour*
⅔ *cup chestnut flour*
⅓ *cup granulated sugar*
1½ *teaspoons baking powder*
¼ *teaspoon cinnamon*
¾ *cup fluid nonfat milk*
½ *cup dry nonfat milk powder*

2 *large egg whites*
2 *tablespoons canola oil*
1 *teaspoon vanilla*
1 *recipe Honey Glazed Chestnuts (recipe follows)*
1 *recipe Raspberry Coulis (recipe on page 11)*

Preheat oven to 375°F. Sift together the two flours, sugar, baking powder and cinnamon. Set aside.

Using an electric mixer, slowly beat together the fluid nonfat milk, dry milk and the egg whites until well blended. Add the oil and vanilla and beat until well blended. Slowly beat in the flour mixture until smooth and fully blended.

Generously spray an 8-inch round nonstick cake pan with nonstick cooking spray. Pour the batter into the pan. Bake at 375°F. for 30 minutes or until an inserted toothpick comes out clean.

Let the cake stand 30 minutes before removing from the pan. Use a thin knife to loosen the cake from the edges of the pan. Lightly tap the bottom of the pan. Place a plate over the pan and invert. No more than 1 hour before serving, spoon the Honey Glazed Chestnuts over the cake.

Slice the cake into 8 portions. Spoon Raspberry Coulis onto individual dessert plates. Set a slice of the Chestnut Cake on the sauce and serve immediately.

YIELD: 8 servings

CALORIES
Per serving: 278
Fat: 14%
Carbohydrates: 75%
Protein: 9%
Alcohol: 2%

CARBOHYDRATES: 53.2 GM
PROTEIN: 6.2 GM
DIETARY FIBER: 4.3 GM
SODIUM: 53 MG
CHOLESTEROL: 1 MG

TOTAL FAT: 4.3 GM
Saturated fat: .4 GM
Monounsaturated fat: 2.5 GM

Pyramid equivalencies: 1 grain, 1 vegetable, 1 fruit, ½ dairy

Honey Glazed Chestnuts

In addition to a topping on cake, I serve Honey Glazed Chestnuts as a holiday candy.

¾ pound fresh chestnuts   *3 tablespoons water*
3 tablespoons honey

Preheat oven to 500°F. With a sharp knife, carefully make cross-cut slashes on flat side of each chestnut. Place nuts on a baking sheet and roast at 500°F. for 25 minutes. Remove nuts from oven, cool and peel. Set aside.

Whisk together the honey and water. Toss the whole peeled chestnuts in the honey mixture until evenly coated. Set on a platter and let stand 30 minutes before serving. May be made a day in advance and refrigerated.

Left whole, the chestnuts make a delicious condiment. For a topping on cake or frozen desserts, slice or quarter the nuts, then toss with the honey.

YIELD: 4 servings as a candy

CALORIES
Per serving: 185
Fat: 3%
Carbohydrates: 92%
Protein: 5%

CARBOHYDRATES: 42.5 GM
PROTEIN: 2.5 GM
DIETARY FIBER: 4.4 GM
SODIUM: 3 MG
CHOLESTEROL: 0 MG

TOTAL FAT: .7 GM
Saturated fat: .1 GM
Monounsaturated fat: .4 GM

Pyramid equivalencies: 2 vegetables

Raspberry Coulis

In addition to the Chestnut Cake, this is a luscious topping for frozen yogurt desserts.

2 cups frozen, unsweetened raspberries
¼ cup frozen, unsweetened berry-apple juice concentrate or plain apple juice concentrate

¼ teaspoon cinnamon
2 tablespoons raspberry or orange liqueur

Combine all of the ingredients in a blender and puree until smooth. Transfer the mixture to a fine strainer or sieve. Press the mixture through the sieve to remove the seeds. Serve the coulis warm or cold as a dessert sauce or topping for pancakes.

YIELD: 8 servings

CALORIES
Per serving: 40
Fat: 4%
Carbohydrates: 75%
Protein: 3%
Alcohol: 18%

CARBOHYDRATES: 8.1 GM
PROTEIN: .3 GM
DIETARY FIBER: 1.4 GM
SODIUM: 2 MG
CHOLESTEROL: 0 MG

TOTAL FAT: .2 GM
Saturated fat: trace
Monounsaturated fat: trace

Pyramid equivalencies: ¾ fruit

Herbal-Flavored Mineral Water

This refreshing calorie-free beverage has a subtle aromatic flavor. I prefer it when it is icy cold.

3 bags chamomile tea
2 bags mint tea
1 cup boiling water
*7 cups unsweetened, lemon-
flavored mineral water,
chilled*

8 wedges fresh lime
*8 leaves fresh basil or sprigs of
other fresh herb*

Place the tea bags in the cup of boiling water. Let stand 20 minutes. Pour the tea through a strainer, pressing the bags against the strainer to extract as much liquid as possible. Chill the liquid.

At serving time, combine the tea and mineral water. Pour into tumblers filled with ice. Garnish with lime wedges and fresh herbs.

YIELD: 8 servings

No nutrients except minerals in the water. Check the bottle of mineral water to determine sodium content.

2

Tropical
Heat Wave

WHEN THE fat is taken away, where do you turn for flavor? This time, the chef turns to the hot, spicy seasonings and exotic fruits and vegetables that are part of tropical cuisines. Why do people in hot climates often favor spicy, piquant food? Spicy foods make you sweat, which in turn cools the body. Spicy foods also speed our metabolism, which causes us to burn a few more calories. Before you think a chile pepper is the next diet pill, realize their best contribution may be bringing exciting flavor to low-fat dishes. This is a festive menu that no one will know is part of light, low-fat cooking!

TROPICAL HEAT WAVE (MENU FOR 4)

Chayote Salad with Mustard Dressing
Pineapple Rice or Tropical Rice Salad
West Indian Plantain
Okra in Spicy Tomato Sauce
Grilled Jerk Chicken
Desert Island Punch
Baked Tropical Fruit Pudding with Pineapple Creme

Additional Recipe:
Jerk Marinade

Squash is a common ingredient in tropical cuisines all over the world. Our menu features a lesser-known squash that is becoming more readily available in American markets. Chayote squash is similar to zucchini, but is less likely to be bitter. It has a slightly buttery flavor. Chayote Salad with Mustard Dressing combines a mildly spicy dressing with peppery watercress.

The secret to spicy foods is also having something that balances the piquant flavors. Pineapple Rice or Tropical Rice Salad has rice to absorb the heat of fresh ginger. West Indian Plantain mixes Garam Masala, a blend of spices that is frequently associated with curry, with the faintly sweet starchy flavor of plantain. In both dishes, starch and fruit tame the spiciness.

Every now and then, I like to offer something that has a lot of fire. Serrano chiles give Okra in Spicy Tomato Sauce a definite wave of heat. Jerk Marinade also fires up the Grilled Jerk Chicken. Don't worry—the Tropical Rice Salad and West Indian Plantain have enough starch to soothe your palate. Remember, the best way to calm a fiery tongue is with starch, not water.

Water is part of the menu, however. Desert Island Punch has a base of fruit-flavored mineral water. Why a desert island when this meal is supposed to be in the tropical zones? Syrupy sweet punches, typical of tropical menus, have never been a favorite of mine. I much prefer dry, faintly sweet beverages. Besides, there are so many other sweet tastes in the meal, I think it's best to offer a lighter beverage. The dessert, Baked Tropical Fruit Pudding with Pineapple Creme, will satisfy your penchant for sweet tropical flavors.

NUTRIENT ANALYSIS FOR TROPICAL HEAT WAVE

The nutrient analysis for the complete meal includes 1 serving each of Chayote Salad with Mustard Dressing, Grilled Jerk Chicken, West Indian Plantain, Tropical Rice Salad, Okra in Spicy Tomato Sauce and Baked Tropical Fruit Pudding with Pineapple Creme. The total includes 2 servings of Desert Island Punch. Persons wanting a heartier meal may want to include a bread.

CALORIES | CARBOHYDRATES: 138.0 GM | TOTAL FAT: 9.8 GM
For total meal: | PROTEIN: 41.7 GM | Saturated fat: 1.7 GM
763 | DIETARY FIBER: 10.8 GM | Monounsaturated fat: 4.1 GM
Fat: 11% | SODIUM: 463 MG |
Carbohydrates: 68% | CHOLESTEROL: 73 MG |
Protein: 21% | |

Pyramid equivalencies: 1½ grains, 5 vegetables, 3⅔ fruits, 1 protein, ⅛ dairy

Chayote Salad with Mustard Dressing

You can use zucchini in this recipe, but I much prefer the chayotes. Chayotes are also called christephenes, pear squash and mirlitons.

> 2 *chayote squash*
> 1 *recipe Mustard Dressing*
>   *(recipe follows)*
>
> 1 *bunch watercress, washed and*
>   *separated into sprigs*

Peel the squash and cut in half. Cut out the center pit. Slice each half into pieces about the size of slices for an apple pie. Toss the squash with Mustard Dressing and marinate in the refrigerator for 2 hours.

To serve, spoon the dressed squash onto plates generously garnished with sprigs of watercress.

YIELD: 4 servings

CALORIES | CARBOHYDRATES: 7.6 GM | TOTAL FAT: 3.6 GM
Per serving: 61 | PROTEIN: .7 GM | Saturated fat: .5 GM
Fat: 49% | DIETARY FIBER: 1.0 GM | Monounsaturated fat: 2.5 GM
Carbohydrates: 47% | SODIUM: 7 MG |
Protein: 4% | CHOLESTEROL: 0 MG |

Pyramid equivalencies: 1 vegetable

Mustard Dressing

This dressing is excellent for both greens and marinated vegetables.

2 tablespoons unsalted Dijon-
  style mustard
2 tablespoons fresh lemon
  juice

1 tablespoon water
1 tablespoon extra-virgin olive
  oil

Whisk together all of the ingredients and refrigerate. Will keep for several days.

YIELD: 4 servings

CALORIES
Per serving: 33
Fat: 93%
Carbohydrates: 6%
Protein: 1%

CARBOHYDRATES: .5 GM
PROTEIN: .1 GM
DIETARY FIBER: trace
SODIUM: 1 MG
CHOLESTEROL: 0 MG

TOTAL FAT: 3.5 GM
Saturated fat: .5 GM
Monounsaturated fat: 2.5 GM

Pyramid equivalencies: No equivalencies

Pineapple Rice

Rice with pineapple or other tropical fruit is part of the cuisine of nearly every tropical region in the world. If you want to make the Tropical Rice Salad for another day, double this recipe for two uses.

2¾ cups boiling water or
   defatted, unsalted chicken
   broth
 1 tablespoon finely minced
   fresh ginger
 1 tablespoon low-sodium soy
   sauce

1½ teaspoons coconut extract
1½ cups brown rice
 1 cup finely chopped fresh
   pineapple, including juice

In a saucepan with the boiling water or broth, stir in the ginger, soy sauce and coconut extract. Stir in the brown rice, cover with a tight-fitting lid and reduce the heat to very low. Cook for 40 minutes.

When the rice is done, immediately stir in the fresh pineapple and serve.

YIELD: 4 servings

CALORIES	CARBOHYDRATES: 42.8 GM	TOTAL FAT: 1.1 GM
Per serving: 198	PROTEIN: 4.2 GM	Saturated fat: trace
Fat: 5%	DIETARY FIBER: 3.1 GM	Monounsaturated fat: .2 GM
Carbohydrates: 86%	SODIUM: 128 MG	
Protein: 9%	CHOLESTEROL: 0 MG	

Pyramid equivalencies: 1½ grains, ½ fruit

Tropical Rice Salad

This salad transforms the previous recipe into a tantalizing new dish. The rice can be hot or cold for the salad.

3 tablespoons fresh orange
  juice
2 tablespoons fresh lime juice
2 green onions, chopped
1 tablespoon finely minced
  fresh parsley
1 tablespoon finely minced
  fresh cilantro

1 recipe Pineapple Rice
  (previous recipe), hot or cold
1 bunch spinach, washed with
  stems removed
½ small papaya, peeled and
  sliced thinly

Combine the orange juice, lime juice, green onions, parsley and cilantro. Stir into the pineapple rice and let marinate 5 minutes.

Arrange the spinach leaves on a platter or on individual serving plates. Mound the rice over the leaves. Arrange the papaya slices around the rice. Serve immediately.

YIELD: 4 servings

CALORIES   CARBOHYDRATES: 50.5 GM   TOTAL FAT: 1.4 GM
Per serving: 232   PROTEIN: 6.3 GM   Saturated fat: .1 GM
Fat: 5%   DIETARY FIBER: 5.0 GM   Monounsaturated fat: .2 GM
Carbohydrates: 84%   SODIUM: 174 MG
Protein: 11%   CHOLESTEROL: 0 MG

Pyramid equivalencies: 1½ grains, 1 vegetable, 1 fruit

West Indian Plantain

Plantain is a pleasant replacement for potatoes or yams in a meal.

        2 plantains   2 teaspoons Garam Masala
        ½ cup dry sherry   (recipe on page 208)
        1 tablespoon rum   ½ teaspoon coconut extract
        1 red onion, coarsely chopped

    Peel the plantains and cut in half crosswise and lengthwise. Place the plantain quarters in a skillet. Add the sherry and rum, then add enough water to cover the bottom of the pan with ¼ inch of liquid.

    Add the remaining ingredients and loosely cover the pan. Simmer at medium temperature for 20 minutes or until the plantains are soft. If necessary, add more liquid. Although they can be served cold or at room temperature, I prefer them hot.

YIELD: 4 servings

CALORIES   CARBOHYDRATES: 34.0 GM   TOTAL FAT: .5 GM
Per serving: 130   PROTEIN: 1.8 GM   Saturated fat: trace
Fat: 3%   DIETARY FIBER: .8 GM   Monounsaturated fat: trace
Carbohydrates: 92%   SODIUM: 7 MG
Protein: 5%   CHOLESTEROL: 0 MG

Pyramid equivalencies: 1 vegetable, 1 fruit

Okra in Spicy Tomato Sauce

People who don't like the gooey texture that is common to okra dishes will be pleasantly surprised by this one. The okra is left whole, keeping the oozy culprit inside. (If you've never had okra before, don't be put off by this rather unappetizing description. Okra is actually quite delicious!)

> 1 pound fresh or frozen whole   1 recipe Spicy Tomato Sauce
>   okra   (recipe follows)

Wash the okra and trim away the stem but do not cut off the ends. Combine the okra and Spicy Tomato Sauce and simmer uncovered 8 minutes or until the okra is tender. Serve immediately.

YIELD: 4 servings

CALORIES	CARBOHYDRATES: 14.0 GM	TOTAL FAT: .5 GM
Per serving: 63	PROTEIN: 3.4 GM	Saturated fat: .1 GM
Fat: 6%	DIETARY FIBER: 3.0 GM	Monounsaturated fat: .1 GM
Carbohydrates: 76%	SODIUM: 105 MG	
Protein: 18%	CHOLESTEROL: 0 MG	

Pyramid equivalencies: 2 vegetables

Spicy Tomato Sauce

This is an excellent sauce for okra, green beans, mushrooms and summer squashes. The advantage to the sauce is that the vegetables can be cooked in the sauce. Fish, seafood and chicken can also be cooked in the sauce.

4 large tomatoes, finely
  chopped
4 cloves garlic, finely minced
1 serrano chile, seeded and
  minced
½ cup water

½ teaspoon curry powder
2 teaspoons low-sodium soy
  sauce
1 to 2 tablespoons unsalted
  tomato paste

Combine all of the ingredients, except the tomato paste, in a saucepan. Cover and simmer at low temperature for 20 minutes. At this point, you can add vegetables, chicken, fish or seafood to the sauce. Cook until the additions are almost done. Stir in the tomato paste to thicken the sauce. Serve immediately.

YIELD: 4 servings

CALORIES
Per serving: 37
Fat: 8%
Carbohydrates: 75%
Protein: 17%

CARBOHYDRATES: 8.2 GM
PROTEIN: 1.9 GM
DIETARY FIBER: 2.0 GM
SODIUM: 101 MG
CHOLESTEROL: 0 MG

TOTAL FAT: .4 GM
Saturated fat: .1 GM
Monounsaturated fat: .1 GM

Pyramid equivalencies: 1 vegetable

Grilled Jerk Chicken

I like this chicken best when prepared over a barbecue grill, although under a broiler will be satisfying.

4 chicken breast halves,
  boneless and without skin

1 recipe Jerk Marinade (recipe
  follows)

With a mallet, pound the breasts until no more than ¼ inch thick. Toss with the Jerk Marinade and marinate in the refrigerator for 2 hours. Turn occasionally while marinating.

Grill over hot coals or under a broiler for 2 to 3 minutes per side. If desired, simmer the leftover marinade for 5 minutes and serve as a sauce with the chicken. Because raw chicken was in the marinade, the sauce needs to be well cooked.

YIELD: 4 servings

CALORIES	CARBOHYDRATES: 4.2 GM	TOTAL FAT: 3.4 GM
Per serving: 161	PROTEIN: 27.4 GM	Saturated fat: .9 GM
Fat: 19%	DIETARY FIBER: .4 GM	Monounsaturated fat: 1.1 GM
Carbohydrates: 11%	SODIUM: 155 MG	
Protein: 70%	CHOLESTEROL: 73 MG	

Pyramid equivalencies: 1 protein

Jerk Marinade

This spicy marinade is excellent for chicken and pork tenderloin.

½ cup coarsely chopped red onion
¼ cup dry sherry
¾ teaspoon crushed dry red chiles
¾ teaspoon ground cinnamon
½ teaspoon ground allspice
¼ teaspoon ground cloves

¼ teaspoon ground black pepper
1 bay leaf
1 tablespoon unsalted Dijon-style mustard
2 teaspoons low-sodium soy sauce

Combine all of the ingredients in a blender and puree until smooth. Refrigerate until ready to use. Will keep 3 or 4 days.

YIELD: 4 servings

CALORIES	CARBOHYDRATES: 18.9 GM	TOTAL FAT: .3 GM
Per serving: 19	PROTEIN: .8 GM	Saturated fat: trace
Fat: 12%	DIETARY FIBER: .4 GM	Monounsaturated fat: trace
Carbohydrates: 74%	SODIUM: 92 MG	
Protein: 14%	CHOLESTEROL: 0 MG	

Pyramid equivalencies: No equivalencies

Desert Island Punch

This low-calorie punch has a dry, sweet flavor. Serve with plenty of ice.

4 bags berry-flavored herb tea
1 bag orange spice-flavored
  herb tea
1 cup boiling water
½ cup unsweetened pineapple
  juice concentrate

6½ cups citrus-flavored,
   unsweetened mineral water,
   chilled
8 orange wedges
8 lime wedges

Place the tea bags in the boiling water and let stand for 20 minutes. Strain the tea, squeezing the liquid from the bags. Mix the concentrated tea with pineapple juice concentrate and chill.

At serving time, combine the tea and juice mixture with the mineral water. Serve in tumblers with plenty of ice. Garnish with a wedge of orange and a wedge of lime.

YIELD: 8 servings

CALORIES
Per serving: 33
Fat: 1%
Carbohydrates: 96%
Protein: 3%

CARBOHYDRATES: 8.2 GM
PROTEIN: .3 GM
DIETARY FIBER: .1 GM
SODIUM: 3 MG
CHOLESTEROL: 0 MG

TOTAL FAT: trace
Saturated fat: 0 GM
Monounsaturated fat: 0 GM

Pyramid equivalencies: ½ fruit

Baked Tropical Fruit Pudding with Pineapple Creme

In addition to dessert, this is a delightful breakfast dish.

1 cup fresh pineapple, coarsely chopped

1 small mango, peeled, stoned and coarsely chopped

1 small papaya, peeled, seeded and coarsely chopped

2 very ripe bananas, peeled and chopped

¼ cup cornstarch

¼ cup frozen, unsweetened apple juice concentrate

2 strawberries, stemmed and sliced, optional garnish

Preheat oven to 375° F. Place all of the fruit in a blender or food processor. Puree until smooth. Dissolve the cornstarch into the juice concentrate and add to the fruit puree. Mix until well blended.

Spray a baking dish with nonstick vegetable spray. Transfer the fruit mixture into the dish, spreading evenly. Bake at 375°F. for 1 hour or until the top is lightly golden.

Cool and refrigerate for 4 hours or until completely chilled. Serve with the Pineapple Creme (recipe follows) drizzled over each serving. If desired, garnish each portion with a small slice of strawberry or other fruit.

YIELD: 8 servings

Nutrient analysis does not include the Pineapple Creme.

CALORIES
Per serving: 88
Fat: 3%
Carbohydrates: 94%
Protein: 3%

CARBOHYDRATES: 22.1 GM
PROTEIN: .7 GM
DIETARY FIBER: .6 GM
SODIUM: 4 MG
CHOLESTEROL: 0 MG

TOTAL FAT: .4 GM
Saturated fat: .1 GM
Monounsaturated fat: .1 GM

Pyramid equivalencies: 1 fruit

Pineapple Creme

This topping is satisfying for both the Baked Tropical Fruit Pudding and fresh tropical fruit.

¾ cup plain nonfat yogurt
¼ cup unsweetened pineapple juice concentrate

1 tablespoon finely grated lemon peel

Whisk together all of the ingredients and chill until ready to use. Use as a topping for the Baked Tropical Fruit Pudding or with fresh tropical fruit. Do not put the creme on raw fruit until ready to serve.

YIELD: 4 servings

CALORIES
Per serving: 28
Fat: 2%
Carbohydrates: 79%
Protein: 19%

CARBOHYDRATES: 5.6 GM
PROTEIN: 1.4 GM
DIETARY FIBER: trace
SODIUM: 17 MG
CHOLESTEROL: trace

TOTAL FAT: trace
Saturated fat: trace
Monounsaturated fat: trace

Pyramid equivalencies: ⅛ fruit, ⅛ dairy

3

Cherries
Jubilation

CHERRIES! THEY may not be preceded by "American as," but they do have truth, honesty and the ghost of George Washington as their spokesperson. Pies, cobblers and flaming ice cream have guaranteed cherries a place in American cookbooks. The cherry season is so short, we've come to accept canned and frozen cherries as a permanent substitute. But nothing really compares to the real thing. Fresh cherries have a subtle, aromatic sweetness that makes them a fantastic subject for more than just desserts. This menu is about fresh cherries in a salad. In addition to the summer season, expensive imported cherries frequently appear around Christmastime. The menu has variations that make it suitable for both summer and winter.

CHERRIES JUBILATION SUMMER MENU (MENU FOR 4)

Cherries Jubilation Salad with Cherry Barbecued Chicken
Garden Bread with Apple Cheese
Iced Mocha Royale

Additional Recipes:
Cherry Salad Dressing
Cherry Barbecue Sauce

25

When I created Cherries Jubilation Salad, it was an outrageously hot day, a day I didn't want to cook or eat very much. That's why the Summer Menu is very simple. The salad, with the addition of Cherry Barbecued Chicken, will definitely please the hot-weather palate. The Cherry Salad Dressing and Cherry Barbecue Sauce have an appealing use any time of year. Salads that have fruit in them go well with breads that are slightly sweet. The Garden Bread with Apple Cheese is a superb complement to the Cherries Jubilation Salad. The bread will keep well, wrapped in plastic and refrigerated. In hot weather I would probably forgo baking and pick up a loaf of date or raisin bread from the bakery. I've never particularly liked iced coffee, but I think the Iced Mocha Royale is a sensational cold beverage. In the summer, it serves as both beverage and dessert.

NUTRIENT ANALYSIS FOR CHERRIES JUBILATION SUMMER MENU

Nutrient analysis for complete meal includes one serving each of Cherries Jubilation Salad with Cherry Barbecued Chicken, Garden Bread with Apple Cheese and Iced Mocha Royale.

CALORIES	CARBOHYDRATES: 95.4 GM	TOTAL FAT: 13.9 GM
For total meal: 673	PROTEIN: 47.8 GM	Saturated fat: 2.4 GM
Fat: 18%	DIETARY FIBER: 10.7 GM	Monounsaturated fat: 7.0 GM
Carbohydrates: 55%	SODIUM: 574 MG	
Protein: 27%	CHOLESTEROL: 78 MG	

Pyramid equivalencies: 2 grains, 2⅓ vegetables, 1½ fruits, 1⅓ dairy, 1 protein

CHERRIES JUBILATION WINTER MENU (MENU FOR 4)

Cherries Jubilation Salad
Cherry Barbecued Chicken
Red Rice
Garden Bread with Apple Cheese
Hot Mocha Royale

Additional Recipe:
Red Beans and Red Rice

This menu was created with a hearty appetite in mind. Imported cherries often appear December and January. This dinner is great for the winter months as well as a mild summer day. For this meal, I would serve the Cherries Jubilation Salad as a first course. The Cherry Barbecued Chicken would accompany Red Rice, a pilaf made with Wehani rice, which is a red, nutty-flavored rice. Vegetarians and hearty eaters may want to add red beans and have Red Beans and Red Rice. Garden Bread with Apple Cheese are also included in this menu. Depending on the climate, and your mood, you may prefer a hot dessert beverage. Hot Mocha Royale is a marvelous finale.

NUTRIENT ANALYSIS FOR CHERRIES JUBILATION WINTER MENU

Nutrient analysis for complete meal includes 1 serving each of Cherries Jubilation Salad, Cherry Barbecued Chicken, Red Rice, Garden Bread with Apple Cheese and Hot Mocha Royale.

CALORIES	CARBOHYDRATES: 120.1 GM	TOTAL FAT: 14.0 GM
For total meal: 790	PROTEIN: 53.2 GM	Saturated fat: 2.4 GM
Fat: 15%	DIETARY FIBER: 14.0 GM	Monounsaturated fat: 7.0 GM
Carbohydrates: 59%	SODIUM: 673 MG	
Protein: 26%	CHOLESTEROL: 73 MG	

Pyramid equivalencies: 3 grains, 2⅓ vegetables, 1½ fruits, 1⅓ dairy, 1 protein

Cherries Jubilation Salad

This exotic composed salad is delicious for light summer dining and winter holiday fare. The different greens can be replaced by prepackaged mixes of salad greens available in the produce section of your market.

4 cups red leaf lettuce, torn in bite-size pieces

2 cups green leaf lettuce, torn in bite-size pieces

1 cup radicchio, torn in bite-size pieces

1 cup curly endive, torn in bite-size pieces

1 recipe Cherry Salad Dressing (recipe follows)

2 green onions, chopped

24 fresh cherries, pitted

1 cup jicama, peeled and cut in 2-inch julienne strips

½ cup enouki mushrooms

¼ cup sliced almonds

After the greens are washed and drained, mix with the Cherry Salad Dressing. Place dressed greens on individual salad plates. Attractively arrange the remaining ingredients over the greens. Serve immediately.

YIELD: 4 servings

CALORIES   CARBOHYDRATES: 32.2 GM   TOTAL FAT: 5.5 GM
Per serving: 185   PROTEIN: 7.2 GM   Saturated fat: .7 GM
Fat: 24%   DIETARY FIBER: 7.0 GM   Monounsaturated fat: 2.9 GM
Carbohydrates: 62%   SODIUM: 169 MG
Protein: 14%   CHOLESTEROL: 0 MG

Pyramid equivalencies: 2 vegetables, 1 fruit

Cherry Salad Dressing

This refreshing sweet and sour dressing is excellent with a variety of greens.

3 tablespoons unseasoned rice   1 tablespoon tomato paste
  vinegar   1 tablespoon water
2 tablespoons frozen, cherry-   ½ teaspoon dry ground ginger
  flavored blended juice
  concentrate

Whisk together all of the ingredients. Store in a glass jar and chill until you are ready to use. Will keep a week in the refrigerator.

YIELD: 4 servings

CALORIES   CARBOHYDRATES: 8.6 GM   TOTAL FAT: .1 GM
Per serving: 36   PROTEIN: .4 GM   Saturated fat: trace
Fat: 2%   DIETARY FIBER: .3 GM   Monounsaturated fat: trace
Carbohydrates: 94%   SODIUM: 79 MG
Protein: 4%   CHOLESTEROL: 0 MG

Pyramid equivalencies: No equivalencies

Cherries Jubilation Salad with Cherry Barbecued Chicken

Cherries Jubilation Salad becomes a main course with the addition of grilled or broiled chicken. The salad is superb with either hot or cold chicken.

For the salad prepare one recipe Cherries Jubilation Salad and one recipe Cherry Barbecued Chicken. When the chicken is cooked, slice each breast in thin strips and arrange over the salad.

YIELD: 4 servings

CALORIES	CARBOHYDRATES: 36.9 GM	TOTAL FAT: 8.8 GM
Per serving: 348	PROTEIN: 34.3 GM	Saturated fat: 1.5 GM
Fat: 21%	DIETARY FIBER: 7.2 GM	Monounsaturated fat: 4.0 GM
Carbohydrates: 41%	SODIUM: 294 MG	
Protein: 38%	CHOLESTEROL: 73 MG	

Pyramid equivalencies: 2 vegetables, 1 fruit, 1 protein

Cherry Barbecued Chicken

Quickly and easily prepared, this chicken is appealing any time of year.

4 chicken breast halves,   *½ recipe Cherry Barbecue Sauce*
boneless and skin free   *(recipe follows)*

With a kitchen mallet, flatten each breast to a thickness of no more than ¼ inch. Marinate the chicken in the Cherry Barbecue Sauce for 30 minutes.

Place the chicken under a hot broiler or on a grill. Cook 3 to 4 minutes on each side. If desired, heat the Cherry Barbecue Sauce and coat the cooked chicken with the sauce. Serve with Cherries Jubilation Salad or with the Red Rice.

YIELD: 4 servings

CALORIES	CARBOHYDRATES: 4.7 GM	TOTAL FAT: 3.2 GM
Per serving: 164	PROTEIN: 27.1 GM	Saturated fat: .9 GM
Fat: 19%	DIETARY FIBER: .2 GM	Monounsaturated fat: 1.1 GM
Carbohydrates: 12%	SODIUM: 125 MG	
Protein: 69%	CHOLESTEROL: 73 MG	

Pyramid equivalencies: 1 protein

Cherry Barbecue Sauce

Cherries don't have to be in season to make this delicious barbecue sauce.

¼ cup frozen, cherry-flavored juice concentrate
2 tablespoons tomato paste
4 teaspoons unseasoned rice vinegar

4 teaspoons unsalted Dijon-style mustard
2 teaspoons low-sodium soy sauce
½ teaspoon curry powder

Whisk together all of the ingredients. Store in the refrigerator until ready to use. Will keep several days. Use as a sauce and marinade for grilled or broiled chicken.

YIELD: 8 servings

CALORIES	CARBOHYDRATES: 4.7 GM	TOTAL FAT: .1 GM
Per serving: 22	PROTEIN: .4 GM	Saturated fat: trace
Fat: 4%	DIETARY FIBER: .2 GM	Monounsaturated fat: trace
Carbohydrates: 88%	SODIUM: 62 MG	
Protein: 8%	CHOLESTEROL: 0 MG	

Pyramid equivalencies: No equivalencies

Red Rice

You can use standard brown rice for this dish, but rusty red Wehani rice offers an exciting color and rich flavor.

2 *cups unsalted, defatted*   2 *teaspoons low-sodium soy*
  chicken broth or water   *sauce*
1 *tablespoon unsalted tomato*   ½ *teaspoon mild chile powder*
  paste   1 *cup uncooked Wehani rice*

Bring the broth or water to a boil. Stir in the tomato paste, soy sauce and chile powder. Add the rice, cover with a tight-fitting lid and reduce the temperature to very low. Cook for 45 minutes. Remove from the heat and stir before serving.

YIELD: 4 servings

CALORIES	CARBOHYDRATES: 27.0 GM	TOTAL FAT: .1 GM
Per serving: 126	PROTEIN: 5.4 GM	Saturated fat: trace
Fat: 1%	DIETARY FIBER: 3.3 GM	Monounsaturated fat: trace
Carbohydrates: 82%	SODIUM: 100 MG	
Protein: 17%	CHOLESTEROL: 0 MG	

Pyramid equivalencies: 1 grain

Red Beans and Red Rice

Adding beans to rice creates a whole protein and makes a hearty dish that appeals to both meat eaters and vegetarians.

In the preceding recipe for Red Rice, add 1 cup diced red onion when you add the rice. After 40 minutes, stir in 1½ cups cooked red beans. Cover again and continue cooking for 10 minutes more.

YIELD: 4 servings

CALORIES   CARBOHYDRATES: 42.2 GM   TOTAL FAT: .4 GM
Per serving: 210   PROTEIN: 11.2 GM   Saturated fat: trace
Fat: 2%   DIETARY FIBER: 5.7 GM   Monounsaturated fat: .1 GM
Carbohydrates: 77%   SODIUM: 102 MG
Protein: 21%   CHOLESTEROL: 0 MG

Pyramid equivalencies: 1 grain, ⅓ protein

Garden Bread

This mildly sweet bread can be served as a breakfast item, an accompaniment to soups or salads or as a dessert.

1½ cups whole wheat flour	½ teaspoon almond extract
½ cup cornstarch	¾ cup water
1½ teaspoons baking soda	1 cup grated carrot
½ teaspoon ground ginger	½ cup grated zucchini
¼ teaspoon ground nutmeg	½ cup grated apple
¼ teaspoon ground cloves	1 tablespoon finely grated lemon
½ cup brown sugar	peel
¼ cup canola oil	¼ cup sliced almonds
2 egg whites	
6 tablespoons frozen, unsweetened apple juice concentrate	

Preheat oven to 350°F. In a bowl, sift together the flour, cornstarch, baking soda and spices. Set aside.

Using a mixer or food processor, beat together the brown sugar, oil, egg whites and apple juice concentrate. When smooth and creamy, add the almond extract and water and process until well blended. Slowly add the flour mixture, mixing until completely incorporated.

By hand, stir in the grated vegetables, apple and lemon peel. Stir until well mixed. Add the almonds and stir until evenly distributed.

Spray an 8-x-5-inch loaf pan with nonstick cooking spray. Pour the batter into the pan and bake for 40 minutes or until an inserted toothpick comes out clean. Allow the bread to cool 30 minutes before slicing. The bread is excellent plain or with Apple Cheese (recipe follows).

YIELD: 10 servings

CALORIES   CARBOHYDRATES: 36.4 GM   TOTAL FAT: 4.7 GM
Per serving: 196   PROTEIN: 4.0 GM   Saturated fat: .4 GM
Fat: 21%   DIETARY FIBER: 3.2 GM   Monounsaturated fat: 2.9 GM
Carbohydrates: 71%   SODIUM: 146 MG
Protein: 8%   CHOLESTEROL: 0 MG

Pyramid equivalencies: 2 grains, ⅓ vegetable, ⅓ fruit

Apple Cheese

This simple spread is excellent for a variety of breads, including bagels and English muffins.

  1 recipe Basic Yogurt Cheese   1 red or green apple
     (page 255)   ⅛ teaspoon ground nutmeg

Prepare the Basic Yogurt Cheese, letting the mixture stand in the strainer for 24 hours.

Peel and core the apple. With a hand grater or food processor, grate the apple. Place the apple in a strainer and press out as much liquid as possible. Immediately mix the grated apple and nutmeg into the Basic Yogurt Cheese. Spoon into a serving dish and refrigerate until ready to serve. Do not make the Apple Cheese more than 4 hours before using.

YIELD: 10 servings

CALORIES   CARBOHYDRATES: 5.4 GM   TOTAL FAT: .1 GM
Per serving: 33   PROTEIN: 2.7 GM   Saturated fat: .1 GM
Fat: 3%   DIETARY FIBER: .3 GM   Monounsaturated fat: trace
Carbohydrates: 65%   SODIUM: 35 MG
Protein: 32%   CHOLESTEROL: 1 MG

Pyramid equivalencies: ⅛ fruit, ⅓ dairy

Iced Mocha Royale

This richly flavored beverage serves beautifully as a replacement for dessert.

3 tablespoons brown sugar   ½ cup dry nonfat milk powder
1 tablespoon cocoa powder   ½ cup fluid nonfat milk
¼ teaspoon cinnamon   ½ teaspoon vanilla extract
3 cups hot coffee

Dissolve the brown sugar, cocoa and cinnamon into the hot coffee. When completely dissolved, refrigerate until fully chilled.

Dissolve the dry milk powder into the fluid milk. Add the vanilla extract. Combine the milk and coffee mixtures and transfer to glasses filled with ice cubes. Serve immediately.

YIELD: 4 servings

CALORIES	CARBOHYDRATES: 16.7 GM	TOTAL FAT: .4 GM
Per cup: 95	PROTEIN: 6.8 GM	Saturated fat: .3 GM
Fat: 4%	DIETARY FIBER: 0 GM	Monounsaturated fat: .1 GM
Carbohydrates: 68%	SODIUM: 99 MG	
Protein: 28%	CHOLESTEROL: 4 MG	

Pyramid equivalencies: 1 dairy

Hot Mocha Royale

Hot Mocha Royale uses the same ingredients as the iced version with a slight reduction in sweetener. Temperature drastically affects our perception of sweetness. Things that are very cold need more sweetener than those dishes served at room temperature. Dishes that are served hot may also need more sweetener than when served at room temperature, but likely will not require as much as when served icy cold.

To make Hot Mocha Royale follow the directions for the iced version, but reduce the brown sugar to 2 tablespoons or 1½ teaspoons per serving. After you have added the dry milk to the liquid milk, heat before adding to the hot coffee. This is easily accomplished in the microwave. Heat the milk until hot but do not boil. Stir together the hot milk and coffee mixtures and serve immediately. If desired garnish each cup with a cinnamon stick.

YIELD: 4 servings

CALORIES	CARBOHYDRATES: 14.4 GM	TOTAL FAT: .4 GM
Per cup: 86	PROTEIN: 6.8 GM	Saturated fat: .3 GM
Fat: 4%	DIETARY FIBER: 0 GM	Monounsaturated fat: .1 GM
Carbohydrates: 65%	SODIUM: 98 MG	
Protein: 31%	CHOLESTEROL: 4 MG	

Pyramid equivalencies: 1 dairy

4

A Chicken in Every Pot

YOU DON'T have to be a fan of Herbert Hoover's or a child of the Great Depression to yearn for chicken in a pot. Prepared in the oven or on top of the stove, chicken in a pot is an old-fashioned comfort dish that offers a sublime flavor achieved only by moist heat and long-term cooking. This menu explores how to re-create the flavor of an old-fashioned chicken stew, using a variety of time-efficient, health-conscious techniques. In fact, this chapter offers five different ways to prepare Chicken in the Pot.

A CHICKEN IN EVERY POT (MENU FOR 4)

Choice of:
Baked Chicken in a Pot
Chicken in a Clay Pot
Steamed Chicken in a Pot
Pressure-Steamed Chicken in a Pot
Chicken in a Crock-Pot

Choice of side dishes:
Roasted Potato Mélange
Kasha and Brown Rice Pilaf
Red Slaw
Savory Poached Pears
Rhubarb Compote

Additional recipes:
Country Chicken Marinade
Basic Rich Chicken Broth
Faster Chicken Broth
Enhanced Canned Broth
Savory Crumb Topping

NUTRIENT ANALYSIS FOR A CHICKEN IN EVERY POT

I would not serve the same side dishes with each version. To determine the nutrient analysis for a complete meal, I have created 5 menu combinations listed below. The nutrient analysis for the complete menu is for 1 serving of each dish. Although it is not included in the total, I would definitely serve a bread with each menu.

Menu I: Baked Chicken in a Pot
Savory Crumb Topping
Roasted Potato Mélange
Red Slaw
Savory Poached Pears
Rhubarb Compote

CALORIES	CARBOHYDRATES: 118.0 GM	TOTAL FAT: 10.0 GM
For total meal: 671	PROTEIN: 36.1 GM	Saturated fat: 1.9 GM
Fat: 13%	DIETARY FIBER: 14.1 GM	Monounsaturated fat: 4.4 GM
Carbohydrates: 67%	SODIUM: 305 MG	
Protein: 20%	CHOLESTEROL: 74 MG	

Pyramid equivalencies: ¼ grain, 4¼ vegetables, 2½ fruits, 1 protein

Menu II: Chicken in a Clay Pot
(Accompanying dishes and nutrient analysis are the same as Menu I.)

Menu III: Steamed Chicken in a Pot
Savory Crumb Topping
Kasha and Brown Rice Pilaf
Savory Poached Pears
Red Slaw
Rhubarb Compote

CALORIES   CARBOHYDRATES: 132.0 GM   TOTAL FAT: 8.3 GM
For total meal: 737   PROTEIN: 40.9 GM   Saturated fat: 1.6 GM
Fat: 10%   DIETARY FIBER: 15.3 GM   Monounsaturated fat: 2.7 GM
Carbohydrates: 69%   SODIUM: 399 MG
Protein: 21%   CHOLESTEROL: 74 MG

Pyramid equivalencies: 1¾ grains, 2¼ vegetables, 2½ fruits, 1 protein

Menu IV: Pressure-Steamed Chicken in a Pot
Kasha and Brown Rice Pilaf
Savory Poached Pears
Red Slaw
Rhubarb Compote

CALORIES   CARBOHYDRATES: 135.0 GM   TOTAL FAT: 7.9 GM
For total meal: 746   PROTEIN: 41.1 GM   Saturated fat: 1.3 GM
Fat: 9%   DIETARY FIBER: 15.6 GM   Monounsaturated fat: 2.6 GM
Carbohydrates: 70%   SODIUM: 343 MG
Protein: 21%   CHOLESTEROL: 73 MG

Pyramid equivalencies: 1¾ grains, 3¼ vegetables, 2½ fruits, 1 protein

Menu V: Chicken in a Crock-Pot
Savory Poached Pears
Red Slaw
Rhubarb Compote

CALORIES   CARBOHYDRATES: 132.0 GM   TOTAL FAT: 7.3 GM
For total meal: 710   PROTEIN: 37.8 GM   Saturated fat: 1.3 GM
Fat: 9%   DIETARY FIBER: 20.2 GM   Monounsaturated fat: 2.5 GM
Carbohydrates: 71%   SODIUM: 222 MG
Protein: 20%   CHOLESTEROL: 73 MG

Pyramid equivalencies: 1¼ grains, 2¾ vegetables, 2½ fruits, 1 protein

Chicken in a pot goes back to a time when young, tender frying chickens were a spring and summer specialty. The rest of the year the butcher shop offered older hens, no longer considered useful for producing eggs. These tough old birds required slow, moist cooking, for 2 or 3 hours. The result was a hearty, subtle, sweet delicacy. The constant availability of tender fryers and the preference for quickly prepared meals have made stewed chicken something of a rarity. In fact, many supermarkets no longer carry stewing chicken. We used to stew the chicken to tenderize the meat. Young frying chickens no longer make that necessary. Lengthy cooking of young chicken results in a mushy-textured meat that ceases to resemble chicken. Short-term cooking of young chicken with moist heat can produce a delicious dish, but often without the sweet, rich flavors that can only develop over time. This chapter explores ways to infuse flavor into chicken that is cooked with moist heat.

I know a lot of people who eat chicken and turkey but refuse to eat beef because they feel it isn't as healthy. This is an assumption that I find difficult to prove. Skinless chicken breast is a marvelous low-fat meat. It is especially low in saturated fat. Removing the skin from a chicken breast cuts the amount of fat in the breast by more than 50%. However, chicken breast *with* the skin still has less fat than the same amount of dark meat *without* skin. And, like the breast, eating the skin of dark meat nearly doubles your fat intake. Comparatively, pork tenderloin has 33% more fat and lean top round has 44% more fat than equal amounts of skinless chicken breast. However, both pork tenderloin and top round have less fat than chicken breast with the skin. Even a well-trimmed leg of lamb has less fat. These cuts score even better against the dark meat of chicken. When you include the skin with the dark meat, you will find that even a filet mignon has less fat. I'm not telling you to never eat the dark meat. Just keep in mind, if you want to reduce the fat in your diet, skinless chicken breast is a superior product. All of these chicken recipes feature skinless chicken breast.

You can use several different methods to create Chicken in a Pot. I've included recipes for Baked Chicken in a Pot, Chicken in a Clay Pot, Steamed Chicken in a Pot, Pressure-Steamed Chicken in a Pot and Chicken in a Crock-Pot. I've included special instructions with each recipe that describe how to use that particular pot. All of the recipes share in common the use of moist heat, begin with the same marinade and have several ingredients that are the same, but I assure you that they will not taste the same. The textures will also vary. If you want to add more of textural and flavor contrast to the dish, you may want to sprinkle Savory Crumb Topping over each serving of chicken. The Chicken in a Pot recipes can be offered as a one-pot meal; however, I generally like to offer a side dish with a contrasting appearance. Roasted Potato Mélange and Kasha and Brown Rice Pilaf are possible choices. Other accompaniments to the chicken dishes include Savory Poached Pears, Red Slaw, and Rhubarb Compote.

ABOUT PREPARING CHICKEN BREASTS

For all of the chicken recipes that follow, I use chicken breasts because they are significantly lower in saturated fat than other parts of the chicken. I also remove the skin from the breast to reduce the fat and cholesterol. Cooking the breast with the skin on and then discarding it before eating is fine, since it really doesn't increase the fat content of the meat it surrounds. However, I usually remove the skin and trim away any visible fat on the breast because it saves me the step of having to skim the fat from the cooking liquid, which will be turned into a sauce for the chicken. Also, the appearance of the skin when cooked in moist heat will have a gray, wrinkled appearance. I prefer leaving the chicken on the bone because it keeps the meat in an attractive rounded shape. A boneless breast, when cooked in moist heat, tends to shrivel and become quite dense. Cooking the breast on the bone also enhances the flavor of the cooking liquid, which in turn creates a more flavorful sauce. Marinating the chicken breasts before cooking also greatly improves the flavor of the dish. To create the moist heat, a deeply flavored chicken broth is a better choice than water. The broth will reinforce the essential chicken flavor. A recipe for Basic Rich Chicken Broth is included in this chapter. Canned broth or dehydrated cubes simply do not offer the fresh flavor of homemade broth or consommé. If you feel you don't have the 3 hours that it takes to cook chicken broth, you can reduce the time to 1 hour in a pressure cooker. This Faster Chicken Broth has all of the flavor of the slower method. If canned broth is the only solution, try Enhanced Canned Broth, which gives added "umph" to the canned product.

Country Chicken Marinade

This simple marinade brings body and richness to chicken breasts and is used in all of the Chicken in Every Pot recipes in this chapter.

1 tablespoon dry white wine
4 cloves garlic, finely minced
2 teaspoons brown sugar
2 teaspoons low-sodium soy
   sauce
2 teaspoons finely grated fresh
   lemon or orange peel

1 bay leaf, finely crushed
1 teaspoon crushed, dry
   rosemary
½ teaspoon dry ground thyme
¼ teaspoon black pepper

Stir together all of the ingredients in a small bowl. Using a pestle or the back of a spoon, mash the ingredients into a paste.

To marinate chicken breasts, first remove the skin from the breasts and discard. With a knife or kitchen scissors, trim away any visible fat. Leave the meat on the bone. Use the knife to make 6 crisscross incisions in the breast, about ¼ inch deep. Spoon the marinade over the breasts and refrigerate for at least 1 hour. Use as directed in the recipes that follow.

YIELD: 4 servings

Nutrient analysis is for marinade only.

CALORIES
Per serving: 17
Fat: 4%
Carbohydrates: 86%
Protein: 10%

CARBOHYDRATES: 4.4 GM
PROTEIN: .5 GM
DIETARY FIBER: trace
SODIUM: 88 MG
CHOLESTEROL: 0 MG

TOTAL FAT: .1 GM
Saturated fat: trace
Monounsaturated fat: trace

Pyramid equivalencies: No equivalencies

Baked Chicken in a Pot

To make this dish, you need a simple ovenproof baking dish. Ovenproof dishes range from simple Pyrex baking dishes to elaborate, decorative casseroles. All you need is a dish big enough to place 4 chicken breasts without overlapping and foil or a lid to tightly cover the dish. When I serve Baked Chicken in a Pot, I like to offer a side dish that has a contrasting texture. Roasted Potato Mélange (recipe in this chapter) can be baked in the oven at the same time.

4 *chicken breast halves, on the bone, with skin and fat removed*

1 *recipe Country Chicken Marinade (preceding recipe)*

1 *medium red onion, peeled and thinly sliced in rings*

2 *large carrots, cut in 3-inch sticks*

½ *cup unsalted, defatted chicken broth, or more (recipes on pages 49–51)*

¼ *cup dry white wine*

2 *tablespoons finely minced fresh parsley*

¼ *cup Savory Crumb Topping (recipe on page 51), optional*

Prepare the chicken breasts and marinade as directed in the recipe for Country Chicken Marinade.

Scatter the onion slices and carrot sticks in the bottom of a baking dish. Arrange the breasts on the vegetables. Drizzle the broth and wine over the chicken and vegetables. If necessary, add more liquid to create a depth of ¼ inch. Cover the dish with foil or a tight-fitting lid. Place in a preheated 375°F. oven and bake for 45 minutes.

Serve with the onion slices and carrot sticks scattered over and around the breasts and the cooking liquid spooned over the top. Sprinkle the fresh parsley over the breasts. If desired, also sprinkle the Savory Crumb Topping over the breasts.

YIELD: 4 servings

CALORIES
Per serving: 195
Fat: 16%
Carbohydrates: 25%
Protein: 59%

CARBOHYDRATES: 11.9 GM
PROTEIN: 28.5 GM
DIETARY FIBER: 1.9 GM
SODIUM: 166 MG
CHOLESTEROL: 73 MG

TOTAL FAT: 3.3 GM
Saturated fat: .9 GM
Monounsaturated fat: 1.1 GM

Pyramid equivalencies: 1 vegetable, 1 protein

Chicken in a Clay Pot

This method requires a special clay baking dish with a cover. Clay pots are somewhat fragile, requiring careful handling. Before using a clay pot, be sure to read the manufacturer's instructions. Generally, the directions require soaking the clay pot, including the lid, in cold water for 15 minutes. After soaking, you immediately place whatever you are cooking in the pot, using minimal liquid. Clay pots are suitable for vegetables, fish, chicken and red meats. Immediately, place the clay pot in a cold oven. Do not preheat the oven. As soon as the pot is in the oven, turn the oven on and set the temperature to high (400°F. to 450°F.).

Clay pots are unique in that they actually steam and roast the food, creating an exquisite flavor and texture that cannot be duplicated by any other method. Although this recipe has essentially the same ingredients as the previous recipe, using a clay pot will produce a very different flavor. I like to serve Roasted Potato Mélange with this dish as well. You can also add potatoes to the Chicken in a Clay Pot and have a one-dish meal.

4 chicken breast halves, bone intact, skin and fat removed
1 recipe Country Chicken Marinade (recipe on page 41)
1 medium red onion, peeled and thinly sliced in rings
2 large carrots, cut in 3-inch sticks
¼ cup dry sherry (more or less)
2 tablespoons finely minced fresh parsley
¼ cup Savory Crumb Topping (recipe on page 51), optional

Prepare the chicken breasts and marinade according to the recipe for Country Chicken Marinade. You do not need to marinate the breasts for the full hour. Twenty minutes will suffice.

Meanwhile, submerge the clay pot, including the lid, in cold water for at least 20 minutes.

Scatter the onion slices and carrot sticks in the bottom of the clay pot. Arrange the breasts on the vegetables and pour the marinade over the breasts. If necessary, add sherry to the pot to just barely cover the bottom. Cover the pot with the lid and place in a cold oven. Set the oven to 450°F. and bake for 50 minutes.

Serve with the onion slices and carrot sticks scattered over and around the breasts and the cooking liquid spooned over the top. Sprinkle the fresh parsley over the breasts. If desired, also sprinkle the Savory Crumb Topping over the breasts.

YIELD: 4 servings

Nutrient analysis is the same as the Baked Chicken in a Pot.

Steamed Chicken in a Pot

Steaming meats is an ancient Chinese technique that is growing in popularity in the United States. Americans are familiar with steamed vegetables, but are just catching on to steamed meats. The availability of electric steamers has widened the use of steaming as a quick, clean cooking method. Steaming produces fresh, crisp flavors and textures. In Steamed Chicken in a Pot, the carrots, onions and chicken retain their distinctively individual flavors. In the other chicken dishes in this chapter, the ingredients tend to synthesize, creating one primary flavor. I like to serve this version of Chicken in a Pot with Kasha and Brown Rice Pilaf or other grain dish.

4 chicken breast halves, bone
  intact, skin and fat
  removed
1 recipe Country Chicken
  Marinade (recipe on
  page 45)
1 cup (or more) unsalted,
  defatted chicken broth
  (recipes on pages 49–51)
¼ cup dry white wine

1 medium red onion, thinly
  sliced
2 large carrots, cut in ¼-inch-
  thick rounds
1 to 2 tablespoons unsalted
  tomato paste
2 tablespoons finely minced
  fresh parsley
¼ cup Savory Crumb Topping
  (recipe on page 51), optional

Prepare the chicken breasts and marinade as directed in the recipe for Country Chicken Marinade.

Pour enough broth into a pot suitable for steaming to create a depth of ⅜ inch. Reserve extra broth for possible later use. Add the wine. Place a steamer rack or basket in the pot. Arrange the onion and carrot slices on the rack and place the breasts on the vegetables. Cover with a tight-fitting lid and steam for 8 minutes. Check the pot to verify there is still plenty of liquid for steaming. If necessary, add more liquid. Re-cover and continue cooking for 3 to 4 minutes.

Lift the steamer basket from the pot. Set aside the chicken and vegetables to keep warm. Stir the tomato paste into the hot liquid and continue cooking at high temperature until the liquid has thickened.

Serve with the onion and carrot slices scattered around the breasts and thickened sauce over the top. Sprinkle the fresh parsley over the breasts and, if desired, Savory Crumb Topping as well.

YIELD: 4 servings

CALORIES
Per serving: 207
Fat: 15%
Carbohydrates: 28%
Protein: 57%

CARBOHYDRATES: 14.2 GM
PROTEIN: 29.2 GM
DIETARY FIBER: 2.2 GM
SODIUM: 171 MG
CHOLESTEROL: 73 MG

TOTAL FAT: 3.4 GM
Saturated fat: .9 GM
Monounsaturated fat: 1.1 GM

Pyramid equivalencies: 1 vegetable, 1 protein

Pressure-Steamed Chicken in a Pot

A lot of cooks are scared of pressure cookers, fearing that somehow they will explode in their kitchen. A pressure cooker, used properly, is no more hazardous than many other pieces of equipment. A kitchen is a dangerous place if you do not observe basic safety procedures. Used improperly, knives, microwaves, food processors, stoves and garbage disposals can cause serious harm. If you follow the safety instructions of the manufacturer, I believe pressure cookers offer a safe, rapid way to prepare tasty, nutritious food. It is especially important to read the instruction book for your specific pressure cooker before adapting or creating recipes.

The first safety check is to observe the quantity of products in relationship to the size of the pot. The pot should never be more than two-thirds filled with vegetables or meats and no more than one-third filled with liquid. Most meats and vegetables will only require enough liquid to create a depth of ½ inch. The measurements in the following recipe are suitable for use in a 6-quart or larger pressure cooker.

Before locking the lid in place, check to see that the lid vent is open and free of any blockage. (I usually run a toothpick back and forth in the vent to verify that it is clear.) Also check to see that the gasket is firmly in place on the inside of the lid before sliding the lid into place.

There are new models of pressure cookers that don't use the rocking valve. The following instructions are for those models with the rocking valve. Set the rocking valve in place on top of the lid. Place the pot on the burner at high. In a few minutes, the safety lock will click into position, followed shortly by the hissing sound of the rocking valve. Reduce the heat, but keep it high enough to maintain the pressure and hissing sound. When the valve begins to rock, set a timer for how long you want it to cook. Cooking time for pressure cooker recipes begins when the valve begins to rock. When the time is up, promptly remove the pot from the heat; be careful not to dislodge the rocking valve. Let the pot stand until the safety lock allows you to release the lid.

Like the Crock-Pot, pressure cookers are also great for preparing tough cuts of meat. The pressure cooker is useful for preparing many other items, but remember it cooks rapidly. Some products in a pressure cooker will cook just as fast if not faster than a microwave. A beef stew that would take 2 or 3 hours on top of the stove, or 8 hours in a Crock-Pot, may be done in 20 to 30 minutes in a pressure cooker. Because the pressure cooker cooks so quickly, I generally do not use it for preparing vegetables (except root vegetables), fish or seafood. Also, be aware that it is very easy to overcook chicken.

4 chicken breast halves, bone intact, skin and fat removed

1 recipe Country Chicken Marinade (recipe on page 41)

2 large carrots, cut in ¼-inch-thick rounds

1 medium red onion, diced

1 cup sliced mushrooms

1 cup (or more) unsalted, defatted chicken broth (recipes on pages 49–51)

2 cups canned, unsalted tomatoes

1 to 2 tablespoons unsalted tomato paste

2 tablespoons finely minced fresh basil

Prepare the chicken breasts and marinade as directed in the recipe for Country Chicken Marinade. Because this cooking method is so rapid, the chicken will be tastier if you marinate it for at least 2 hours.

Place the rack in the bottom of the pressure cooker. Place the carrot slices, onion, and mushroom slices on the rack. Set the chicken breasts on the vegetables. Pour the marinade, broth and tomatoes over the chicken.

Lock the lid in place and turn the heat to high. Adjust the heat to maintain high pressure and cook for 7 minutes and absolutely no longer. Promptly remove the pot from the heat. Let the pot stand until the safety lock allows you to release the lid.

With a slotted spoon, transfer the chicken and vegetables to a serving platter. Stir the tomato paste into the hot liquid. Pour the thickened sauce over the chicken. Sprinkle the basil over the top and serve immediately. I like to serve this with a Kasha and Brown Rice Pilaf (recipe in this chapter) or other grain pilaf. It's also excellent with pasta.

YIELD: 4 servings

CALORIES   CARBOHYDRATES: 20.5 GM   TOTAL FAT: 3.8 GM
Per serving: 195   PROTEIN: 30.8 GM   Saturated fat: 1.0 GM
Fat: 14%   DIETARY FIBER: 3.3 GM   Monounsaturated fat: 1.2 GM
Carbohydrates: 35%   SODIUM: 189 MG
Protein: 51%   CHOLESTEROL: 73 MG

Pyramid equivalencies: 2 vegetables, 1 protein

Chicken in a Crock-Pot

The primary advantage of a Crock-Pot (electric slow cooker) is that you
can turn it on, leave it unattended and return 6 to 8 hours later to a
finished meal. Crock-Pots are best known for creating one-pot meals
that include a mix of vegetables and meat. This version of Chicken in a
Pot includes barley, making it a complete meal in one pot. My favorite
use of the Crock-Pot is for preparing tough cuts of meat that require
longer cooking. A low, moist heat and long-term cooking tenderize the
meat and intensify the flavor of the dish. I am less satisfied with chicken
cooked in a Crock-Pot and would never use it for preparing fish, seafood or any vegetable other than firm root vegetables. I've included this
recipe with chicken because I know that, no matter how gourmet our
tastes, the convenience of a ready and waiting hot meal is often totally
satisfying.

 1 recipe Country Chicken   2 large carrots, cut in ⅜-inch-
    Marinade (recipe on page   thick rounds
    41)   1 cup pearl barley, rinsed and
1¼ cups unsalted, defatted   drained
    chicken broth (recipes on   4 chicken breast halves, bone
    pages 49–51)   intact, skin and fat removed
 ½ cup dry white wine   2 tablespoons finely minced
 ½ pound sliced mushrooms   fresh parsley
 1 medium red onion, diced

Prepare the Country Chicken Marinade and mix it with the broth and
wine. In the bottom of a 3-quart or larger Crock-Pot, stir together the
liquid mixture with the sliced mushrooms, diced onion, carrot rounds

and barley. Place the breasts on the barley-vegetable mixture. In this recipe, the breasts do not need to be scored with the knife or marinated before cooking begins. Cover and cook at low for 6 to 7 hours or until the barley is tender.

Serve with the parsley sprinkled over the barley and chicken breasts.

YIELD: 4 servings

CALORIES	CARBOHYDRATES: 54.3 GM	TOTAL FAT: 4.0 GM
Per serving: 388	PROTEIN: 33.7 GM	Saturated fat: 1.0 GM
Fat: 9%	DIETARY FIBER: 10.2 GM	Monounsaturated fat: 1.2 GM
Carbohydrates: 56%	SODIUM: 170 MG	
Protein: 35%	CHOLESTEROL: 73 MG	

Pyramid equivalencies: 1 grain, 1½ vegetables, 1 protein

Basic Rich Chicken Broth

Combining chicken and turkey parts make an extra-rich stock.

2 *pounds chicken backs, necks or wings*
1 *pound turkey necks or wings*
1 *large onion, including skin, coarsely chopped*
1 *whole bulb garlic*
2 *carrots, sliced*
2 *stalks celery*
1 *sprig fresh parsley*
1 *teaspoon dry rosemary*
2 *bay leaves*
8 *cups water, plus additional water*
1 *cup dry sherry*

Combine all of the ingredients in a large pot and simmer for 3 hours, uncovered. Periodically add more water, enough to keep the vegetables covered. Remove from the heat and strain, discarding everything but the liquid. If necessary, add more water to the stock to yield a total of 8 cups.

Skim the fat from the stock. The easiest way to do this is to chill the stock overnight. When ready to use, skim the fat off the top. Underneath will be a rich, gelatinous consommé.

YIELD: 8 servings

CALORIES   CARBOHYDRATES: 5.5 GM   TOTAL FAT: trace
Per serving: 34   PROTEIN: 2.6 GM   Saturated fat: trace
Fat: 0%   DIETARY FIBER: 0 GM   Monounsaturated fat: trace
Carbohydrates: 68%   SODIUM: 5 MG
Protein: 32%   CHOLESTEROL: trace

Pyramid equivalencies: No equivalencies

Faster Chicken Broth

Using a pressure cooker, you can have rich chicken broth in less than 1 hour! See the note about pressure cookers at the beginning of the Pressure-Steamed Chicken in a Pot recipe.

The measurements in the previous recipe, except the water, are suitable for use in a 6-quart pressure cooker. Instead of 8 cups of water, use only 4. Place the rack in the bottom of the pressure cooker. Place the vegetables and poultry parts on the rack. Add the seasonings and pour 4 cups of water and 1 cup of sherry into the pot.

Lock the lid in place and turn the heat to high. Adjust the heat to maintain high pressure and cook for 25 minutes. Promptly remove the pot from the heat. Let the pot stand until the safety lock allows you to release the lid.

Strain the contents, discarding all but the liquid. Add enough water to the pot to yield 8 cups of liquid. Skim the fat from the broth before using.

YIELD: 8 cups

Nutrient analysis is the same as the previous recipe.

Enhanced Canned Broth

The flavor of canned broth simply does not have the fresh, rich flavor of homemade broth. I realize that when we are in a hurry, we may sometimes need to use the canned product. This simple recipe shows how you can enhance the canned product with a few flavorful additions. Because soy is added to this recipe, it is very important to use only unsalted broth. If the enhanced broth is going to be used in a cooked dish, you can simply whisk the ingredients together and use immediately without cooking.

56 *ounces canned unsalted*
chicken broth (4 fourteen-
ounce cans)
1 *cup dry sherry*

2 *tablespoons unsalted tomato*
paste
1 *tablespoon low-sodium soy*
sauce

Skim the fat from the broth. Whisk together the broth, sherry, tomato paste and soy sauce. If adding to a dish that does not require cooking, simmer the broth ingredients in a small saucepan for 4 minutes before using.

YIELD: 8 cups

Nutrient analysis is nearly the same as Basic Rich Chicken Broth except sodium increases to 30 milligrams per cup.

Savory Crumb Topping

These flavorful crumbs, sprinkled over meat or vegetables just before serving, enhance both flavor and texture.

1 *slice whole wheat or mixed*
grain bread
1 *tablespoon finely grated*
fresh Parmesan cheese
1 *teaspoon finely grated fresh*
lemon peel

$1/4$ *teaspoon dry ground sage*
$1/8$ *teaspoon dry ground thyme*
$1/8$ *teaspoon ground black pepper*

Lightly toast the bread. Tear the bread into small pieces and place in a food processor or blender and pulse until the bread is ground. If you do not have a processor or blender, use a rolling pin to crush the bread into crumbs. Stir in the seasonings and store in dry, airtight container. Do not refrigerate, but use within 24 hours.

YIELD: 4 servings

CALORIES	CARBOHYDRATES: 3.2 GM	TOTAL FAT: .8 GM
Per serving: 25	PROTEIN: 1.3 GM	Saturated fat: .3 GM
Fat: 28%	DIETARY FIBER: .8 GM	Monounsaturated fat: .1 GM
Carbohydrates: 51%	SODIUM: 74 MG	
Protein: 21%	CHOLESTEROL: 1 MG	

Pyramid equivalencies: ¼ grain

Roasted Potato Mélange

Steaming vegetables before roasting produces vegetables that are soft on the inside and crisp on the outside. They make an appealing contrast in flavor and texture to the Baked Chicken in a Pot or Chicken in a Clay Pot.

2 *medium red potatoes, washed and cut in bite-size pieces*

1 *small yam or sweet potato, peeled and cut in bite-size pieces*

1 *turnip or rutabaga, peeled and cut in bite-size pieces*

2 *teaspoons olive oil*

1 *teaspoon granulated garlic powder*

½ *teaspoon paprika*

1 *tablespoon finely minced fresh rosemary*

4 *sprigs fresh rosemary for garnish (optional)*

Place the vegetable pieces in a steamer basket. Pour enough water in the pot to make a depth of ⅜ inch. Steam, covered, for 8 minutes or until vegetables are just tender.

Remove the vegetables from the basket and toss while still hot with the olive oil, garlic powder, paprika and rosemary. Spread the vegetables on a baking sheet and roast at 450°F. for 10 minutes.

YIELD: 4 servings

CALORIES
Per serving: 130
Fat: 17%
Carbohydrates: 76%
Protein: 7%

CARBOHYDRATES: 25.7 GM
PROTEIN: 2.2 GM
DIETARY FIBER: 1.3 GM
SODIUM: 14 MG
CHOLESTEROL: 0 MG

TOTAL FAT: 2.5 GM
Saturated fat: .4 GM
Monounsaturated fat: 1.7 GM

Pyramid equivalencies: 2 vegetables

Kasha and Brown Rice Pilaf

Kasha brings an aromatic, wild flavor to the rice.

1 cup finely diced white or yellow onion
2¾ cups boiling chicken broth (recipes on pages 49–51)
1 cup brown rice
½ cup kasha (buckwheat groats)

1 small egg white
1 cup finely diced white or yellow onion
1 cup brown rice
2 teaspoons low-sodium soy sauce

Combine the onion and broth in a saucepan and bring the broth to a boil. Stir in the rice, and when the broth returns to a boil reduce the heat to low and cover. Allow the rice to cook for 20 minutes.

Meanwhile, mix the kasha (groats) and egg white in a small nonstick skillet. Cook over medium heat, stirring regularly until the kasha is dry. Stir the kasha into the rice, cover tightly and continue cooking at very low heat for 20 minutes.

Remove the grains from the heat, stir in the soy sauce and serve immediately.

YIELD: 4 servings

CALORIES   CARBOHYDRATES: 37.6 GM   TOTAL FAT: .8 GM
Per serving: 184   PROTEIN: 6.3 GM   Saturated fat: trace
Fat: 4%   DIETARY FIBER: 2.3 GM   Monounsaturated fat: .3 GM
Carbohydrates: 82%   SODIUM: 103 MG
Protein: 14%   CHOLESTEROL: 0 MG

Pyramid equivalencies: 1½ grains

Savory Poached Pears

This is a wonderful condiment to serve with almost any meat dish. Cooked in broth and dry wine, the pears have a flavor more like a vegetable than a fruit.

> 4 small Bosc pears, peeled   1 cup dry red wine
>   and cored
> 1 cup defatted, unsalted
>   chicken broth, more if
>   necessary

Cut a thin slice off the bottom of the pears so that they will easily stand upright. Combine pears, broth and wine in a small pan. If necessary, add enough liquid to barely cover the pears. Simmer at moderate heat until the pears are just tender. Allow to cool in the liquid. Refrigerate, stored in the liquid. Reheat just before serving. Offer as a condiment with any meat dish. The pears are best made 1 or 2 days ahead.

YIELD: 4 servings

CALORIES   CARBOHYDRATES: 30.3 GM   TOTAL FAT: .8 GM
Per serving: 120   PROTEIN: .8 GM   Saturated fat: trace
Fat: 5%   DIETARY FIBER: 5.2 GM   Monounsaturated fat: .2 GM
Carbohydrates: 92%   SODIUM: 1.7 MG
Protein: 3%   CHOLESTEROL: 0 MG

Pyramid equivalencies: 1 fruit

Red Slaw

Although green cabbage will work, the red variety will have a superior appearance when mixed with the dressing.

½ cup red wine vinegar
2 tablespoons tomato paste
2 tablespoons frozen, unsweetened apple juice concentrate
¼ teaspoon allspice
⅛ teaspoon cayenne pepper

2 cups shredded red cabbage
1 medium carrot, grated
½ cup finely diced red onion
½ cup finely diced red bell pepper
¼ cup raisins

Whisk together the vinegar, tomato paste, juice concentrate, allspice and cayenne pepper. Toss with the remaining ingredients and marinate 1 to 4 hours before serving. Mix two or three times while marinating. Serve cold or at room temperature.

YIELD: 4 servings

CALORIES
Per serving: 79
Fat: 4%
Carbohydrates: 89%
Protein: 7%

CARBOHYDRATES: 20.2 GM
PROTEIN: 1.6 GM
DIETARY FIBER: 2.7 GM
SODIUM: 19 MG
CHOLESTEROL: 0 MG

TOTAL FAT: .4 GM
Saturated fat: .1 GM
Monounsaturated fat: trace

Pyramid equivalencies: 1 vegetable, ½ fruit

Rhubarb Compote

This old-fashioned dessert is a delightful way to complete a meal of comfort foods.

¼ cup unsweetened frozen apple juice concentrate
¼ cup fruit-sweetened strawberry preserves
¼ cup water
½ teaspoon cinnamon
1 cup diced fresh rhubarb

1 teaspoon orange-flavored liqueur
1 cup freshly sliced strawberries
2 tablespoons sliced almonds
2 tablespoons nutty-style cereal (Grape-Nuts, for example)

Whisk together the juice concentrate, preserves, water and cinnamon in a small saucepan. Place over moderate heat and add the rhubarb. Simmer 8 minutes or until the rhubarb is tender. Stir in the liqueur and allow to cool to room temperature. Stir in the fresh strawberries and transfer to individual serving dishes. Serve immediately or chill for later use. Just before serving, crush the almonds and mix with the nutty cereal. Sprinkle the mixture over the compote and serve.

YIELD: 4 servings

CALORIES
Per serving: 123
Fat: 14%
Carbohydrates: 81%
Protein: 5%

CARBOHYDRATES: 26.8 GM
PROTEIN: 1.6 GM
DIETARY FIBER: 2.1 GM
SODIUM: 31 MG
CHOLESTEROL: 0 MG

TOTAL FAT: 2.1 GM
Saturated fat: .2 GM
Monounsaturated fat: 1.2 GM

Pyramid equivalencies: ¼ vegetable, 1 fruit

5

Spring Holiday

TURKEY IS more than just a Thanksgiving dish. This menu shows how turkey can be used to create a fabulous springtime meal. I created this dinner to celebrate my friend Carol's birthday, which is on the first day of spring. Her favorite foods include turkey, strawberries and chocolate (not necessarily in that order!). A lot of times when I entertain I like to create several courses with many different dishes. This time I kept it simple with three basic courses.

SPRING HOLIDAY (MENU FOR 8)

Swiss Chard, Bean and Potato Soup
Turkey with Asparagus and Penne
Carol's Chocolate Cake and Mixed Berry Compote

Additional Recipes:
Swiss Chard, Bean and Potato Soup with Turkey Sausage
Basic Turkey Sausage
Spicy Sausage
Country Sausage
Chorizo-Style Sausage
Chocolate Raspberry Frosting

Swiss Chard, Bean and Potato Soup is a hearty soup that we often associate with meals in which soup is the main course. When I'm entertaining with a simple meal with few dishes, I like to feature a robust soup because it tends to fill people up. I would probably double the recipe so I can have more soup later in the week. The main course, Turkey with Asparagus and Penne, requires raw turkey breast. Because a whole turkey breast is likely a better buy, I've included recipes for homemade turkey sausage that can be made at the same time you are cutting the turkey for the pasta dish. Starting with a Basic Turkey Sausage, you can add seasoning blends to create Spicy Sausage, Country Sausage or Chorizo-Style Sausage. If you like, you can add some of your homemade sausage to the soup, creating Swiss Chard, Bean and Potato Soup with Turkey Sausage.

In keeping with a meal of robust flavors, Carol's Chocolate Cake has a dark chocolate flavor but is still low in fat. The cake is delicious with just Chocolate Raspberry Frosting, but I like to also serve a Mixed Berry Compote. I would likely serve this menu accompanied by mineral water with wedges of orange and a Muscadet wine. Although a bread recipe is not included in this chapter, I would definitely include bread. Since the soup is so robust, Hearty Whole Wheat Rolls (page 293) would be a good choice.

NUTRIENT ANALYSIS FOR SPRING HOLIDAY

The nutrient analysis includes 1 serving each of Swiss Chard, Bean and Potato Soup, Turkey with Asparagus and Penne, Carol's Chocolate Cake and Mixed Berry Compote. Beverage and bread are not included.

CALORIES	CARBOHYDRATES: 143.5 GM	TOTAL FAT: 14.7 GM
For total meal: 840	PROTEIN: 48.2 GM	Saturated fat: 2.0 GM
Fat: 15%	DIETARY FIBER: 11.7 GM	Monounsaturated fat: 6.1 GM
Carbohydrates: 64%	SODIUM: 537 MG	
Protein: 21%	CHOLESTEROL: 60.0 MG	

Pyramid equivalencies: 3 grains, 3 vegetables, 1¼ fruits, 1¼ proteins, 1 extra

Swiss Chard, Bean and Potato Soup

This is an earthy soup that is satisfying any time of year.

1 cup dry garbanzo beans
Water
1 red onion, finely diced
4 cloves garlic, finely minced
1 teaspoon dry crushed rosemary
1 teaspoon dry oregano leaves
¼ teaspoon ground black pepper
½ cup dry white wine
1 celery root, peeled and cut in 1-inch cubes
1 large potato, cubed
2 carrots, cut in ¼-inch-thick rounds
4 cups water
2 cups canned, unsalted tomatoes, chopped
12 ounces unsalted vegetable juice cocktail (e.g., V–8 juice)
6 cups Swiss chard, torn in 1-inch pieces

Rinse the beans in cold water, checking for any stones or foreign matter. Place the garbanzos in a pot and cover with 3 inches of cold water. Bring the water to a boil, then reduce to low. Simmer for 3 hours or until the beans are tender. If necessary, add more water to the pot. When the beans are done, drain and rinse under cold water. Refrigerate until you are ready to use.

Combine the onion, garlic, rosemary, oregano, black pepper and wine in a large pot. Cover and cook at medium heat for 20 minutes. Add the celery root, potato, carrots and water and simmer for 25 minutes uncovered. Add the tomatoes, vegetable juice cocktail and garbanzo beans and cook for 10 minutes. At this point, the soup can be completed or stored and reheated at a later time.

Add the Swiss chard just before serving. Cook the chard in the soup for 3 or 4 minutes. Serve immediately.

YIELD: 8 servings

CALORIES   CARBOHYDRATES: 28.8 GM   TOTAL FAT: 1.6 GM
Per serving: 159   PROTEIN: 7.7 GM   Saturated fat: trace
Fat: 9%   DIETARY FIBER: 2.2 GM   Monounsaturated fat: trace
Carbohydrates: 72% SODIUM: 137 MG
Protein: 19%   CHOLESTEROL: 0 MG

Pyramid equivalencies: 2 vegetables, ¼ protein

Swiss Chard, Bean and Potato Soup with Turkey Sausage

Sausage adds a wonderful robust flavor to soups. Unfortunately, traditional sausage is quite high in fat. I've found that you can flavor ground turkey breast with traditional sausage seasonings and attain a marvelous sausage taste.

Add a half recipe of Spicy Turkey Sausage (recipe follows) to one complete recipe of Swiss Chard, Bean and Potato Soup.

YIELD: 8 servings

CALORIES   CARBOHYDRATES: 30.6 GM   TOTAL FAT: 2.1 GM
Per serving: 232   PROTEIN: 22.0 GM   Saturated fat: .2 GM
Fat: 8%   DIETARY FIBER: 2.7 GM   Monounsaturated fat: .1 GM
Carbohydrates: 54% SODIUM: 232 MG
Protein: 38%   CHOLESTEROL: 35 MG

Pyramid equivalencies: 2 vegetables, ¾ protein

Basic Turkey Sausage

Ground turkey breast, seasoned with traditional sausage spices, takes on the flavor of sausage without the fat. This turkey sausage is not intended as a dish by itself. I use it to give a "sausage flavor" to dishes that often include sausage. It's delicious added to soups, stews, pilafs, grain-stuffed vegetables, pizzas and scrambled egg whites.

2 pounds ground turkey
  breast, without skin or fat
1 recipe Sausage Seasoning
  Blend (recipes follow)
1 cup dry sherry

1 cup water
2 tablespoons low-sodium soy
  sauce
1 tablespoon unsulfured
  molasses

In a large bowl, mix together the ground turkey breast and one of the Sausage Seasoning Blends (recipes follow). Mix until well incorporated.

Heat the sherry, water, soy sauce and molasses in a skillet until almost boiling. Reduce the heat to low and stir in the turkey mixture. Stirring occasionally, simmer until most of the liquid evaporates.

Refrigerate for up to 3 days or freeze for later use.

YIELD: 16 servings (when used in soup)

There are only minor differences in nutrient values with each seasoning blend.

CALORIES
Per serving: 73
Fat: 6%
Carbohydrates: 10%
Protein: 84%

CARBOHYDRATES: 1.8 GM
PROTEIN: 14.3 GM
DIETARY FIBER: .1 GM
SODIUM: 95 MG
CHOLESTEROL: 35 MG

TOTAL FAT: .5 GM
Saturated fat: .2 GM
Monounsaturated fat: .1 GM

Pyramid equivalencies: ½ protein

Sausage Seasoning Blend #1: Spicy Sausage

This blend produces a faintly sweet, piquant flavor. For those who want a little less heat, reduce the cayenne pepper to ¼ teaspoon.

4 cloves garlic, finely minced
2 teaspoons paprika
1 teaspoon crushed dry
  oregano
1 teaspoon crushed dry sage

1 teaspoon ground black pepper
½ teaspoon ground nutmeg
½ teaspoon ground cinnamon
½ teaspoon ground cloves
½ teaspoon cayenne pepper

Combine all of the ingredients and use as directed in the recipe for Basic Turkey Sausage. Use this blend with 2 pounds of ground turkey breast.

Sausage Seasoning Blend #2: Country Sausage

This blend produces a mildly spicy, herbal sausage.

8 cloves garlic, finely minced	1 teaspoon paprika
2 teaspoons dry crushed sage	½ teaspoon black pepper
1 teaspoon dry crushed rosemary	¼ teaspoon ground cinnamon
	1 cup very dry white wine
1 teaspoon ground fennel seed	2 teaspoons honey

In the Basic Turkey Sausage recipe, omit the sherry and molasses. Combine all of the ingredients for the Sausage Seasoning Blend and use as directed in the recipe for Basic Turkey Sausage. Use this blend with 2 pounds of ground turkey breast.

Sausage Seasoning Blend #3: Chorizo-Style Sausage

The flavor will remind you of a robust Mexican sausage.

1½ cups water	1 teaspoon black pepper
8 cloves garlic, finely minced	¼ teaspoon ground cloves
2 ounces dry ancho chile	⅔ cup apple cider vinegar
2 teaspoons dry ground oregano	⅓ cup frozen unsweetened apple juice concentrate
2 teaspoons ground cumin	

In the Basic Turkey Sausage Recipe, replace the sherry with ⅔ cup apple cider vinegar and ⅓ cup frozen unsweetened apple juice concentrate. Omit the molasses and water. In a saucepan, combine all of the ingredients for the seasoning blend and simmer until the chile has softened and the water is reduced to 1 cup. If necessary, add water to yield 1 cup. Puree the mixture in a blender until smooth. Add to Basic Turkey Sausage recipe and proceed as directed. Use this blend with 2 pounds of ground turkey breast.

Turkey with Asparagus and Penne

This is a wonderful dish that is great for parties and everyday dining.

2 pounds raw turkey breast, without skin or bone

4 shallots, finely minced

6 cloves garlic, finely minced

2 cups Marsala

2 pounds fresh asparagus

¼ cup frozen, unsweetened orange juice concentrate

2 tablespoons extra-virgin olive oil

2 tablespoons unsalted tomato paste

4 teaspoons low-sodium soy sauce

2 tablespoons capers, rinsed

1 pound dry penne pasta

6 quarts boiling water

2 tablespoons finely minced fresh basil

8 sprigs fresh basil for garnish

8 orange slices for garnish

Slice the raw turkey breast into very thin slices, no more than 2½ inches across and no more than ⅛ inch thick. In a skillet, combine the turkey with the shallots, garlic and Marsala. Cover and simmer at low temperature for 20 minutes or until the turkey is just tender.

Meanwhile, cut the lower, tough portion from the asparagus stalks and discard. Cut each stalk into 2-inch pieces. Set aside.

Add the juice concentrate, olive oil, tomato paste, soy sauce and capers to the turkey mixture. Increase the heat and cook until the sauce has started to thicken. Add the asparagus and cook until tender. If necessary, add water to the pan.

The pasta can be prepared while the turkey is cooking. Place the pasta in the boiling water and stir. Cook in boiling water for 10 minutes or until desired tenderness. Drain the pasta and toss with the turkey and asparagus mixture. Add the fresh basil and serve immediately. Garnish with sprigs of fresh basil and orange slices.

YIELD: 8 servings

CALORIES	CARBOHYDRATES: 53.6 GM	TOTAL FAT: 7.6 GM
Per serving: 428	PROTEIN: 37.0 GM	Saturated fat: 1.5 GM
Fat: 16%	DIETARY FIBER: 2.9 GM	Monounsaturated fat: 3.0 GM
Carbohydrates: 50%	SODIUM: 285 MG	
Protein: 34%	CHOLESTEROL: 59 MG	

Pyramid equivalencies: 2 grains, 1 vegetable, 1 protein

Carol's Chocolate Cake

Carol adores both chocolate and berries. This cake brings those delights together in a surprisingly light cake.

1¼ cups unbleached all-purpose
   flour
⅓ cup cocoa powder
1 teaspoon baking soda
¼ cup almond oil or canola
   oil
1 cup brown sugar, tightly
   packed

1 cup nonfat milk
¼ cup plain nonfat yogurt
1 teaspoon almond extract
1 recipe Chocolate Raspberry
   Frosting (recipe follows)
½ cup fresh raspberries or
   strawberries, optional

Preheat oven to 350°F. Sift together the flour, cocoa and baking soda. Set aside.

Whisk together the oil and brown sugar. Add the milk, stirring until the sugar is thoroughly dissolved. Add the yogurt and almond extract and stir until blended. Pour the liquid mixture into the dry ingredients. Whisk until well blended.

Spray two 8-inch, round cake pans with nonstick cooking spray. Pour the batter evenly into the 2 pans. Bake 20 minutes or until an inserted toothpick comes out clean. Allow cakes to cool 10 minutes before removing from the pans.

Gently loosen the edges of the cakes with a spatula. Invert one of the cakes onto a plate. Spread half of the Chocolate Raspberry Frosting over the bottom layer while still warm. Place second layer on top. Do not frost second layer until it has cooled completely. Spread the remaining frosting over the top of the cake. If desired, decorate with a few raspberries and refrigerate until serving time. Let stand at room temperature 10 minutes before cutting. Serve plain or with Mixed Berry Compote.

YIELD: 12 servings

Nutrient information does not include Mixed Berry Compote.

CALORIES	CARBOHYDRATES: 47.5 GM	TOTAL FAT: 5.1 GM
Per serving: 197	PROTEIN: 3.0 GM	Saturated fat: .4 GM
Fat: 18%	DIETARY FIBER: 4.2 GM	Monounsaturated fat: 3.0 GM
Carbohydrates: 77%	SODIUM: 111 MG	
Protein: 5%	CHOLESTEROL: 1 MG	

Pyramid equivalencies: 1 grain, ¼ fruit, 1 extra

Chocolate Raspberry Frosting

This is delicious as a topping for nonfat frozen yogurt as well.

½ cup fruit-sweetened seedless raspberry preserves
¼ cup water
2 tablespoons cocoa powder

2 tablespoons berry-flavored liqueur
1 teaspoon fresh lemon juice

Place all of the ingredients in a blender or food processor and puree until smooth. Use as a frosting for Carol's Chocolate Cake or as a sauce for frozen yogurt.

YIELD: 12 servings

CALORIES   CARBOHYDRATES: 16.6 GM   TOTAL FAT: .4 GM
Per serving: 72   PROTEIN: .4 GM   Saturated fat: .1 GM
Fat: 4%   DIETARY FIBER: .6 GM   Monounsaturated fat: .1 GM
Carbohydrates: 94%   SODIUM: 100 MG
Protein: 2%   CHOLESTEROL: 0 MG

Pyramid equivalencies: ½ fruit

Mixed Berry Compote

This compote is for diners who prefer berries tart, with little sweetener.

*1 cup fresh or frozen
  raspberries*
*1 cup fresh or frozen
  blueberries*
*1 pint fresh strawberries,
  stemmed and quartered*

*1 tablespoon fruit-sweetened
  berry preserves*
1 tablespoon water
¼ teaspoon cinnamon
*1 tablespoon berry-flavored
  liqueur, optional*

In a bowl, stir together the raspberries and blueberries. Transfer half of the combination to a blender or food processor. To the half remaining in the bowl, add the strawberries and set aside.

Add the preserves, water, cinnamon and liqueur (optional) to the processor. Puree until smooth. Stir the berry puree into the bowl of whole berries and refrigerate for 1 hour, but not longer than 3 hours. Serve alone or with Carol's Chocolate Cake.

YIELD: 4 servings

CALORIES   CARBOHYDRATES: 13.6 GM   TOTAL FAT: .4 GM
Per serving: 56   PROTEIN: .5 GM   Saturated fat: trace
Fat: 6%   DIETARY FIBER: 2.4 GM   Monounsaturated fat: trace
Carbohydrates: 90%   SODIUM: 4 MG
Protein: 4%   CHOLESTEROL: 0 MG

Pyramid equivalencies: 1 fruit

6

Native Harvest

THIS WINTER holiday menu for two is a celebration of Native American ingredients. Of course, it doesn't have to be a holiday to enjoy this hearty dinner. I find cooking for one or two is often more difficult than cooking for a large crowd. Most holiday recipe books don't even mention menus for one or two. We may wish that we could be spending the holiday with others, but it doesn't always happen. You can still make the day a special occasion. This menu is one I developed especially for Thanksgiving. Most of the ingredients are native to North America. Alone, or with others, we can celebrate the joys of our native culinary heritage.

NATIVE HARVEST (MENU FOR 2)

Festive Squash Soup
Salsa Succotash with Hearts of Palm
Cranberry Chutney
Peanut-Crusted Roast Turkey with Yams
Wild Rice and Mushrooms
Persimmons with Pecans

Additional Recipe:
Chutney Marinade

Native Americans cultivated a wide variety of squash. Of all the winter squash, none has etched a more important role in our culture than pumpkin. For the Festive Squash Soup, you can use pumpkin or any other winter squash. In addition to being rich in culinary history, winter squash is also high in beta-carotene, an important nutrient for maintaining our immune systems.

Succotash is one of the few Native American dishes that contemporary diners recognize by name. Succotash refers to the combination of beans and corn. Salsa Succotash with Hearts of Palm is a hearty salad that can be served with the soup for an appealing lunch. Hearts of palm is native to Florida and the Caribbean. The Seminoles continue to harvest this wonderful delicacy.

Cranberry Chutney offers a bold twist to the traditional holiday condiment. The chutney is also part of Chutney Marinade, which is used in preparing Peanut-Crusted Roast Turkey with Yams. Cranberries, peanuts, turkey and yams are all native to our continent. Together, they create a richly flavored entrée.

Wild Rice and Mushrooms has a slightly gamy flavor that complements assertively flavored dishes. Wild rice is still harvested by Native Americans in Minnesota. Persimmons with Pecans is another dish based on Native American cooking. The persimmons that were enjoyed by the earliest Americans have now been replaced by trees native to Asia. The pecans and maple syrup that season the dish originate from trees that have shaded our nation for centuries.

NUTRIENT ANALYSIS FOR NATIVE HARVEST

The nutrient analysis for the complete meal includes 1 serving each of Festive Squash Soup, Salsa Succotash with Hearts of Palm, Cranberry Chutney, Peanut-Crusted Roast Turkey with Yams, Wild Rice and Mushrooms and Persimmons with Pecans.

CALORIES	CARBOHYDRATES: 232.1 GM	TOTAL FAT: 11.6 GM
For total meal: 1,170	PROTEIN: 52.8 GM	Saturated fat: 1.9 GM
Fat: 8%	DIETARY FIBER: 13.8 GM	Monounsaturated fat: 5.0 GM
Carbohydrates: 75%	SODIUM: 555 MG	
Protein: 17%	CHOLESTEROL: 52 MG	

Pyramid equivalencies: 2½ grains, 3 vegetables, 3¾ fruits, 1½ proteins, ¼ dairy, 1 extra

Festive Squash Soup

A simple squash soup becomes a lively holiday dish when served with a variety of condiments.

The soup:

> 1 cup cooked, pureed winter squash
> 1 cup fluid nonfat milk
> 1/4 cup finely diced red onion
> 1 teaspoon finely minced fresh ginger
> 3/4 cup water or defatted, unsalted chicken broth

> 1/2 cup dry sherry
> 1 1/2 teaspoons low-sodium soy sauce
> 1/8 teaspoon ground nutmeg (or more to taste)
> 1/8 teaspoon ground white pepper (or more to taste)

The condiments:

> 1 tablespoon water
> 1 teaspoon frozen, unsweetened orange juice concentrate
> 1 small red apple, cored and diced
> 1/4 cup finely diced red onion

> 2 tablespoons finely minced fresh celery leaves
> 1 tablespoon finely minced fresh mint
> 1 tablespoon finely minced fresh parsley

For the soup:

You need 1 cup of cooked and pureed winter squash for 4 servings. Acorn, Hubbard, banana, butternut and pumpkin are all suitable. The squash can be easily cooked in the oven or microwave. After the squash is tender, allow it to cool before peeling. Place chunks of squash in a blender and puree until smooth. Carrots, yams, sweet potatoes and canned pumpkin can also be used in the recipe.

In the blender, combine the cooled, pureed squash with the milk and process until well blended.

Meanwhile, combine the red onion, ginger, water or broth, sherry, soy sauce, nutmeg and white pepper in a pot and simmer covered for 20 minutes. Pour the onion mixture into the blender with the pureed squash and milk. Process until completely smooth. Transfer the soup to a pot and heat through. Serve the soup hot with a choice of condiments to be sprinkled over the top of each bowl.

For the condiments:
Stir together the water and orange juice concentrate and toss with the diced apple immediately after dicing. Place the coated apple in a small condiment dish. Place the diced onion in another small dish. Combine the minced herbs in a third small bowl. Serve the condiments as a topping for the soup.

YIELD: 4 servings

CALORIES	CARBOHYDRATES: 14.9 GM	TOTAL FAT: .3 GM
Per serving: 70	PROTEIN: 3.5 GM	Saturated fat: .1 GM
Fat: 4%	DIETARY FIBER: .8 GM	Monounsaturated fat: trace
Carbohydrates: 78%	SODIUM: 99 MG	
Protein: 18%	CHOLESTEROL: 1 MG	

Pyramid equivalencies: 1 vegetable, ¼ fruit, ¼ dairy

Salsa Succotash with Hearts of Palm

For the fruit in this salad, you can choose just about any firm fruit you want. Apples, pears, pineapple, nectarines, peaches, apricots, mango, papaya and cantaloupe are likely possibilities.

4 stalks canned hearts of palm, well rinsed
½ cup diced fresh fruit (see above note)
1 cup frozen corn kernels, thawed
½ cup cooked black beans, well rinsed
¼ cup diced canned pimento, well rinsed
2 green onions, diced

1 small fresh serrano chile, seeded and finely minced
1 clove garlic, finely minced
2 tablespoons fresh orange juice
1 tablespoon fresh lime juice
1 tablespoon unseasoned rice vinegar
2 tablespoons finely minced fresh cilantro
2 large leaves lettuce or red cabbage

Slice the stalks of hearts of palm in ½-inch-thick rounds. Combine with all of the other ingredients, except the lettuce leaves, and marinate 4 hours before serving. Serve on salad plates garnished with the leaves.

YIELD: 2 servings

CALORIES	CARBOHYDRATES: 54.3 GM	TOTAL FAT: .7 GM
Per serving: 230	PROTEIN: 8.6 GM	Saturated fat: .1 GM
Fat: 3%	DIETARY FIBER: 5.7 GM	Monounsaturated fat: .1 GM
Carbohydrates: 84%	SODIUM: 133 MG	
Protein: 13%	CHOLESTEROL: 0 MG	

Pyramid equivalencies: 1 grain, ½ vegetable, ½ fruit, ¼ protein

Cranberry Chutney

This tantalizing condiment makes a marvelous holiday gift from the kitchen.

½ cup water or dry sherry
2 tablespoons finely minced
    fresh ginger
1 cup fresh or frozen whole
    cranberries
1 large apple, cored and diced
⅔ cup frozen, unsweetened
    apple juice concentrate

⅓ cup raisins
2 tablespoons fresh lemon juice
2 tablespoons finely grated fresh
    orange peel
1 teaspoon ground cinnamon
½ teaspoon ground allspice
⅛ teaspoon cayenne pepper

Pour the water or sherry in a saucepan with the ginger. Simmer at medium temperature until most of the liquid has evaporated.

Add all of the remaining ingredients and cook at medium heat for 25 minutes or until the cranberries have softened and the chutney has thickened. Will keep 2 or 3 weeks stored in a glass jar in the refrigerator. Use this chutney in the Chutney Marinade (recipe follows).

YIELD: 8 servings

CALORIES   CARBOHYDRATES: 19.2 GM   TOTAL FAT: .3 GM
Per serving: 74   PROTEIN: .5 GM   Saturated fat: 0 GM
Fat: 3%   DIETARY FIBER: .7 GM   Monounsaturated fat: 0 GM
Carbohydrates: 95% SODIUM: 8 MG
Protein: 2%   CHOLESTEROL: 0 MG

Pyramid equivalencies: 1 fruit

Chutney Marinade

This marinade is a great way to bring robust flavor to meats without using fat.

> 2 *tablespoons Cranberry*   1 *tablespoon dry sherry*
>   *Chutney (previous recipe)*   1½ *teaspoons low-sodium soy*
> 1 *tablespoon low-sodium*   *sauce*
>   *tomato ketchup*   ⅛ *teaspoon hot pepper sauce*

Place all of the ingredients in a blender and process until smooth. Will keep several days stored in a glass jar in the refrigerator. Use as a marinade for grilled or roasted chicken, turkey or pork.

YIELD: 2 servings

CALORIES   CARBOHYDRATES: 21.6 GM   TOTAL FAT: .4 GM
Per serving: 85   PROTEIN: 1.3 GM   Saturated fat: trace
Fat: 4%   DIETARY FIBER: .8 GM   Monounsaturated fat: trace
Carbohydrates: 91% SODIUM: 165 MG
Protein: 5%   CHOLESTEROL: 0 MG

Pyramid equivalencies: 1 fruit

Peanut-Crusted Roast Turkey with Yams

A variety of turkey breast cuts are available for making this dish. I prefer to purchase a portion with the skin and bone attached. These cuts will yield a moister meat.

¾ pound turkey breast
1 recipe Chutney Marinade
2 tablespoons dry-roasted peanuts, crushed
1 large yam, peeled and cut in rounds, ½ inch thick

½ teaspoon cinnamon
Unsalted, defatted chicken broth or dry wine

Remove any skin or fat from the turkey breast. Coat the meat with the Chutney Marinade and marinate for 3 hours in the refrigerator.

Place the meat in a baking dish. Sprinkle the crushed peanuts over the turkey. Place the yam slices around the turkey. Sprinkle the yam slices with cinnamon. Pour enough broth or wine into the dish to create a depth of ¼ inch. Cover the dish with a tight-fitting lid or foil. Bake in a preheated oven at 375°F. for 1 hour.

Serve the turkey and yams garnished with the Cranberry Chutney.

YIELD: 2 servings

CALORIES
Per serving: 404
Fat: 15%
Carbohydrates: 58%
Protein: 27%

CARBOHYDRATES: 60.7 GM
PROTEIN: 29.0 GM
DIETARY FIBER: 3.4 GM
SODIUM: 210 MG
CHOLESTEROL: 51 MG

TOTAL FAT: 6.9 GM
Saturated fat: 1.5 GM
Monounsaturated fat: 3.0 GM

Pyramid equivalencies: 1¼ proteins, 1 vegetable

Wild Rice and Mushrooms

Wild rice has an assertive flavor that makes it an appealing companion to richly flavored meat and poultry dishes.

1 cup unsalted, defatted
   chicken broth or water
½ cup wild rice
1 cup sliced mushrooms
2 cloves garlic, finely minced

1 teaspoon low-sodium soy
   sauce
⅛ teaspoon ground black
   pepper

Pour the broth into a saucepan and bring to a boil. Add all of the remaining ingredients. Stir and reduce the heat to low. Cover with a tight-fitting lid and cook for 40 minutes or until the rice is tender. If necessary, remove the lid and increase the temperature to evaporate away any excess liquid.

YIELD: 2 servings

CALORIES
Per serving: 173
Fat: 4%
Carbohydrates: 74%
Protein: 22%

CARBOHYDRATES: 33.2 GM
PROTEIN: 9.8 GM
DIETARY FIBER: 1.2 GM
SODIUM: 100 MG
CHOLESTEROL: 0 MG

TOTAL FAT: .6 GM
Saturated fat: trace
Monounsaturated fat: trace

Pyramid equivalencies: 1½ grains, ½ vegetable

Persimmons with Pecans

A ripe persimmon has a rich honeylike flavor. Remember, an unripe persimmon has an unpleasant astringent taste. The Fuyu are ripe when firm but not hard. Other persimmons are not ripe until soft.

> 2 ripe persimmons
> 1 tablespoon pure maple
>   syrup
> 1 tablespoon honey
> 1 tablespoon water
>
> 1 teaspoon nut-flavored liqueur,
>   optional
> 4 dry-roasted, unsalted pecan
>   halves, crushed

Carefully cut out the stem end of each persimmon. Cut each fruit lengthwise in half. Set the halves on a serving platter or individual serving plates. With a sharp knife, cut an X across each persimmon half, penetrating almost to the skin.

Whisk together the maple syrup, honey, water and liqueur. Gently squeeze each persimmon half to force the slits to open slightly. Slowly pour the syrup mixture over each persimmon half, allowing the liquid to enter the slits. Sprinkle the crushed pecans over the top and serve immediately.

YIELD: 2 servings

CALORIES
Per serving: 219
Fat: 11%
Carbohydrates: 87%
Protein: 2%

CARBOHYDRATES: 49.8 GM
PROTEIN: 1.4 GM
DIETARY FIBER: 2.0 GM
SODIUM: 5 MG
CHOLESTEROL: 0 MG

TOTAL FAT: 2.8 GM
Saturated fat: .2 GM
Monounsaturated fat: 1.9 GM

Pyramid equivalencies: 1 fruit

7

Southwestern Holiday

THANKSGIVING IS synonymous with tradition. In some form or another, we always expect turkey, dressing, gravy, cranberry relish, yams and, of course, pumpkin pie. Thanksgiving fare typically has reflected New England cooking styles. Since I live in San Diego, at the opposite end of the mainland, I decided it would be fun to create a Thanksgiving feast with a distinctly southwestern character. In addition to European influences, Mexican, Native American and Pacific Rim flavors are essential components of our region's culinary personality. Our mild climate and outdoor lifestyle call for dishes that are lighter and lower in fat. This feast is certainly lighter than most Thanksgiving menus, but don't think for a moment it is any less flavorful!

The menu for Southwestern Holiday is designed to allow you time to enjoy your guests. All too often holiday cooking chains us to the stove without time to sit down with our company. Sometimes we work so hard getting our celebration feast together that we can't enjoy the fruits of our labor. This meal was created so that almost all of the work can be done 1 or 2 days before the event. You will be able to savor the meal as much as your guests do!

Planning ahead is the key to ease and comfort in the holiday kitchen. If you are buying a frozen turkey, you need to allow 3 to 4 days for it to thaw properly in the refrigerator. To make things especially easy, I like

76

to make the turkey stuffing and gravy 1 or 2 days before the party. This requires making a flavorful stock or consommé. I assure you, the advance effort is worth the time it saves you on the actual holiday as well as offering a flavor bonus to the meal. A strong turkey consommé enables you to provide a deep, rich flavor without using fat. And for that everyone will be thankful!

Southwestern Holiday is a salute to great healthy dining. Good health is the greatest treasure any of us can possess. What better way to give thanks to ourselves than celebrate with a healthy, delicious feast!

SOUTHWESTERN HOLIDAY (MENU FOR 8)

Southwestern Turkey with Orange-Chile Gravy
Baja Turkey Dressing
Borrego Springs Cranberry Salsa
California Waldorf Salad with Waldorf Vinaigrette
Autumn Vegetable Medley
Nisei Yams and Persimmons
Old Town Pumpkin Flan

Additional Recipes:
Orange-Chile Paste
Turkey Consommé
Light Waldorf Vinaigrette

The recipe for Southwestern Turkey uses only the breast of the turkey, however, the general preparation method can be applied to a whole turkey as well. Turkey breast by itself, without skin, is extremely low in fat (only 6% of calories from fat). Compare this with the dark meat of the turkey, which without skin is 36% fat and with the skin is 47% fat. Even without the skin, the dark meat of turkey has more fat than some cuts of beef. On the other hand, Thanksgiving comes only once a year. A little indulgence now and then is certainly compatible with healthy dining!

The turkey breast has a lot of flavor because it is coated with an Orange-Chile Paste. This is also used to create Orange-Chile Gravy to top the turkey and dressing. To make the gravy, you can use defatted juices from the pan or make Turkey Consommé a few days before the party. I prefer using the Consommé because it enables me to prepare the gravy long before the guests arrive. At a later time, I usually add the pan juices and carcass to a pot of boiling water to create turkey soup.

Turkey Consommé made in advance also enables you to prepare the Baja Turkey Dressing a day before the actual feast. Here, the traditional flavors of a sage dressing are mixed with the piquant addition of chile and cactus. Although unfamiliar to many cooks, cactus is readily available in the Mexican food section of most markets. Starting with a base of brown rice, the dressing has a tantalizing variety of textures.

Borrego Springs Cranberry Salsa has a wonderfully wild flavor, a kind of mix between traditional cranberry relish and a fresh salsa. Its sweet-sour flavor is a pleasant accompaniment to other meat and poultry dishes, as well.

Autumn Vegetable Medley is an explosion of color that also dazzles the taste buds. Even people who say they hate turnips usually find they like this dish. If you are tired of the same old yams and marshmallows, Nisei Yams and Persimmons is a delightful alternative. It celebrates the Asian influence that has become an important part of southwestern cuisine.

Flan is typically thought of as one of the world's richest dishes. Old Town Pumpkin Flan is made with egg whites and nonfat milk, dramatically reducing the calories and fat without sacrificing a marvelously rich flavor. This dessert is still, nonetheless, an indulgence. The sugar content is high. My feeling is that you can be healthy and indulge in an occasional extravagance.

NUTRIENT ANALYSIS FOR SOUTHWESTERN HOLIDAY

When you include beverage and bread, this meal could easily exceed 1,500 calories. That seems like a lot of food. For ordinary daily eating, it is high for one meal, but for holiday dining, it is quite acceptable. In fact, consider that more-traditional American holiday menus may easily have as much as 4,000 calories! A notable feature of this menu is that it is superrich in beta-carotene and vitamin C. Analysis is for 1 serving each of Southwestern Turkey with Orange-Chile Gravy, Baja Turkey Dressing, Borrego Springs Cranberry Salsa, California Waldorf Salad with Waldorf Vinaigrette, Autumn Vegetable Medley, Nisei Yams and Persimmons and Old Town Pumpkin Flan.

CALORIES   CARBOHYDRATES: 233.9 GM   TOTAL FAT: 10.6 GM
For total meal: PROTEIN: 47.3 GM   Saturated fat: 1.6 GM
  1,129   DIETARY FIBER: 15.2 GM   Monounsaturated fat: 4.6 GM
Fat: 8%   SODIUM: 819 MG
Carbohydrates: 76% CHOLESTEROL: 67 MG
Protein: 16%

Pyramid equivalencies: 1¼ grains, 4½ vegetables, 4¼ fruits, 1½ proteins, ½ dairy, 1 extra

Southwestern Turkey

Southwestern Turkey is oven steamed, creating deliciously moist meat without ever having to baste the turkey. Even if you elect to serve a whole turkey, oven steaming is still a superb technique. It makes cooking the turkey easy, healthy and delicious and eliminates the need for buying a prebasted, chemically treated bird.

1 whole turkey breast	1 large onion, quartered
½ recipe for Orange-Chile Paste (recipe follows)	1 bulb garlic, sliced or broken into cloves
4 large carrots	Water
4 stalks celery	3 tablespoons pine nuts

Trim any excess fat from the turkey. Lift the skin around the breast to cut away the visible fat. Carefully pull back the skin, exposing as much of the breast as possible.

With a pastry brush or paper towel paint the breast with ¼ cup of the Orange-Chile Paste. Immediately cover the breast with the skin. Set aside the Orange-Chile Paste for later use.

Make a rack of vegetables by placing the carrots, celery, onion and garlic in the bottom of a roasting pan. Place the turkey on top of the vegetables. Pour water into the pan to the depth of 2 inches. Cover the turkey with foil, completely sealing the turkey in the pan. Roast the turkey breast at 350°F., for 20 minutes per pound.

Fifteen minutes before completion of the allotted cooking time, take the turkey out of the oven. Remove the foil. Carefully pull away the skin covering the breast. Generously coat the breast with ½ cup of the Orange-Chile Paste. Return the exposed turkey breast to the oven and roast uncovered for 15 minutes more.

Remove the turkey from the oven and let stand 15 minutes before slicing. Just before serving, crush the pine nuts and sprinkle over the breast. Serve with the Orange-Chile Gravy, Baja Dressing and Borrego Springs Cranberry Salsa.

YIELD: 8 servings

CALORIES	CARBOHYDRATES: 22.0 GM	TOTAL FAT: 2.7 GM
Per serving: 219	PROTEIN: 26.5 GM	Saturated fat: .4 GM
Fat: 11%	DIETARY FIBER: 1.4 GM	Monounsaturated fat: 1.0 GM
Carbohydrates: 40%	SODIUM: 192 MG	
Protein: 49%	CHOLESTEROL: 64 MG	

Pyramid equivalencies: 1 fruit, 1 protein

Orange-Chile Paste

Three-fourths cup of this recipe is used to baste the turkey (previous recipe) and the remaining ½ cup is used to create the Orange-Chile Gravy (recipe follows). The paste is also excellent as a coating for broiled or grilled chicken breasts, game hen, fish steaks or shrimp.

1 cup frozen, unsweetened orange juice concentrate
2 tablespoons low-sodium soy sauce
1 tablespoon tomato paste
1 tablespoon fresh lemon juice
2 tablespoons mild chile powder
1 teaspoon ground cumin
½ teaspoon ground coriander seed
¼ teaspoon ground cinnamon

Place all of the ingredients in a bowl and whisk until completely blended. May be stored in the refrigerator for 5 days before using.

YIELD: 10 servings (2 tablespoons each)

CALORIES
Per serving: 76
Fat: 4%
Carbohydrates: 90%
Protein: 6%

CARBOHYDRATES: 14.4 GM
PROTEIN: 1.0 GM
DIETARY FIBER: .5 GM
SODIUM: 70 MG
CHOLESTEROL: 0 MG

TOTAL FAT: .3 GM
Saturated fat: trace
Monounsaturated fat: trace

Pyramid equivalencies: ¾ fruit

Orange-Chile Gravy

This is a delicious gravy for chicken dishes as well as turkey.

½ cup Orange-Chile Paste
(previous recipe)
3 cups Turkey Consommé
(recipe follows) or defatted
broth from cooking the
turkey

¼ cup cornstarch
¼ cup cold water

In a saucepan, combine ½ cup of the Orange-Chile Paste with 3 cups of Turkey Consommé. Heat until almost boiling. Dissolve the cornstarch into the cold water, then whisk into the heated mixture. Stirring regularly, cook until thickened.

YIELD: 8 servings

CALORIES
Per serving: 66
Fat: 2%
Carbohydrates: 88%
Protein: 10%

CARBOHYDRATES: 12.9 GM
PROTEIN: 1.5 GM
DIETARY FIBER: .2 GM
SODIUM: 37 MG
CHOLESTEROL: 0 MG

TOTAL FAT: .2 GM
Saturated fat: trace
Monounsaturated fat: trace

Pyramid equivalencies: ¼ fruit

Turkey Consommé

This recipe is used in the Baja Turkey Dressing and Orange-Chile Gravy. The purpose of a consommé is to give a rich, meaty flavor. Canned products or dehydrated cubes simply do not offer the flavor of a freshly prepared broth or consommé. If you feel you don't have the time to make it yourself, I suggest buying a canned chicken broth free of salt and MSG. Buy enough to yield 12 cups. Place the broth in a pot and add 1 cup of dry sherry. Boil the liquid until it is reduced to 8 cups. You can always reduce it to less than that and later add water to bring it back to 8 cups. After chilling, skim the fat from the broth. Of course, I hope you will opt for the homemade version! Although our turkey recipe only calls for the breast, you may want to buy a whole turkey, setting aside the breast and using the wings and legs to prepare the Consommé.

3 pounds turkey wings, legs or other parts	1 turnip, quartered
1 large onion, including skin, coarsely chopped	2 stalks celery
6 cloves garlic	3 bay leaves
2 carrots, sliced	8 cups water, plus additional water
	1 cup dry sherry

Combine all of the ingredients in a large pot and simmer uncovered for 3 hours. Periodically add more water to keep the vegetables covered.

Remove from the heat and strain. The vegetables and turkey wings can be discarded or used for other dishes. If necessary, add more water to the stock to yield a total of 8 cups.

Chill the stock overnight. When ready to use, skim the fat off the top. Underneath will be a rich, gelatinous consommé. In addition to the previous recipes, it may also be used for making soups and sauces.

YIELD: 8 servings

CALORIES
Per serving: 34
Fat: 0%
Carbohydrates: 68%
Protein: 32%

CARBOHYDRATES: 5.5 GM
PROTEIN: 2.6 GM
DIETARY FIBER: 0 GM
SODIUM: 5 MG
CHOLESTEROL: 0 MG

TOTAL FAT: 0 GM
Saturated fat: 0 GM
Monounsaturated fat: 0 GM

Pyramid equivalencies: No equivalencies

Baja Turkey Dressing

Turkey Consommé (previous recipe) gives the dressing a rich turkey taste without the usual fat. The mildly flavored nopalitos (cactus leaves) provide an appealing texture similar to well-cooked, diced celery. In fact, you can substitute 2 stalks of diced celery. Nopalitos are readily found in the Mexican-foods section of most major supermarkets.

¾ cup canned, diced nopales (nopalitos)
1 cup fresh or frozen white corn kernels
2¼ cups uncooked brown rice
2 large red apples, cored and finely diced
1 large yellow onion, finely diced
½ cup raisins
8 cloves garlic, minced
1 tablespoon dry pasilla chile powder
2 teaspoons mild California chile powder

2 teaspoons crushed dry sage
½ teaspoon ground coriander seed
½ teaspoon crushed dry oregano
¼ teaspoon ground cinnamon
1 cup dry sherry, Marsala or Madeira
4 teaspoons low-sodium soy sauce
Turkey Consommé (previous recipe)
¼ cup pine nuts, finely diced
1 tablespoon freshly minced parsley

Place the nopalitos in a strainer and rinse under cold water for 30 seconds. In a large ovenproof casserole dish, mix the nopalitos with the corn and uncooked brown rice and set aside.

In a large saucepan, combine all of the remaining ingredients, except the turkey consommé, pine nuts and parsley. Cover and simmer for 8 minutes. Using a strainer, pour the liquid from saucepan into a large measuring cup. To this liquid, add enough Turkey Consommé to yield 4 cups of liquid. Stir the liquid and ingredients from the saucepan into the casserole dish with the nopalitos, corn and rice.

Cover the dish with foil or tightly fitting lid. Bake at 325°F. for 1 hour and 15 minutes. Before serving, stir the casserole. This dish can easily be made a day ahead and reheated. If reheating, you will likely need to add ½ cup Consommé or other liquid. Just before serving, sprinkle the pine nuts and parsley over the top of the dish.

YIELD: 8 servings

CALORIES	CARBOHYDRATES: 51.1 GM	TOTAL FAT: 3.2 GM
Per serving: 246	PROTEIN: 6.2 GM	Saturated fat: .5 GM
Fat: 11%	DIETARY FIBER: 4.8 GM	Monounsaturated fat: 1.2 GM
Carbohydrates: 79%	SODIUM: 118 MG	
Protein: 10%	CHOLESTEROL: 0 MG	

Pyramid equivalencies: 1¼ grains, ½ vegetable, ½ fruit

Borrego Springs Cranberry Salsa

If seedless red grapes are unavailable, substitute traditional grapes, but do remove the seeds. Two large Delicious apples can also be substituted for the grapes, although I personally like the deep red-violet color the grapes give the dish.

2 cups fresh cranberries
2 cups red seedless grapes
4 ripe plum tomatoes (Romas)
1 red bell pepper, diced
½ cup finely diced red onion
½ cup fresh orange juice
1 tablespoon fresh lime juice

1 tablespoon frozen grape juice concentrate
¼ teaspoon ground cinnamon
¼ teaspoon Tabasco (more or less to taste)
Fresh sprigs of mint and cilantro (optional)

Coarsely chop the cranberries, grapes, tomatoes, pepper and onion. A food processor can be used, remembering that a better texture will be achieved if you process only one of the ingredients at a time.

Mix all of the freshly chopped ingredients with the juices, cinnamon and Tabasco. Marinate for at least 4 hours or overnight.

When ready to serve, place in a bowl surrounded by sprigs of fresh mint and cilantro.

YIELD: 8 servings

CALORIES	CARBOHYDRATES: 12.5 GM	TOTAL FAT: .5 MG
Per serving: 52	PROTEIN: 1.0 GM	Saturated fat: trace
Fat: 7%	DIETARY FIBER: 1.4 GM	Monounsaturated fat: trace
Carbohydrates: 86%	SODIUM: 61 MG	
Protein: 7%	CHOLESTEROL: 0 MG	

Pyramid equivalencies: ½ vegetable, 1 fruit

California Waldorf Salad

This is a carefree revision of Waldorf Salad. Made with fruits and vegetables in shades of green, the salad offers a luscious burst of mono-chromatic color.

1 small green apple, cored and sliced

1 recipe Waldorf Vinaigrette (recipe follows)

½ cup canned water chestnuts, drained and rinsed

1 cup honeydew melon, cut in balls or cubes

1 cup seedless green grapes

1 cup diced fresh cucumber, peeled and seeded

2 stalks celery, diced

1 small head green leaf lettuce, washed and torn in bite-size pieces

1 kiwi, peeled and sliced

3 tablespoons fresh pomegranate seeds, optional

3 tablespoons slivered almonds, optional

Toss the sliced green apple with Waldorf Vinaigrette. Mix in the water chestnuts, melon, grapes, cucumber and celery and marinate in the refrigerator for at least 1 hour, but no more than 8 hours.

Toss the mixture just before serving. Serve over lettuce garnished with the kiwi slices. If desired, also garnish with fresh pomegranate seeds and sliced almonds. Decorating with slivered almonds, of course, increases the fat content.

YIELD: 8 servings

Nutrient information does not include the almonds.

CALORIES	CARBOHYDRATES: 12.5 GM	TOTAL FAT: 1.9 GM
Per serving: 64	PROTEIN: .7 GM	Saturated fat: .3 GM
Fat: 25%	DIETARY FIBER: 1.6 GM	Monounsaturated fat: 1.3 GM
Carbohydrates: 71%	SODIUM: 15 MG	
Protein: 4%	CHOLESTEROL: 0 MG	

Pyramid equivalencies: 1 vegetable, 1 fruit

Waldorf Vinaigrette

In addition to the California Waldorf Salad, the dressing is delicious on a simple green salad.

2 tablespoons fresh lime juice
2 tablespoons frozen, unsweetened apple juice concentrate
2 tablespoons water
1 tablespoon plain rice vinegar
1 tablespoon extra-virgin olive oil
1 tablespoon finely minced fresh basil
1 tablespoon finely minced fresh mint

Stir together all of the ingredients and use immediately. The vinaigrette may be stored for 2 days before using; however, I prefer the flavor when the herbs have just been freshly added. This dressing is also excellent on green salads.

YIELD: ½ cup, 8 tablespoons

CALORIES	CARBOHYDRATES: 2.2 GM	TOTAL FAT: 1.7 GM
Per tablespoon: 23	PROTEIN: .4 GM	Saturated fat: .2 GM
Fat: 60%	DIETARY FIBER: trace	Monounsaturated fat: 1.3 GM
Carbohydrates: 34%	SODIUM: 9 MG	
Protein: 6%	CHOLESTEROL: 0 MG	

Pyramid equivalencies: No equivalencies

Light Waldorf Vinaigrette

This is the previous recipe for Waldorf Vinaigrette with the olive oil omitted. This is also an appealing dressing for the California Waldorf Salad or other fruit-type salads.

YIELD: ½ cup, 8 tablespoons, approximately

CALORIES	CARBOHYDRATES: 2.2 GM	TOTAL FAT: .1 GM
Per tablespoon: 8	PROTEIN: .4 GM	Saturated fat: trace
Fat: 60%	DIETARY FIBER: trace	Monounsaturated fat: trace
Carbohydrates: 34%	SODIUM: 9 MG	
Protein: 6%	CHOLESTEROL: 0 MG	

Pyramid equivalencies: No equivalencies

Autumn Vegetable Medley

This dish of root vegetables and apples has all the brilliant colors of autumn and an equally sprightly flavor. All of the vegetables can be peeled and sliced the day before cooking. Cover with water and store in the refrigerator. Do, however, store the beets separately from the other vegetables.

2 large beets, peeled and
  julienned in ¼-inch strips
2 carrots, peeled and sliced in
  rounds
2 parsnips, peeled and sliced
  in rounds
1 large rutabaga, peeled and
  julienned in ¼-inch strips
1 large turnip, peeled and
  julienned in ¼-inch strips

1 red apple, cored and sliced in
  ¼-inch-thick pieces
1 yellow apple, cored and sliced
  in ¼-inch-thick pieces
¼ cup frozen, unsweetened apple
  juice concentrate
1 tablespoon finely minced fresh
  tarragon, mint or basil

Place all of the vegetables and apples in a steamer basket. If necessary, steam in separate batches. Steam covered for 7 to 8 minutes. Remove and immediately transfer to a serving dish. Toss with the apple juice and fresh herb. Serve immediately.

YIELD: 8 servings

CALORIES	CARBOHYDRATES: 32.0 GM	TOTAL FAT: .2
Per serving: 80	PROTEIN: 2.0 GM	Saturated fat: trace
Fat: 3%	DIETARY FIBER: 3.8 GM	Monounsaturated fat: trace
Carbohydrates: 91%	SODIUM: 138 MG	
Protein: 6%	CHOLESTEROL: 0 MG	

Pyramid equivalencies: 1½ vegetables, ½ fruit

Nisei Yams and Persimmons

Both the yams and Japanese persimmons have a rich sweetness that blends well in this easily prepared casserole. The Fuyu are ripe when firm but not hard. Other persimmons are not ripe until soft.

4 medium yams or sweet
  potatoes, washed and
  trimmed
2 Fuyu persimmons
⅓ cup dry sherry
3 tablespoons frozen,
  unsweetened apple juice
  concentrate

2 tablespoons low-sodium soy
  sauce
1 tablespoon finely minced fresh
  ginger

Tightly wrap the yams in foil. Bake at 325°F. for 30 minutes. Remove from the oven and cool. This much can be done the day before.

When ready to prepare the casserole, unwrap the yams and pull away the peel. Cut the yams in half lengthwise. Slice each section in ¼-inch pieces.

Remove and discard the stem from the persimmons. Slice the fruit thinly and toss with the yam slices. Mix together all the remaining ingredients and toss with the yam and persimmon slices.

Spray a baking dish with nonstick cooking spray. Evenly distribute the yam and persimmon slices. Pour all of the sauce into the dish. Cover with a tight-fitting lid or foil and bake at 325°F. for 15 minutes. Remove the cover and stir the mixture, coating the yam and persimmons in sauce. Bake 10 minutes more uncovered.

YIELD: 8 servings

CALORIES	CARBOHYDRATES: 25.5 GM	TOTAL FAT: .2 GM
Per serving: 104	PROTEIN: 1.7 GM	Saturated fat: trace
Fat: 1%	DIETARY FIBER: 1.7 GM	Monounsaturated fat: trace
Carbohydrates: 93%	SODIUM: 136 MG	
Protein: 6%	CHOLESTEROL: 0 MG	

Pyramid equivalencies: 1 vegetable, ¼ fruit

Old Town Pumpkin Flan

The dessert is definitely better when made a day before. It can be made in individual custard cups, custard mold or 9-inch square baking pan.

1 cup brown sugar	¼ teaspoon ground cloves
⅓ cup water	¾ cup egg whites
2 cups fluid nonfat milk	1 cup canned pumpkin
1 cup nonfat dry milk powder	¾ cup honey
1½ teaspoons ground	2 tablespoons molasses
cinnamon	3 tablespoons toasted, sliced
½ teaspoon ground ginger	almonds

In a nonstick pan, stir together the brown sugar and water. Place the pan over medium heat. As the sugar melts, stir regularly to prevent sticking. When the sugar has melted, pour into a 2-quart baking mold, 9-inch baking pan or individual custard dishes. Tilt the dish to coat the bottom and sides of the dish with the caramelized sugar. Set the dish aside.

In a bowl, blend together the fluid and dry milk. Add the cinnamon, ginger and cloves. Mix well. Stir in the egg whites and whisk until evenly blended. Add the pumpkin, honey and molasses. Whisk until the mixture is evenly and thoroughly blended.

Pour the mixture into the mold with the caramelized sugar. Place the mold into a larger baking pan and fill the pan halfway up the sides with hot water. Bake approximately 1¼ hours at 325°F. or until a knife inserted in the center comes out clean. Remove from the hot water and set aside to cool.

Chill several hours or overnight. When it comes time to serve, you have two choices for presenting the flan. First, loosen the outer edges of the flan with a thin knife. Place a serving dish over the flan and invert. Spoon any remaining sauce over the flan. Sprinkle the almonds over the top. If inverting the flan makes you nervous, you can cut the flan in pieces as you would for a cake. When removing the pieces, invert each piece onto individual dessert plates. Spoon some of the sauce over each serving and sprinkle almonds over the top.

YIELD: 8 servings

CALORIES	CARBOHYDRATES: 65.4 GM	TOTAL FAT: 1.7 GM
Per serving: 298	PROTEIN: 7.7 GM	Saturated fat: .3 GM
Fat: 10%	DIETARY FIBER: .3 GM	Monounsaturated fat: 1.0 GM
Carbohydrates: 85%	SODIUM: 122 MG	
Protein: 5%	CHOLESTEROL: 3 MG	

Pyramid equivalencies: ¼ vegetable, ¼ protein, ½ dairy, 1 extra

8

Farm Fresh

IF YOU have ever had your own garden, you know how wonderful a tomato can really be. Field-ripened fruits and vegetables have a sweet, robust flavor that is rarely equaled by supermarket products. Produce that is picked green and held in cold storage never develops its full, complete flavor. Of course, if we allowed everything to mature on the vine, we would have huge shortages at one time and too much produce to use at another time. This is a menu to celebrate that time of year when your garden is at its most abundant or truck farmers have filled stands with glorious freshly picked produce.

FARM FRESH (MENU FOR 4)

Tomato and Cucumber Salad with Summer Marinade
Twice-Cooked Salmon with Sesame Crust
Corn on the Cob with Fresh Herbs
Natural Candied Carrots
Peaches and Creme

Additional Recipes:
Light Summer Marinade
Apricot Glaze
Fruit Sweet
Honey Yogurt Creme
Yogurt Crème Fraîche

Although tomatoes are available the year round, there are many months when their bland flavor contributes little to a salad. Tomato and Cucumber Salad with Summer Marinade needs sweet, robust tomatoes. Twice-Cooked Salmon with Sesame Crust is a celebration of fresh fish. The cooking technique keeps the fish moist, yet produces a slight crispy exterior that we associate with broiling. This is one dish in which frozen fish would definitely not be as satisfying. The fish has an Apricot Glaze that is also delicious with chicken. In the area where I live, sweet white corn is frequently available from nearby farms. Corn on the Cob with Fresh Herbs depends on a fragrant sweet corn. Freshly picked sweet white corn has a luscious flavor without ever adding butter. Natural Candied Carrots is a great example of how a cooking technique greatly enhances the innate sweetness of the vegetable. Peaches and Creme with a choice of Honey Yogurt Creme and Yogurt Crème Fraîche is a great example of how low-fat cooking can still have an "old-fashioned flavor." Although the dish is best when the peaches are superb, Fruit Sweet demonstrates how the natural flavor of fruit can be enhanced by this method of sweetening.

NUTRIENT ANALYSIS FOR FARM FRESH

Nutrient analysis includes one serving each of Tomato and Cucumber Salad with Summer Marinade, Twice-Cooked Salmon with Sesame Crust, Natural Candied Carrots, Corn on the Cob with Fresh Herbs and Peaches and Creme (made with Honey Yogurt Creme). Persons wanting a higher-calorie meal should elect to add bread. Yogurt Crème Fraîche with chives can serve as a spread for the bread.

CALORIES	CARBOHYDRATES: 79.7 GM	TOTAL FAT: 12.7 GM
For total meal: 537	PROTEIN: 34.2 GM	Saturated fat: 2.1 GM
Fat: 20%	DIETARY FIBER: 10.7 GM	Monounsaturated fat: 5.7 GM
Carbohydrates: 56%	SODIUM: 465 MG	
Protein: 24%	CHOLESTEROL: 43 MG	

Pyramid equivalencies: 1 grain, 2 vegetables, 1¼ fruits, 1 protein, ½ dairy

Tomato and Cucumber Salad with Summer Marinade

This salad is a great way to enjoy homegrown tomatoes at the peak of their season.

1 *large cucumber, peeled, seeded and diced*
½ *cup diced red onion*
1 *recipe Summer Marinade (recipe follows)*
4 *large ripe tomatoes, stemmed and cut in 8 sections*

1 *tablespoon finely minced fresh dill*
8 *black olives, pitted and sliced*
4 *lemon wedges*

Toss the cucumber and red onion with the Summer Marinade and let stand at room temperature for 20 minutes.

Add the tomatoes, dill and olives and toss again. Serve immediately with a wedge of lemon on the side.

YIELD: 4 servings

CALORIES
Per serving: 86
Fat: 44%
Carbohydrates: 47%
Protein: 9%

CARBOHYDRATES: 11.8 GM
PROTEIN: 2.2 GM
DIETARY FIBER: 3.0 GM
SODIUM: 217 MG
CHOLESTEROL: 0 MG

TOTAL FAT: 4.8 GM
Saturated fat: .7 GM
Monounsaturated fat: 3.2 GM

Pyramid equivalencies: 1 vegetable

Summer Marinade

Summer Marinade is a pleasant enhancement to farm-fresh vegetables, raw or cooked. In addition to the Tomato and Cucumber Salad, I like to use it on green salads, warm boiled potatoes and fresh steamed vegetables.

3 tablespoons red wine
   vinegar

3 tablespoons fresh orange
   juice

1 tablespoon extra-virgin olive
   oil

1 teaspoon low-sodium soy
   sauce

2 teaspoons finely grated lemon
   peel

1 clove garlic, finely minced

¼ teaspoon black pepper

⅛ teaspoon ground cayenne
   pepper

Whisk together the vinegar, orange juice, olive oil and soy sauce. Add the lemon peel, garlic, black pepper and cayenne pepper. Store in a glass container and refrigerate 1 hour before using. May be kept in the refrigerator for 4 days.

YIELD: 4 servings

CALORIES	CARBOHYDRATES: 2.6 GM	TOTAL FAT: 3.4 GM
Per serving: 38	PROTEIN: .3 GM	Saturated fat: .4 GM
Fat: 73%	DIETARY FIBER: .1 GM	Monounsaturated fat: 2.5 GM
Carbohydrates: 24%	SODIUM: 43 MG	
Protein: 3%	CHOLESTEROL: 0 MG	

Pyramid equivalencies: No equivalencies

Light Summer Marinade

For a lower-fat dressing, omit the olive oil in the previous recipe. Add 1 more tablespoon of fresh orange juice.

YIELD: 4 servings

CALORIES	CARBOHYDRATES: 3.0 GM	TOTAL FAT: trace
Per serving: 10	PROTEIN: .3 GM	Saturated fat: trace
Fat: 3%	DIETARY FIBER: .1 GM	Monounsaturated fat: trace
Carbohydrates: 88%	SODIUM: 43 MG	
Protein: 9%	CHOLESTEROL: 0 MG	

Pyramid equivalencies: No equivalencies

Twice-Cooked Salmon with Sesame Crust

Salmon fillets that are cut in strips, about 2 inches wide, are ideal for this dish.

4 salmon fillets (3 or 4 ounces
    each)
¼ cup dry sherry
1 recipe Apricot Glaze (recipe
    follows)

1 teaspoon black or white
    sesame seeds

Do not remove the skin from the salmon, as it is necessary to hold the fish together. In a glass bowl, toss the salmon with the sherry. Marinate for 10 minutes.

Drain the sherry into a pot with a steamer rack. Add enough water to create a depth of ½ inch. Place the fillets on the steamer rack, skin side down. Cover the pot and steam the salmon for about 3 minutes, or until the fish has changed color but is not cooked all the way through.

While the salmon is steaming, you can prepare the Apricot Glaze. Lift the steamer rack with the salmon from the pot. Spoon the glaze over each piece of salmon, then sprinkle with the sesame seeds. Transfer the salmon to a tray or dish that can be placed under a preheated broiler. Broil for 2 minutes or until browned. Serve immediately.

YIELD: 4 servings

CALORIES	CARBOHYDRATES: 3.8 GM	TOTAL FAT: 6.9 GM
Per serving: 177	PROTEIN: 23.9 GM	Saturated fat: 1.2 GM
Fat: 36%	DIETARY FIBER: trace	Monounsaturated fat: 2.2 GM
Carbohydrates: 9%	SODIUM: 136 MG	
Protein: 55%	CHOLESTEROL: 42 MG	

Pyramid equivalencies: 1 protein

Apricot Glaze

This quickly prepared glaze instantly turns a plain piece of chicken or fish into a delectable favorite.

1 tablespoon fruit-sweetened apricot preserves	1 tablespoon dry sherry
1 tablespoon unsalted Dijon-style mustard	2 teaspoons low-sodium soy sauce

Whisk together all of the ingredients. If the glaze seems too thick, add 1 tablespoon of water. Use as a sauce for broiled or grilled fish or chicken. Do not put the glaze on the meat until the meat has partially cooked.

YIELD: 4 servings

CALORIES	CARBOHYDRATES: 3.8 GM	TOTAL FAT: .2 GM
Per serving: 16	PROTEIN: .4 GM	Saturated fat: trace
Fat: 7%	DIETARY FIBER: trace	Monounsaturated fat: trace
Carbohydrates: 83%	SODIUM: 86 MG	
Protein: 10%	CHOLESTEROL: 0 MG	

Pyramid equivalencies: No equivalencies

Corn on the Cob with Fresh Herbs

I prefer using fresh white corn on the cob.

4 ears fresh corn in husks	4 leaves fresh sage
4 sprigs fresh rosemary	2 cloves garlic, split in half

Carefully pull back husks (do not remove) and expose corn. Remove silk and rinse corn.

Pull husks back into place while tucking fresh herbs and garlic between the husks and kernels of corn. Tie string around the end of each ear to keep closed.

Drop the corn in boiling water and cook for about 6 minutes. Remove the string and husks and serve immediately.

YIELD: 4 servings

CALORIES	CARBOHYDRATES: 17.2 GM	TOTAL FAT: .6 GM
Per serving: 71	PROTEIN: 2.4 GM	Saturated fat: .1 GM
Fat: 6%	DIETARY FIBER: 3.1 GM	Monounsaturated fat: .2 GM
Carbohydrates: 83%	SODIUM: 3 MG	
Protein: 11%	CHOLESTEROL: 0 MG	

Pyramid equivalencies: 1 grain

Natural Candied Carrots

Carrots and onions naturally contain more sugar than most other vegetables. Cooking them slowly at a low temperature gently releases the sugar, creating a delicious, natural glaze.

- ½ large red onion, cut in ¼-inch-thick slices
- 2 tablespoons dry sherry
- 2 tablespoons water
- 2 cups carrots, cut in ¼-inch-thick rounds
- 1 tablespoon finely minced fresh mint

Cut the onion slices in quarters. Place the onion in a small saucepan. Add the sherry and water. If necessary, add more to just barely cover the bottom of the pan.

Add the carrot slices. Cover with a tight-fitting lid and cook at very low temperature for 30 to 40 minutes or until the vegetables are tender and the liquid has turned to a sticky glaze.

Toss with the fresh mint and serve immediately.

YIELD: 4 servings

CALORIES	CARBOHYDRATES: 10.2 GM	TOTAL FAT: .2 GM
Per serving: 43	PROTEIN: 1.1 GM	Saturated fat: trace
Fat: 4%	DIETARY FIBER: 3.2 GM	Monounsaturated fat: trace
Carbohydrates: 87%	SODIUM: 53 MG	
Protein: 9%	CHOLESTEROL: 0 MG	

Pyramid equivalencies: 1 vegetable

Peaches and Creme

Nonfat yogurt and specially sweetened peaches give an old favorite a new twist.

4 large ripe peaches
1 recipe Fruit Sweet (recipe follows)

1 recipe Honey Yogurt Creme or
1 recipe Yogurt Crème Fraîche (recipes follow)

Peeling peaches before eating is a matter of individual preference. Some varieties of peaches have a fuzzy, unappealing surface. Others do not. To peel, drop the peaches in a pot of boiling water. Very ripe peaches should be removed from the water within 30 seconds, others may need to remain in the boiling water slightly longer.

Peeling and slicing fresh peaches should not occur until just before serving. Slice the peaches and taste. How much sweetener, if any, do they need? To bring out the "peachy" flavor, toss with Fruit Sweet.

Serve the fresh peaches in bowls with Honey Yogurt Creme or Yogurt Crème Fraîche served on the side.

YIELD: 4 servings

Nutrient analysis includes Fruit Sweet and Honey Yogurt Creme

CALORIES	CARBOHYDRATES: 36.7 GM	TOTAL FAT: .2 GM
Per serving: 160	PROTEIN: 4.6 GM	Saturated fat: .1 GM
Fat: 1%	DIETARY FIBER: 1.4 GM	Monounsaturated fat: .1 GM
Carbohydrates: 88%	SODIUM: 56 MG	
Protein: 11%	CHOLESTEROL: 1 MG	

Pyramid equivalencies: 1¼ fruits, ½ dairy

Fruit Sweet

This sweetener is created to sweeten and strengthen the natural flavor of fresh fruit. Choose a fruit-sweetened preserve that is in the flavor of the fruit being sweetened (peach preserves for peaches, strawberry preserves for strawberries). In addition to sweetening, the preserve reinforces the innate flavor of the fruit. Apricot and pineapple preserves are excellent for their respective fruits as well as sweetening nectarines and tropical fruit. Adding a splash of fruit-flavored brandy or liqueur also helps enhance the fruit's natural flavor as well as helping to retard spoilage.

¼ cup fruit-sweetened preserves
¼ cup water

½ teaspoon ground ginger or cinnamon, optional
1 tablespoon brandy, optional

Whisk all of the ingredients together until completely blended. Use as a sweetener for fresh fruit.

YIELD: 4 servings

CALORIES
Per serving: 52
Fat: 0%
Carbohydrates: 90%
Protein: 0%
Alcohol: 10%

CARBOHYDRATES: 13.1 GM
PROTEIN: 0 GM
DIETARY FIBER: trace
SODIUM: 1 MG
CHOLESTEROL: 0 MG

TOTAL FAT: 0 GM
Saturated fat: 0 GM
Monounsaturated fat: 0 GM

Pyramid equivalencies: ¼ fruit

Honey Yogurt Creme

This easy sauce is delicious with any fruit.

1 cup plain nonfat yogurt
2 tablespoons dry nonfat milk powder

2 tablespoons honey
¼ teaspoon almond or rum extract, optional

Whisk together the yogurt and milk powder. Add the honey and extract. Whisk until smooth. Chill until ready to serve.

YIELD: 4 servings

CALORIES	CARBOHYDRATES: 14.0 GM	TOTAL FAT: .1 GM
Per serving: 72	PROTEIN: 4.0 GM	Saturated fat: trace
Fat: 1%	DIETARY FIBER: trace	Monounsaturated fat: trace
Carbohydrates: 77%	SODIUM: 56 MG	
Protein: 22%	CHOLESTEROL: 1 MG	

Pyramid equivalencies: ½ dairy

Yogurt Crème Fraîche

This is a marvelous topping for fresh fruit. Without the sweetener, use it with vegetables or as a spread for bread.

½ cup plain nonfat yogurt
½ cup nonfat cottage cheese

2 tablespoons honey or brown sugar, optional

Place the yogurt and cottage cheese in a food processor. Puree until completely smooth and creamy. Taste the mixture. If you desire a more tart product, add more yogurt. If you want it less acidic, add more cottage cheese. Puree again if you have added more yogurt or cottage cheese. Refrigerate until ready to serve.

For desserts, place the Yogurt Crème Fraîche in an attractive serving bowl. Drizzle the honey or sprinkle the brown sugar over the top of the creme. Spoon the creme over fresh fruit, gingerbread or other cakes.

The Yogurt Crème Fraîche, without the honey or brown sugar, is ideal for baked potatoes. For a savory topping, you may elect to add chives or other herbs to the creme.

YIELD: 4 servings

Nutrient analysis with brown sugar.

CALORIES | CARBOHYDRATES: 9.8 GM | TOTAL FAT: .1 GM
Per serving: 61 | PROTEIN: 5.1 GM | Saturated fat: trace
Fat: 1% | DIETARY FIBER: 0 GM | Monounsaturated fat: trace
Carbohydrates: 65% | SODIUM: 74 MG
Protein: 34% | CHOLESTEROL: 2 MG

Pyramid equivalencies: ½ dairy

Nutrient analysis without any sweetener.

YIELD: 4 servings. (As a spread for bread, the Yogurt Crème Fraîche should provide 8 to 12 servings.)

CALORIES | CARBOHYDRATES: 3.2 GM | TOTAL FAT: .1 GM
Per serving: 36 | PROTEIN: 5.1 GM | Saturated fat: trace
Fat: 1% | DIETARY FIBER: 0 GM | Monounsaturated fat: trace
Carbohydrates: 38% | SODIUM: 72 MG
Protein: 61% | CHOLESTEROL: 2.0 MG

Pyramid equivalencies: ½ dairy

9

Tapas Party

TAPAS ARE a kind of Spanish meal between meals. Strictly translated, the word "tapas" means "little lids" or "covers." Their origin dates to a time when taverns would serve a glass or cup of wine, then set a small plate of snacks on top of the glass. These plates of foods now represent a hugely popular dining ritual among all walks of Spanish life. Tapas are to Spain what afternoon tea is to England. You could also say tapas are sort of like an American "happy hour." The difference is that the Spanish focus more on the food than the drink. Restaurants become famous for their tapas, offering a huge selection of delectable specialties. Many travelers to Spain turn this so-called little meal of appetizers into a major feast. Forgoing the traditional structure of specific meal courses, I like to offer an array of tapas as a complete dinner. This casual way of dining creates a relaxed, festive atmosphere that family and guests thoroughly enjoy. From the nutritional perspective, a meal of lots of little portions is an excellent way to keep quantities of high-cholesterol products low while bringing great variety to the diet.

TAPAS PARTY (MENU FOR 8)

Marinated Olives
Cucumber and Olive Salad
Radishes with Citrus Vinegar
Toasted Bread Rounds

Roasted Pepper and Anchovy Spread
Sardines and Spanish Sauce
Steamed Mussels with Tomato-Wine Broth
Spicy Braised Shrimp
Crab-Stuffed Eggs
Spanish Potato Salad
Herbed Asparagus
Fruit Wedges with Honey Dip
Madeira Spritzer

Additional Recipes:
Spanish Sauce
Mustard Yogurt Spread
Spanish Potato Salad with Tuna

A tapas party wouldn't be a tapas party without olives in some form or another. Spanish diners delight in numerous varieties of olives, pickled and seasoned in a myriad of ways. Although high in fat, olives offered in small quantities can be a tasty treasure. My version of Marinated Olives is delectable by itself or as an addition to other dishes, such as Cucumber and Olive Salad. Since I am one of those persons who can ravish a plate of olives in seconds, I'm better off mixing my olives into other dishes. Although it is the same spiced olive, the two dishes are different enough so that I wouldn't hesitate to serve both the Marinated Olives and the Cucumber and Olive Salad at the same party. The dual use of recipes is repeated with other dishes featured in this menu. This shortens the time needed to prepare for the party. If you don't like olives, or you are making a super effort to control your fat intake, Radishes with Citrus Vinegar is a pleasant substitute. For a large group, I would offer both the radish and olive dishes.

Along with olives, olive oil is hugely important in the preparation of Spanish cuisine. Olives and olive oil are primarily monounsaturated fat, often called "the healthy fat." Although olive oil offers many benefits, my tapas recipes use about one-fourth the oil that would be typically used in Spain. I find that because of major differences in physical activity, most Americans can't afford the extra calories from using so much olive oil. I've attempted to compensate for the loss in flavor by enhancing the use of seasonings. The result might be described as American tapas with a Spanish accent!

Dishes with little bits of seafood are frequent choices on tapas menus.

Another common item is small slices of bread, plain, toasted or fried and served with a variety of toppings. These toppings may often include seafood. I'll forgo the frying of bread and offer Toasted Bread Rounds. Toppings include Roasted Pepper and Anchovy Spread and Sardines and Spanish Sauce. Because anchovies and sardines have such an assertive sapor, very little is needed to create a pleasant savoriness. The Toasted Bread Rounds can be served with the topping already on the bread or served with the toppings on the side. In addition to the Toasted Bread Rounds, I would also serve plain rounds of bread.

Preparing a meal of several appetizers or little dishes can be more time consuming than cooking a full-course dinner. For that reason, I've created recipes with multiple uses. A basic Spanish Sauce is used to make Sardines and Spanish Sauce, Steamed Mussels with Tomato-Wine Broth and Spicy Braised Shrimp. Crab-Stuffed Eggs and Spanish Potato Salad have the same Mustard Yogurt Spread as a foundation. The Mustard Yogurt Spread is also delicious with Herbed Asparagus. Crab-Stuffed Eggs places a seafood filling inside halves of boiled eggs (yolk discarded). The crab filling could just as easily be used as a topping on the toast, and, in turn, the Roasted Pepper and Anchovy Spread and Sardines and Spanish Sauce could be used to stuff eggs. If you want a complete seafood menu, tuna can be added to create a Spanish Potato Salad with Tuna.

Although sweets are not usually part of a tapas party, I like to serve wedges of fresh fruit as a palate refresher. Fruit Wedges with Honey Dip is a satisfying complement to the tapas. Because there are so many flavors in the Tapas Party, I would keep the beverages simple. For the summertime, I suggest a Madeira Spritzer, iced mineral water or a chilled rosé wine. In cooler temperatures, I like chilled, but not iced, mineral water or a glass of fine dry sherry.

NUTRIENT ANALYSIS FOR TAPAS PARTY

The nutrient analysis includes 1 serving each of Marinated Olives, Cucumber and Olive Salad, Radishes with Citrus Vinegar, Steamed Mussels with Tomato-Wine Broth, Spicy Braised Shrimp, Crab-Stuffed Eggs, Spanish Potato Salad, Herbed Asparagus, Fruit Wedges with Honey Dip and Madeira Spritzer. The analysis also includes 4 servings of Toasted Bread Rounds and 4 servings of a plain baguette cut into the same-size rounds. Also in the total data are 2 servings each of

Roasted Pepper and Anchovy Spread and Sardines and Spanish Sauce. Note that this meal has a high sodium content. The main sources of sodium in this meal are: olives, anchovies, sardines, shrimp and bread. If you serve this complete menu, you may want to adjust your intake of salt at other meals or eliminate 1 or 2 of the menu items. One possibility, without changing the menu, is to use low-sodium breads. Nearly 600 milligrams of the sodium in this menu come from bread. Although they are not always easy to find, low-sodium breads are a helpful contribution.

CALORIES   CARBOHYDRATES: 127.8 GM   TOTAL FAT: 18.6 GM
For total   PROTEIN: 45.0 GM   Saturated fat: 3.4 GM
   meal: 893   DIETARY FIBER: 15.3 GM   Monounsaturated fat: 8.3 GM
Fat: 19%   SODIUM: 1,922 MG
Carbohydrates: 58%   CHOLESTEROL: 114 MG
Protein: 20%
Alcohol: 3%

Pyramid equivalencies: 4 grains, 5 vegetables, 1 fruit, 1½ proteins, ¾ dairy, 2 extras

Marinated Olives

These olives have a teasing spiciness that's delicious by themselves or mixed into other dishes.

2 cups stuffed green olives, drained and rinsed

1 tablespoon fennel seed

2 sprigs fresh thyme or rosemary

3 cloves garlic, slivered

2 teaspoons green peppercorns, drained

1 lemon, cut in very thin slices

½ cup sherry vinegar

Place all of the ingredients in a glass jar and cover. Refrigerate 1 week before serving. Will keep several weeks refrigerated. Use as a condiment or in recipes calling for olives.

YIELD: 4 olives per serving

CALORIES   CARBOHYDRATES: .1 GM   TOTAL FAT: 2.0 GM
Per serving: 15   PROTEIN: .4 GM   Saturated fat: .2 GM
Fat: 84%   DIETARY FIBER: .4 GM   Monounsaturated fat: 1.4 GM
Carbohydrates: 8% SODIUM: 242 MG
Protein: 8%   CHOLESTEROL: 0 MG

Pyramid equivalencies: ½ vegetable

Cucumber and Olive Salad

By using the flavorful Marinated Olives, this salad seems to have more
olives than it really does.

2 *large cucumbers, peeled*   4 *green onions, chopped*
32 *Marinated Olives*   8 *plum tomatoes, quartered*
  (previous recipe)   ¼ *cup finely minced fresh*
½ *cup liquid from Marinated*   *parsley*
  Olives

Cut the cucumber in half lengthwise. With a spoon, scrape out the
seeds. Cut each half crosswise in ¼-inch-thick slices. Toss with the
Marinated Olives, liquid from the olives and the onions. Chill 1 hour.
  Add the tomatoes and parsley to the cucumber mixture just before
serving. Mix and serve immediately.

YIELD: 8 servings

CALORIES   CARBOHYDRATES: 4.7 GM   TOTAL FAT: 2.1 GM
Per serving: 34   PROTEIN: 1.2 GM   Saturated fat: .2 GM
Fat: 45%   DIETARY FIBER: 1.7 GM   Monounsaturated fat: 1.4 GM
Carbohydrates: 44% SODIUM: 328 MG
Protein: 11%   CHOLESTEROL: 0 MG

Pyramid equivalencies: 1 vegetable

Radishes with Citrus Vinegar

Sometimes the simplest dishes offer a major contribution to a meal. In this case, the radishes have a crispness that is unlike any of the other tapas. While a humble plate of radishes doesn't seem like much, the bright color and contrasting texture increase the appeal of the other dishes. Specialty radishes include elongated radishes or white or purple radishes. If you can't find any of these specialty radishes, use all red radishes or use a small daikon. Daikon, a large Japanese radish, will need to be peeled and sliced and tossed with lemon juice to prevent discoloring.

⅓ cup red wine vinegar or sherry vinegar	1 bunch specialty radishes, washed and trimmed
¼ cup fresh orange juice	1 lemon cut in 8 wedges
1 bunch red radishes, washed and trimmed	

Whisk together the vinegar and orange juice and place in small bowl suitable for dipping. Place the bowl on a platter and arrange the assorted radishes around the bowl. Intersperse lemon wedges between the radishes. Chill before serving.

YIELD: 8 servings

CALORIES	CARBOHYDRATES: 3.0 GM	TOTAL FAT: trace
Per serving: 9	PROTEIN: .2 GM	Saturated fat: 0 GM
Fat: 45%	DIETARY FIBER: .1 GM	Monounsaturated fat: 0 GM
Carbohydrates: 44%	SODIUM: 6 MG	
Protein: 11%	CHOLESTEROL: 0 MG	

Pyramid equivalencies: ¼ vegetable

Toasted Bread Rounds

Supermarkets feature many different seasoning blends without salt. A lemon-herb mixture is excellent on the Toasted Bread Rounds. In addition to preparing the Toasted Bread Rounds, I usually slice another baguette into rounds and serve it plain with the assorted spreads.

1 *twelve-inch (8 ounces)*	*Salt-free seasoning blend*
baguette or similar bread	2 *tablespoons finely grated*
Nonstick cooking spray	*Parmesan cheese*
made with extra-virgin olive	
oil	

Slice the baguette in ⅜-inch-thick rounds. A 12-inch baguette should yield about 32 slices. Place the rounds on a cookie sheet, close together but not overlapping. Place the cookie sheet under a preheated broiler. Leave under the broiler for 45 seconds and check to see if it has lightly browned. If necessary, leave the bread under the broiler for a few seconds more.

Remove the tray and turn the bread rounds over. Lightly spray the bread with the olive oil spray. Generously sprinkle the bread with the no-salt seasoning blend. Follow with a light sprinkling of the Parmesan cheese. Return the bread rounds to the broiler. Toast for 45 seconds or until the bread is lightly browned. Serve hot or put in a dry container and store 2 or 3 days at room temperature. Serve with Sardines and Spanish Sauce or Roasted Pepper and Anchovy Spread.

YIELD: 32 servings, 1 bread round per serving

CALORIES	CARBOHYDRATES: 4.0 GM	TOTAL FAT: .6 GM
Per serving: 26	PROTEIN: .9 GM	Saturated fat: .2 GM
Fat: 22%	DIETARY FIBER: .2 GM	Monounsaturated fat: .2 GM
Carbohydrates: 63%	SODIUM: 50 MG	
Protein: 15%	CHOLESTEROL: .4 MG	

Pyramid equivalencies: ⅓ grain

Roasted Pepper and Anchovy Spread

People love or hate anchovies. There seems to be no middle ground. However, I have found that when anchovies are used in very small quantities, they contribute a tantalizing flavor without overpowering the dish. The anchovy hater may never realize there's an anchovy present. To make this dish, I suggest you add 1 or 2 fillets at a time, tasting after each addition. Before using the anchovies, be sure to rinse well under cold water. This will take away a lot of the salt, oil and fishiness.

2 large red bell peppers	1 tablespoon fresh orange juice
2 garlic cloves, peeled	1 tablespoon fresh lemon juice
2 tablespoons unsalted tomato paste	3 or 4 anchovy fillets or more to taste
	4 to 6 leaves fresh basil

Place the bell peppers on the grate over a burner on a gas stove. You may use metal tongs to hold the peppers in place. Rotate the peppers until the outside skin is completely blackened. Immediately wrap the pepper in a clean towel or place in a brown paper bag and tightly close. After 20 minutes, remove the peppers and pull away the blackened skin. Rinse under cold water. Open the peppers and remove the seeds and white ribs.

If you do not have a gas stove, place the peppers under a broiler or in a very hot oven. Rotate the peppers four or five times. This method of roasting takes longer than the burner method, usually at least 30 minutes. When the peppers have softened, remove from the heat and rinse under cold water. Although the skin may not have blackened, peel away the skin. Open the peppers and discard the seeds and white ribs. If the peppers aren't tender, simmer a few minutes in wine or water.

Rinse the anchovies under cold water. Combine all of the ingredients in a blender jar and puree until smooth and creamy. If necessary, add a little water to create the desired consistency. Taste the mixture and decide if you want to add more anchovy.

Use as a spread for Toasted Bread Rounds, plain bread rounds or as a filling for boiled egg halves.

YIELD: 1½ cups, 16 servings of 1½ tablespoons each

Nutrient information does not include bread rounds.

CALORIES	CARBOHYDRATES: 2.4 GM	TOTAL FAT: .3 GM
Per serving: 15	PROTEIN: 1.1 GM	Saturated fat: .1 GM
Fat: 15%	DIETARY FIBER: .3 GM	Monounsaturated fat: .1 GM
Carbohydrates: 60%	SODIUM: 60 MG	
Protein: 25%	CHOLESTEROL: 1.0 MG	

Pyramid equivalencies: ¼ vegetable

Spanish Sauce

This traditional sauce has been modified to exclude oil. It is a marvelous sauce for vegetables, chicken, fish and seafood. For the Tapas Party, it is used for Sardines and Spanish Sauce, Steamed Mussels with Tomato-Wine Broth and Spicy Braised Shrimp. It is also excellent as a spread for the Toasted Bread Rounds.

12 plum tomatoes, finely diced
1 cup diced red onion
6 cloves garlic, finely minced
1 fresh serrano chile, seeded and finely minced
½ teaspoon saffron
½ teaspoon paprika
½ teaspoon cumin
¼ teaspoon ground black pepper
½ cup Madeira or dry sherry
2 teaspoons low-sodium soy sauce
1 bell pepper, seeded and finely diced
1 to 3 tablespoons unsalted tomato paste

In a saucepan, combine all of the ingredients except the bell pepper and tomato paste. Simmer uncovered at low temperature for 10 minutes. Add the bell pepper and simmer 5 minutes more. If necessary, add water to the pan.

Stir in the tomato paste and continue cooking until the sauce has thickened. Serve immediately or refrigerate for later use. Use as a spread or sauce.

YIELD: 3½ cups, 40 servings of 1½ tablespoons each

Nutrient information is for 1½ tablespoons.

CALORIES	CARBOHYDRATES: 1.3 GM	TOTAL FAT: trace
Per serving: 6	PROTEIN: .3 GM	Saturated fat: trace
Fat: 9%	DIETARY FIBER: .3 GM	Monounsaturated fat: trace
Carbohydrates: 77%	SODIUM: 3.8 MG	
Protein: 14%	CHOLESTEROL: 0 MG	

Pyramid equivalencies: ⅙ vegetable

Sardines and Spanish Sauce

Although a traditional Spanish appetizer, this was a popular item on Victorian American menus.

> 1 can (3.75 ounces) water-
>   packed sardines
> 1⅓ cups Spanish Sauce
>   (previous recipe)
>
> 1 tablespoon fresh orange juice
> 1 tablespoon fresh lemon juice
> 1 teaspoon brown sugar

Place the sardines in a strainer and rinse under cold water. Transfer the sardines to a small saucepan and mash with a fork. Add the other ingredients and mix well. Warm the mixture and serve immediately. Serve warm as a spread for Toasted Bread Rounds, crackers or other bread.

YIELD: 16 servings, 1½ tablespoons per serving

Nutrient information does not include bread rounds.

CALORIES	CARBOHYDRATES: 1.6 GM	TOTAL FAT: 1.3 GM
Per serving: 23	PROTEIN: 1.4 GM	Saturated fat: .4 GM
Fat: 49%	DIETARY FIBER: .2 GM	Monounsaturated fat: .4 GM
Carbohydrates: 27%	SODIUM: 20 MG	
Protein: 24%	CHOLESTEROL: 5 MG	

Pyramid equivalencies: ¼ vegetable, ⅛ protein

Steamed Mussels with Tomato-Wine Broth

This simple preparation of mussels in a tomato-wine broth is popular throughout the Mediterranean area. Various wines and tomato sauces can be used to create the tomato-wine broth.

16 mussels
1 cup dry sherry
Water
½ cup Spanish Sauce (recipe on page 110)

3 tablespoons finely chopped fresh parsley

Carefully wash the mussels with cold water. Using a knife, scrape any "beard" that protrudes from the shell.

Pour the sherry into a pot with a steamer basket. Add enough water to create a depth of ½ inch. Bring the liquid to a boil. Place the mussels in the steamer basket and cover the pot. Steam for 3 or 4 minutes or until the mussels open.

Transfer the mussels to a serving platter. Open the shells completely so that a sauce can be easily poured over the mussels. Combine ½ cup of the cooking liquid and ½ cup of the Spanish Sauce. Spoon the sauce over the mussels and sprinkle with the fresh parsley. Serve immediately.

YIELD: 8 servings (2 mussels each)

CALORIES	CARBOHYDRATES: 1.8 GM	TOTAL FAT: .7 GM
Per serving: 31	PROTEIN: 4.3 GM	Saturated fat: .1 GM
Fat: 19%	DIETARY FIBER: .2 GM	Monounsaturated fat: .1 GM
Carbohydrates: 23%	SODIUM: 83 MG	
Protein: 58%	CHOLESTEROL: 5.3 MG	

Pyramid equivalencies: ⅙ vegetable, ⅓ protein

Spicy Braised Shrimp

Although high in cholesterol, shrimp has so little fat that it can be comfortably enjoyed on a health-conscious diet. Of course, you want to avoid adding fat when you cook the shrimp!

8 slices whole wheat bread
1 cup Spanish Sauce (recipe on page 110)
¼ cup water
1 pound raw shrimp, peeled and deveined

2 tablespoons finely minced fresh cilantro
8 wedges fresh lemon or orange

Trim the crust from the slices of bread. Cut each slice diagonally, creating 2 triangles. Arrange the bread triangles on a baking sheet and place under a broiler. When the bread is lightly browned, in 1 or 2 minutes, turn the bread and toast on the other side. Set the toasted triangles aside.

In a skillet, combine the Spanish Sauce and water. At high heat, bring the mixture to a boil and immediately add the shrimp. Stirring constantly and continuing at high heat, cook the shrimp for 1 or 2 minutes or until they have developed their white and coral colors. Stir the cilantro into the shrimp mixture and remove from the heat.

Arrange the bread triangles around the outside of a serving platter. Mound the hot shrimp in the middle of the platter and serve immediately, garnished with lemon or orange wedges.

YIELD: 8 servings

CALORIES
Per serving: 132
Fat: 15%
Carbohydrates: 42%
Protein: 43%

CARBOHYDRATES: 12.7 GM
PROTEIN: 12.4 GM
DIETARY FIBER: 3.3 GM
SODIUM: 279 MG
CHOLESTEROL: 82 MG

TOTAL FAT: 1.9 GM
Saturated fat: .3 GM
Monounsaturated fat: .3 GM

Pyramid equivalencies: 1 grain, ¼ vegetable, ½ protein

Crab-Stuffed Eggs

Stuffed eggs are always a popular appetizer.

8 large hard-boiled eggs, shell
removed
½ recipe Mustard Yogurt
Spread (recipe follows)
2 tablespoons capers, drained
and rinsed
1 tablespoon extra-virgin olive
oil

1 teaspoon fresh lemon juice
¼ teaspoon ground black pepper
⅔ cup cooked crab
2 green onions, finely chopped
¼ cup diced, canned pimento

Halve the eggs lengthwise and discard the yolks. Rinse away any fragment of yolks and set aside.

Stir together the Mustard Yogurt Spread, capers, olive oil, lemon juice and black pepper. Mix in the crab, green onions and pimento. Stuff the egg halves and chill until serving time. Do not make more than 3 hours before serving. This filling can also be used as a spread for bread rounds.

YIELD: 8 servings, 2 halves each

CALORIES	CARBOHYDRATES: 4.2 GM	TOTAL FAT: 2.2 GM
Per serving: 69	PROTEIN: 8.1 GM	Saturated fat: .3 GM
Fat: 28%	DIETARY FIBER: trace	Monounsaturated fat: 1.3 GM
Carbohydrates: 25%	SODIUM: 181 MG	
Protein: 47%	CHOLESTEROL: 11.8 MG	

Pyramid equivalencies: ¼ dairy, ⅓ protein

Mustard Yogurt Spread

This simple spread is satisfying as a dip for raw vegetables or as a spread for sandwiches. The spread is used for making Crab-Stuffed Eggs (previous recipe) and Spanish Potato Salad (following recipe).

2 cups plain nonfat yogurt
¼ cup dry nonfat milk powder
2 tablespoons unsalted Dijon-
  style mustard

1 teaspoon dry dill

Line a strainer with cheesecloth or a paper coffee filter. Fill the strainer with the yogurt and place in a bowl to drain for 2 hours in a refrigerator.

Transfer the drained yogurt to a mixing bowl. Whisk the milk powder into the yogurt. Add the mustard and dill and continue whisking until well blended.

YIELD: 1½ cups, 16 servings of 1½ tablespoons each

CALORIES	CARBOHYDRATES: 2.9 GM	TOTAL FAT: .1 GM
Per serving: 22	PROTEIN: 2.1 GM	Saturated fat: trace
Fat: 4%	DIETARY FIBER: 0 GM	Monounsaturated fat: trace
Carbohydrates: 56%	SODIUM: 23 MG	
Protein: 40%	CHOLESTEROL: .7 MG	

Pyramid equivalencies: ¼ dairy

Spanish Potato Salad

This salad would be made traditionally with mayonnaise, but a yogurt dressing is equally appealing. It can be served cold, although I prefer it while the potatoes are still slightly warm. Hot or cold, do not add the tomato until you are ready to serve. A recipe follows that includes tuna.

12 small red potatoes, carefully
   washed and quartered
1 tablespoon extra-virgin olive
   oil
1 tablespoon fresh lemon juice
½ cup diced red onion
3 boiled eggs, shell removed
½ cup diced red bell pepper or
   ¼ cup diced, canned red
   pimento

½ recipe Mustard Yogurt Spread
   (previous recipe)
8 green olives, sliced
2 tablespoons finely chopped
   fresh parsley
1 cup diced fresh tomato

Place the potatoes in a pot of boiling water and cook until tender, about 10 minutes. When the potatoes are tender, drain and rinse under cold water for 30 seconds. Immediately toss with the olive oil, lemon juice and red onion. Let stand 10 minutes.

Meanwhile, halve the boiled eggs. Discard the yolk and chop the egg whites. After the potatoes have cooled for 10 minutes, toss with the egg whites and bell pepper. Add ½ recipe of the Mustard Yogurt Spread and mix well. Stir in the sliced olives, parsley and fresh tomato. Serve immediately.

YIELD: 8 servings

CALORIES	CARBOHYDRATES: 15.3 GM	TOTAL FAT: 2.4 GM
Per serving: 100	PROTEIN: 4.8 GM	Saturated fat: .4 GM
Fat: 21%	DIETARY FIBER: 1.1 GM	Monounsaturated fat: 1.6 GM
Carbohydrates: 60%	SODIUM: 268 MG	
Protein: 19%	CHOLESTEROL: .7 MG	

Pyramid equivalencies: 1½ vegetables, ¼ dairy

Spanish Potato Salad with Tuna

Fish and seafood are common ingredients in potato salad in Spain and other European countries.

To the above recipe add 1 cup tuna chunks. Use water-packed canned tuna that has been rinsed under cold water.

YIELD: 8 servings

CALORIES	CARBOHYDRATES: 15.3 GM	TOTAL FAT: 2.8 GM
Per serving: 126	PROTEIN: 10.4 GM	Saturated fat: .5 GM
Fat: 20%	DIETARY FIBER: 1.2 GM	Monounsaturated fat: 1.6 GM
Carbohydrates: 48%	SODIUM: 179 MG	
Protein: 32%	CHOLESTEROL: 8.2 MG	

Pyramid equivalencies: 1½ vegetables, ¼ dairy, ⅓ protein

Herbed Asparagus

Spears of chilled asparagus are delicious by themselves or accompanied by a sauce. I like to serve the asparagus with a dollop of the Mustard Yogurt Spread.

32 *spears of fresh asparagus*
1 *tablespoon finely minced fresh mint*
1 *tablespoon finely minced fresh parsley*

1 *clove garlic, finely minced*
Mustard Yogurt Spread, optional (recipe on page 114)

On a cutting board, line up the asparagus with the tip ends forming a straight line. With a knife, cut away the coarse ends so that the spears are all the same length. You will likely need to cut away 1 to 2 inches of stalk.

Tie a string around the asparagus or use a piece of aluminum foil to wrap around the tip end of the complete bunch. Stand the asparagus upright in a pot with about 1 inch of water. Cover the pot and steam for 2 to 4 minutes, or until the asparagus is tender.

Drain the asparagus and immediately rinse in cold water. Gently toss the asparagus with the mint, parsley and garlic. Refrigerate for at least 1 hour before serving. Arrange the asparagus on a serving plate and top with a dollop of Mustard Yogurt Spread, if desired.

YIELD: 8 servings

Nutrient information does not include the Mustard Yogurt Spread.

CALORIES	CARBOHYDRATES: 2.7 GM	TOTAL FAT: .2 GM
Per serving: 15	PROTEIN: 1.5 GM	Saturated fat: .1 GM
Fat: 2%	DIETARY FIBER: 1.8 GM	Monounsaturated fat: trace
Carbohydrates: 95%	SODIUM: 3 MG	
Protein: 3%	CHOLESTEROL: 0 MG	

Pyramid equivalencies: 1 vegetable

Fruit Wedges with Honey Dip

This simple fruit platter is intended as an appetizer or refresher between courses.

⅓ cup honey
3 tablespoons Spanish sherry
3 tablespoons water
1 pink grapefruit, peeled and sectioned

2 large oranges, peeled and sectioned
1 pint strawberries, washed and left whole with stems intact

Whisk together the honey, sherry and water in a small saucepan. Bring to almost boiling, then remove from the heat. This step can also be done in a microwave. Allow mixture to cool uncovered at room temperature. If desired, chill before serving.

Pour the mixture into a small dipping bowl. Place the bowl in the center of a platter and arrange the fruit around the bowl.

YIELD: 8 servings

CALORIES
Per serving: 80
Fat: 2%
Carbohydrates: 95%
Protein: 3%

CARBOHYDRATES: 20.4 GM
PROTEIN: .7 GM
DIETARY FIBER: 2.2 GM
SODIUM: 2 MG
CHOLESTEROL: 0 MG

TOTAL FAT: .2 GM
Saturated fat: trace
Monounsaturated fat: trace

Pyramid equivalencies: 1 fruit

Madeira Spritzer

In addition to Madeira, Marsala or a fine sherry can be used in this aromatic cooler. There are many sherries to choose from, but do not use a cream sherry.

2 cups Madeira   8 thin strips of orange peel
2 cups unsweetened, orange-
    flavored mineral water

Place 8 wineglasses in the freezer. When chilled, fill with crushed ice and chill again. Meanwhile, chill but do not combine the Madeira and mineral water.

When ready to serve, pour equal amounts of Madeira and mineral water into each glass. Wipe the rim of each glass with the orange peel. Serve immediately.

YIELD: 8 servings

CALORIES	CARBOHYDRATES: 22.0 GM	TOTAL FAT: .5 GM
Per serving: 126	PROTEIN: .3 GM	Saturated fat: .1 GM
Fat: 3%	DIETARY FIBER: 0 GM	Monounsaturated fat: trace
Carbohydrates: 66%	SODIUM: 4 MG	
Protein: 1%	CHOLESTEROL: 0 MG	
Alcohol: 30%		

Pyramid equivalencies: 1 extra

10

California
Mediterrania

CALIFORNIA IS sometimes described as America's version of Mediterrania. Comparable climates produce similar agricultural products. With all of the attention recently given to the health benefits of Mediterranean cuisine, I decided it would be fun to create a menu that gives a California twist to some traditional Mediterranean dishes.

California cuisine has long been noted for Mexican and Asian influences. This menu incorporates some of those influences into dishes with Mediterranean roots. More important than the origin of the dishes, California Mediterrania is a celebration of farm-fresh produce. Fresh fruit and vegetables are the soul of this tantalizing menu. Make this meal in the summertime, when you have the widest selection of fresh produce.

CALIFORNIA MEDITERRANIA (MENU FOR 4)

Pacific Rim Gazpacho
Green Apple Tabouli
Garlicky Artichokes with Lemon-Herb Dipping Sauce
Golden Salad Niçoise with Golden State Vinaigrette

Pale Passion
Berry Almond Tea

Additional Recipe:
Alternative Green Apple Tabouli

Gazpacho is a chilled Spanish soup that is popular worldwide. Sometimes called "salad soup," our Pacific Rim Gazpacho incorporates Asian flavors into the soup.

Parsley in the Middle East is commonly used as a salad green as well as a seasoning herb. Tabouli is a parsley and tomato salad, laced with little flecks of bulgur. American versions usually add more bulgur and decrease the parsley. One time when I went to make tabouli I couldn't find any tomatoes that had flavor. I decided to experiment, replacing the tomatoes with green apples. Green Apple Tabouli was the result. A version with more bulgur and less parsley is also included. If green apples turn you off, use red ones or stick with the traditional tomatoes.

One of my favorite California trips is to drive through Gilroy, the Garlic Capital of America. The region is also famous for artichokes. Garlicky Artichokes with Lemon-Herb Dipping Sauce allows you to enjoy the pleasures of the choke without the fat of the typical dipping sauces. Our dipping sauce is a superb low-fat alternative for other vegetables as well.

Salad Niçoise, with tuna, green beans and potatoes is one of the French Riviera's most famous recipes. It has also become standard fare on many American restaurant menus. My version isn't much different except for color. I replaced the tuna with salmon and then used yellow vegetables to complete the salad. You don't have to do this, but wax beans, Finnish potatoes and yellow peppers and tomatoes make a gorgeous presentation. For a dazzling display of gold, try Golden Salad Niçoise with Golden State Vinaigrette.

An assertive white wine is a tantalizing addition to this meal. In the interest of reducing alcohol or calories, some diners may prefer de-alcoholized wine or other soft drink. Pale Passion is an easily made beverage with just a hint of grape, so that the sweetness won't detract from the rest of the meal. Although a dessert is not included with this menu, I would recommend the Almond Cake (page 265). Almond desserts are extremely popular in the Mediterranean region, and California is a major producer of almonds. A cup of hot Berry Almond Tea is also a sensational way to complete this meal.

NUTRIENT INFORMATION FOR CALIFORNIA MEDITERRANIA

Nutrient information for total meal is based on 1 serving each of Pacific Rim Gazpacho, Green Apple Tabouli, Garlicky Artichokes with Lemon-Herb Dipping Sauce, Golden Salad Niçoise with Golden State Vinaigrette and Berry Almond Tea. The analysis includes two servings of Pale Passion. Persons wanting more calories may add bread, fresh fruit or an extra serving of the Pacific Rim Gazpacho.

CALORIES	CARBOHYDRATES: 102.1 GM	TOTAL FAT: 17.2 GM
For total meal: 717	PROTEIN: 40.3 GM	Saturated fat: 2.6 GM
Fat: 21%	DIETARY FIBER: 16.9 GM	Monounsaturated fat: 8.2 GM
Carbohydrates: 57%	SODIUM: 692 MG	
Protein: 22%	CHOLESTEROL: 43 MG	

Pyramid equivalencies: ¼ grain, 5 vegetables, 1 fruit, 1 protein, ¼ dairy

Pacific Rim Gazpacho

Use the ripest, sweetest tomatoes you can find for this chilled soup.

2 cups water
1 cup unsalted tomato puree
½ cup rice vinegar
4 teaspoons low-sodium soy sauce
¼ teaspoon hot pepper sauce
1 tablespoon frozen orange juice concentrate
1 teaspoon dark sesame oil
3 cups finely diced ripe tomatoes

1 cup cucumber, peeled, seeded and diced
1 cup green or red bell pepper, seeded and finely diced
½ cup diced green onion
2 cloves garlic, finely minced
½ cup sliced canned water chestnuts
¼ cup minced fresh cilantro or parsley

Stir together the water, tomato puree, vinegar, soy sauce, hot pepper sauce, juice concentrate and sesame oil. Chill for 2 hours.

Add the tomatoes, cucumber, bell pepper, green onion and garlic. Refrigerate 1 hour.

When ready to serve, sprinkle the water chestnuts and cilantro over each bowl.

YIELD: 8 servings

CALORIES	CARBOHYDRATES: 11.3 GM	TOTAL FAT: .9 GM
Per serving: 53	PROTEIN: 2.0 GM	Saturated fat: .1 GM
Fat: 13%	DIETARY FIBER: 2.3 GM	Monounsaturated fat: .3 GM
Carbohydrates: 74%	SODIUM: 102 MG	
Protein: 13%	CHOLESTEROL: 0 MG	

Pyramid equivalencies: 1 vegetable

Green Apple Tabouli

This version is basically like the traditional Middle Eastern version, except green apples replace tomatoes.

⅓ cup bulgur
⅓ cup boiling water
2 green apples
⅓ cup fresh lemon juice
¼ cup fresh orange juice
1 tablespoon extra-virgin olive oil

1 clove garlic, finely minced
¼ teaspoon ground black pepper
¼ teaspoon ground allspice
2 cups finely chopped fresh parsley
1 cup finely chopped fresh mint
1 green onion, finely chopped

Pour boiling water over bulgur and cover. Let rest for 10 minutes or until water is absorbed.

Core and finely dice the apples. Immediately toss with the lemon and orange juice. Add the olive oil, garlic, black pepper and allspice. Toss until well mixed.

When the bulgur has cooled, add to apple mixture. Also stir in the parsley, mint and green onion. Chill 2 hours before serving.

YIELD: 4 servings

CALORIES   CARBOHYDRATES: 29.6 GM   TOTAL FAT: 4.0 GM
Per serving: 152   PROTEIN: 2.7 GM   Saturated fat: .5 GM
Fat: 22%   DIETARY FIBER: 6.5 GM   Monounsaturated fat: 2.5 GM
Carbohydrates: 71%   SODIUM: 20 MG
Protein: 7%   CHOLESTEROL: 0 MG

Pyramid equivalencies: ¼ grain, 1 vegetable, ½ fruit

Alternative Green Apple Tabouli

This version emphasizes the grain over the herbs. The seasonings have
been adjusted to account for the increased starch.

1 cup bulgur	1 clove garlic, finely minced
1 cup boiling water	¼ teaspoon ground black pepper
2 green apples	¼ teaspoon ground allspice
⅓ cup fresh lemon juice	1 cup finely chopped fresh
⅓ cup fresh orange juice	parsley
1 tablespoon extra-virgin olive	½ cup finely chopped fresh mint
oil	1 green onion, finely chopped
1 teaspoon low-sodium soy	
sauce	

Pour boiling water over bulgur and cover. Let rest for 10 minutes or
until water is absorbed.

Core and finely dice the apples. Immediately toss with the lemon and
orange juice. Add the olive oil, soy sauce, garlic, black pepper and
allspice. Toss until well mixed.

When the bulgur has cooled, add to apple mixture. Also stir in the
parsley, mint and green onion. Chill 2 hours before serving.

YIELD: 4 servings

CALORIES   CARBOHYDRATES: 29.6 GM   TOTAL FAT: 4.0 GM
Per serving: 251   PROTEIN: 2.7 GM   Saturated fat: .5 GM
Fat: 15%   DIETARY FIBER: 1.2 GM   Monounsaturated fat: 2.5 GM
Carbohydrates: 78%   SODIUM: 20 MG
Protein: 7%   CHOLESTEROL: 0 MG

Pyramid equivalencies: 1 grain, ¾ vegetable, ½ fruit

Garlicky Artichokes with Lemon-Herb Dipping Sauce

Garlic subtly enhances the flavor of the artichokes.

4 large artichokes	2 tablespoons rice vinegar
Boiling water	1 recipe Lemon-Herb Dipping
1 bulb garlic	Sauce (recipe follows)

With a serrated knife, slice ½ inch off the top of the artichoke. Cut away most of the stems, so that the artichokes will sit upright. Using scissors, trim the thorny portion from the leaves. Place the artichokes standing upright in a pot.

Slice the garlic bulb in half. Add the garlic to the pot. Add enough boiling water to the pot to just cover the artichokes. Add the vinegar and simmer with lid slightly ajar at moderate temperature for 30 to 40 minutes or until the leaves just barely pull away. Remove the pot from the heat, but let the artichokes stand in the hot water for 20 minutes.

The artichokes may be served hot or cold. Serve with the Lemon-Herb Dipping Sauce.

YIELD: 4 servings

Nutrient information also includes the sauce.

CALORIES	CARBOHYDRATES: 19.4 GM	TOTAL FAT: .5 GM
Per serving: 96	PROTEIN: 6.3 GM	Saturated fat: .1 GM
Fat: 4%	DIETARY FIBER: 4.1 GM	Monounsaturated fat: .1 GM
Carbohydrates: 72%	SODIUM: 125 MG	Polyunsaturated fat: .1 GM
Protein: 24%	CHOLESTEROL: 1 MG	

Pyramid equivalencies: 1 vegetable, ¼ dairy

Lemon-Herb Dipping Sauce

This is also excellent as a dipping sauce for fresh vegetable crudités.

¾ cup plain nonfat yogurt
2 tablespoons dry nonfat milk
  powder
1 tablespoon unsalted Dijon-
  style mustard
1 tablespoon frozen,
  unsweetened orange juice
  concentrate

1 tablespoon fresh lemon juice
1 tablespoon capers, well rinsed
2 tablespoons finely minced
  fresh basil, parsley or
  tarragon
1 tablespoon finely grated fresh
  lemon peel

Whisk together the yogurt and milk powder. Whisk in the mustard, orange juice concentrate and lemon juice. Slightly crush the capers and add with the fresh herbs and lemon peel to the yogurt mixture. Mix well and set aside for 30 minutes before serving.

YIELD: 4 servings

CALORIES
Per serving: 43
Fat: 5%
Carbohydrates: 63%
Protein: 32%

CARBOHYDRATES: 7.0 GM
PROTEIN: 3.5 GM
DIETARY FIBER: .1 GM
SODIUM: 46 MG
CHOLESTEROL: 1 MG

TOTAL FAT: .3 GM
Saturated fat: .1 GM
Monounsaturated fat: trace

Pyramid equivalencies: ½ dairy

Golden Salad Niçoise

If Finnish potatoes are not available, you may substitute any other yellow potato.

2 large Finnish potatoes, peeled and cut in bite-size pieces

½ pound yellow wax beans, cut in 2-inch pieces

1 carrot, peeled and thinly sliced in rounds

1 pound fresh salmon fillets

½ cup dry white wine (approximately)

1 bay leaf

1 large head butter lettuce, torn in bite-size pieces

1 recipe Golden State Vinaigrette (recipe follows)

2 boiled eggs, each peeled and cut in eight parts with yolks discarded

8 black olives, pitted and sliced

4 teaspoons capers, drained and rinsed

1 yellow bell pepper, cut in slivers

1 cup yellow teardrop or yellow cherry tomatoes (halved or whole)

In a saucepan, place the potatoes on a steamer rack over hot water. Cover and steam 4 minutes. Add the beans and carrot and steam until all of the vegetables are tender. Immediately rinse the vegetables in cold water. Drain and set aside in refrigerator to chill.

Using pliers or tweezers remove any bones from the salmon. Place the salmon in a skillet, skin side down. Add enough wine to the pan to create a depth of ¼ inch. Add the bay leaf and poach at moderate heat, covered. Allow about 4 minutes per ½ inch of thickness. Using a spatula, transfer the salmon to a plate and chill. Just before serving, pull away the skin and discard. Break the salmon into bite-size pieces.

In a large bowl, toss the lettuce with ¼ cup of Golden State Vinaigrette. Transfer the lettuce to individual serving plates. After removing the lettuce from the bowl, toss the cooked potatoes, beans and carrot with some of the dressing, adding more as needed. Arrange the dressed vegetables in a line over the lettuce. Create a parallel column by alternately placing bits of salmon and egg white slices over the lettuce. Drizzle the remaining dressing over the entire salad. Sprinkle the olive slices and capers over the salad. Attractively arrange the pepper slivers and tomatoes on the salad. Serve immediately.

YIELD: 4 servings

Nutrient information includes the dressing.

CALORIES	CARBOHYDRATES: 28.7 GM	TOTAL FAT: 11.6 GM
Per serving: 326	PROTEIN: 29.1 GM	Saturated fat: 1.9 GM
Fat: 31%	DIETARY FIBER: 3.8 GM	Monounsaturated fat: 5.4 GM
Carbohydrates: 34%	SODIUM: 439 MG	
Protein: 35%	CHOLESTEROL: 42 MG	

Pyramid equivalencies: 2 vegetables, 1 protein

Golden State Vinaigrette

This is also excellent as a dressing for a simple green salad.

⅓ cup rice vinegar
2 tablespoons frozen, unsweetened orange juice concentrate
2 tablespoons water
1 tablespoon unsalted, Dijon-style mustard
1 teaspoon unsalted tomato paste
1 tablespoon extra-virgin olive oil
1 clove garlic, finely minced
3 or 4 leaves fresh basil

Place all of the ingredients in a blender and process until the basil is finely chopped and the liquid is well blended. Use immediately or chill for later use. Do not make more than 24 hours before serving.

YIELD: 4 servings

CALORIES	CARBOHYDRATES: 5.1 GM	TOTAL FAT: 3.6 GM
Per serving: 51	PROTEIN: .5 GM	Saturated fat: .5 GM
Fat: 59%	DIETARY FIBER: .2 GM	Monounsaturated fat: 2.5 GM
Carbohydrates: 37%	SODIUM: 3 MG	
Protein: 4%	CHOLESTEROL: 0 MG	

Pyramid equivalencies: No equivalencies

Pale Passion

With only a hint of sweetness, this simple beverage has a light, refreshing flavor that can be enjoyed throughout a meal.

1 liter unsweetened, lemon-
    flavored mineral water

1 cup unsweetened, white grape
    juice (regular strength)

Chill the mineral water and grape juice. When ready to serve, pour ½ cup mineral water into each glass and stir in 1 tablespoon of white grape juice. Pale Passion can be served in wine or champagne glasses without ice or in other glasses with ice.

YIELD: 8 servings

CALORIES	CARBOHYDRATES: 5.1 GM	TOTAL FAT: .1 GM
Per serving: 20	PROTEIN: .1 GM	Saturated fat: 0 GM
Fat: 2%	DIETARY FIBER: .1 GM	Monounsaturated fat: 0 GM
Carbohydrates: 96%	SODIUM: 3 MG	
Protein: 2%	CHOLESTEROL: 0 MG	

Pyramid equivalencies: ¼ fruit

Berry Almond Tea

A hint of aromatic sweetness makes this a pleasant conclusion to a delicious meal.

3 bags almond-flavored tea
4 cups boiling water
2 tablespoons berry-flavored
    juice concentrate

4 large strawberries for garnish,
    optional

Place the tea bags in a teapot and add the boiling water. Let steep for 5 minutes. Remove the bags, squeezing the liquid from the bags into the teapot. Add the juice and serve immediately. This is one tea that I would not serve with a wedge of lemon or other citrus. The acid knocks out the subtle almond flavor. If desired, garnish the plate with a simple straw-berry.

YIELD: 8 servings

CALORIES	CARBOHYDRATES: 3.0 GM	TOTAL FAT: trace
Per serving: 15	PROTEIN: trace	Saturated fat: 0 GM
Fat: 1%	DIETARY FIBER: .1 GM	Monounsaturated fat: 0 GM
Carbohydrates: 97%	SODIUM: 3 MG	
Protein: 2%	CHOLESTEROL: 0 MG	

Pyramid equivalencies: ¼ fruit

11

Extraordinary Fare

ORDINARY DISHES, with a few extra touches, can become extraordinary fare. This dinner is about bringing creativity to a commonplace meal. Minestrone, garlic bread, fish cakes and bread pudding are given a zesty new look that will make family or friends feel this meal is a special occasion. In addition to creating an appealing new look and taste, you will also offer extraordinary nutrition! This menu was deliberately created to produce leftovers for the next day's lunch.

EXTRAORDINARY FARE (MENU FOR 4 WITH LEFTOVERS FOR TOMORROW'S LUNCH)

Red and Gold Minestrone
Garlic Cheese Bread
Salmon Cakes with Papaya Salsa
Vibrant Orange-Scented Beets
Banana Bread Pudding with Orange-Honey Yogurt Creme

It's amazing what a little color will do. Altering traditional minestrone soup so that all of the ingredients are in shades of red or yellow

131

produces a soup that is a blaze of color. Red and Gold Minestrone has a hearty appeal for any season. Soup needs bread. Garlic Cheese Bread sounds wonderful, but what about the fat? This version uses a tiny amount of blue cheese and Parmesan blended with yogurt. Because the cheeses are so strongly flavored, a cheese taste is created with very little fat.

Fish cakes, often made with canned fish, have been part of American family cooking for several generations. This version of Salmon Cakes is made with fresh salmon and is bolstered with three grains: corn, oats and wheat. Instead of a heavy cream sauce, these cakes are topped with a lively Papaya Salsa. The bright yellow of the papaya brings out the yellow corn kernels in the cakes. Vibrant Orange-Scented Beets completes the hot colors of the plate. Although vivid in color, the beets are subtly seasoned, making an ideal partner for the bold salsa.

One of the best bread puddings I've ever tasted was one made with banana bread. But who ever has leftover banana bread for making a pudding? I created Banana Bread Pudding using ordinary sandwich bread mixed with a puree of bananas. It tastes as if it were made with banana bread and has much less fat than most bread puddings. Orange-Honey Yogurt Creme is a delightful substitute for the more traditional whipped cream.

NUTRIENT ANALYSIS FOR EXTRAORDINARY FARE

The nutrient analysis for the complete meal includes 1 serving each of Red and Gold Minestrone, Vibrant Orange-Scented Beets, Garlic Cheese Bread and Banana Bread Pudding with Orange-Honey Yogurt Creme. It also includes 2 servings each of Salmon Cakes with Papaya Salsa.

CALORIES	CARBOHYDRATES: 167.4 GM	TOTAL FAT: 15.8 GM
For total meal: 1,012	PROTEIN: 61.6 GM	Saturated fat: 3.1 GM
Fat: 13%	DIETARY FIBER: 14.4 GM	Monounsaturated fat: 5.5 GM
Carbohydrates: 64%	SODIUM: 1,027 MG	
Protein: 23%	CHOLESTEROL: 47 MG	

Pyramid equivalencies: 4¼ grains, 3 vegetables, 1⅓ fruits, 1 dairy, ½ protein

NUTRIENT ANALYSIS FOR LEFTOVER LUNCH FROM EXTRAORDINARY FARE

The nutrient analysis for the complete meal includes 1 serving each of Red and Gold Minestrone, Garlic Cheese Bread and Banana Bread Pudding with Orange-Honey Yogurt Creme.

CALORIES	CARBOHYDRATES: 107.9 GM	TOTAL FAT: 7.8 GM
For total meal: 575	PROTEIN: 23.7 GM	Saturated fat: .8 GM
Carbohydrates: 72%	DIETARY FIBER: 9.6 GM	Monounsaturated fat: 3.0 GM
Protein: 16%	SODIUM: 572 MG	
	CHOLESTEROL: 5 MG	

Pyramid equivalencies: 2¼ grains, 2 vegetables, ⅔ fruit, 1 dairy, ½ protein

Red and Gold Minestrone

This colorful soup is delicious any time of year.

1 cup dry sherry
1 large red onion, peeled and diced
4 cloves garlic, finely minced
½ teaspoon crushed dry oregano
½ teaspoon crushed dry rosemary
½ teaspoon hot red pepper flakes
¼ teaspoon black pepper
3 cups water
2 medium carrots, sliced into rounds
1½ cups unsalted vegetable juice cocktail (e.g., V–8 juice)

1 cup fresh or frozen yellow wax beans, cut in 1-inch pieces
½ cup dry macaroni
2 cups unsalted canned tomatoes
1 yellow crookneck squash, sliced into rounds
1 cup cooked kidney beans or other red bean
½ cup finely diced red bell pepper
¼ cup finely minced fresh basil
8 basil sprigs for garnish
8 wedges fresh lemon

In a soup pot, combine the sherry, red onion, garlic, oregano, rosemary, hot pepper flakes and black pepper. Simmer covered at medium temperature for 5 minutes. Add the water and carrots, cover and simmer another 5 minutes.

Add the vegetable juice cocktail and wax beans. When the liquid begins to simmer, add the macaroni and continue cooking for 5 minutes without the cover. Add the next 5 ingredients and cook uncovered at low temperature for 10 minutes. Add water to pot any time it seems necessary.

Serve hot with basil sprinkled over each serving. Garnish with additional basil sprigs and lemon wedges.

YIELD: 8 servings

CALORIES	CARBOHYDRATES: 21.3 GM	TOTAL FAT: .5 GM
Per serving: 99	PROTEIN: 4.3 GM	Saturated fat: .1 GM
Fat: 4%	DIETARY FIBER: 4.3 GM	Monounsaturated fat: trace
Carbohydrates: 80%	SODIUM: 31 MG	
Protein: 16%	CHOLESTEROL: 0 MG	

Pyramid equivalencies: ¼ grain, 2 vegetables, ⅛ protein

Garlic Cheese Bread

Because the sodium content of the bread and cheese is usually quite high, use an unsalted mustard with this dish. I like to use whole wheat French rolls with this cheese spread. Unfortunately, the whole wheat rolls are frequently hard to find. Try a health food store or bakery that offers many varieties of bread. Nutrient analysis is provided for the garlic cheese spread by itself and with a basic supermarket French roll.

¼ cup plain nonfat yogurt
2 tablespoons unsalted Dijon-style mustard
2 tablespoons finely grated Parmesan cheese
½ ounce blue cheese
2 cloves garlic

1 teaspoon dry Italian herb blend
4 sourdough French rolls (80 grams or about 3¼ ounces each)
Paprika or cayenne pepper to taste

Combine the yogurt, mustard, Parmesan cheese, blue cheese, garlic and Italian herbs in a blender. Puree until smooth. Check to make sure that the blue cheese has been thoroughly incorporated into the mixture. Chill until ready to use. Will keep 1 week in the refrigerator.

Split the French rolls in half lengthwise. Spread the yogurt and cheese mixture evenly over each half. Sprinkle the bread with a little paprika or hot cayenne pepper. Place the bread under a broiler for 1 to 2 minutes or until the bread has lightly browned. Serve immediately.

YIELD: 8 servings

CALORIES	CARBOHYDRATES: 19.2 GM	TOTAL FAT: 2.0 GM
Per serving: 119	PROTEIN: 5.5 GM	Saturated fat: 1.0 GM
Fat: 15%	DIETARY FIBER: .5 GM	Monounsaturated fat: .5 GM
Carbohydrates: 66%	SODIUM: 227 MG	
Protein: 19%	CHOLESTEROL: 3 MG	

Pyramid equivalencies: 1 grain, ¼ dairy

Nutrient analysis for the garlic cheese spread without the bread:

CALORIES	CARBOHYDRATES: .7 GM	TOTAL FAT: 1.0 GM
Per serving: 19	PROTEIN: 1.5 GM	Saturated fat: .7 GM
Fat: 31%	DIETARY FIBER: .0 GM	Monounsaturated fat: .2 GM
Carbohydrates: 22%	SODIUM: 57 MG	
Protein: 47%	CHOLESTEROL: 3 MG	

Pyramid equivalencies: ¼ dairy

Salmon Cakes

Salmon Cakes are always best when made with fresh salmon. Leftover salmon is quite suitable and out of season you may elect to use canned salmon.

¾ pound cooked salmon (from 1 pound raw salmon)

1 slice whole wheat bread, torn in pieces

2 cups fresh or frozen corn kernels (divided use)

3 large egg whites

1 tablespoon unsalted Dijon-style mustard

2 tablespoons low-sodium Worcestershire sauce

2 cloves garlic, finely minced

¼ teaspoon black pepper

½ cup uncooked oatmeal, or one-minute oatmeal, not instant

2 green onions, finely chopped

If you are using fresh salmon, use tweezers or pliers to pull out any fine bones. Place the salmon on a flat rack or steamer basket. Fill the pan with ½ inch water or wine, cover and steam for 5 minutes. Allow to cool slightly, then remove the skin. Refrigerate until ready to use.

Place the bread in a food processor and process until the bread is ground into crumbs. Remove the bread crumbs and set aside.

Place 1 cup corn kernels in the processor. Add the egg whites, mustard, Worcestershire sauce, garlic and black pepper. Process until nearly smooth. Transfer the mixture to a large bowl and stir in the remaining corn, salmon, oatmeal and green onions. Mix well. Add enough bread crumbs to make the mixture hold together.

Form the mixture into 8 patties. The salmon cakes may be cooked on a griddle or skillet sprayed with a nonstick cooking spray or baked in the oven on a nonstick baking sheet. On top of the stove, cook for 3 to 4 minutes, then turn and cook another 3 minutes or until lightly browned. In the oven, bake at 450°F. for 7 minutes, turn and bake another 7 minutes. Serve immediately with Papaya Salsa (recipe follows).

YIELD: 8 cakes

Nutrient analysis does not include salsa.

CALORIES | CARBOHYDRATES: 14.2 GM | TOTAL FAT: 3.8 GM
Per serving: 153 | PROTEIN: 16.3 GM | Saturated fat: .7 GM
Fat: 22% | DIETARY FIBER: 1.5 GM | Monounsaturated fat: 1.2 GM
Carbohydrates: 36% | SODIUM: 203 MG
Protein: 42% | CHOLESTEROL: 21 MG

Pyramid equivalencies: 1 grain, ½ protein

Papaya Salsa

This chunky sauce is a marvelous topping for grilled chicken, fish and shrimp.

½ small papaya, peeled, seeded and diced

½ yellow or red bell pepper, seeded and diced

¼ cup coarsely chopped dried apricots

1 teaspoon finely minced fresh ginger

1 teaspoon finely minced fresh serrano chile, without seeds

3 tablespoons fresh lime juice

1 tablespoon finely minced fresh cilantro

1 tablespoon finely minced fresh mint

Stir together all of the ingredients, except the cilantro and mint. Refrigerate and allow to marinate for at least 30 minutes, but not longer than 4 hours. Add the fresh herbs and serve immediately.

YIELD: 8 servings

CALORIES | CARBOHYDRATES: 12.7 GM | TOTAL FAT: .2 GM
Per serving: 52 | PROTEIN: 2.2 GM | Saturated fat: 0 GM
Fat: 3% | DIETARY FIBER: .4 GM | Monounsaturated fat: trace
Carbohydrates: 83% | SODIUM: 7 MG
Protein: 14% | CHOLESTEROL: 0 MG

Pyramid equivalencies: ½ fruit

Vibrant Orange-Scented Beets

There are many sauces that combine well with beets. However, on a plate with many different flavors, beets with little or no seasoning are a delicious complement to an entrée. Using fresh beets instead of canned creates a far superior dish.

4 medium-sized beets	¼ teaspoon cinnamon
Boiling water	¼ teaspoon black pepper
1 tablespoon finely grated	4 small sprigs fresh mint for
orange peel	garnish, optional

Avoid buying large beets because they tend to be tough and woody. Some cooks prefer wearing latex gloves when handling beets to avoid staining their hands. Although I usually don't, the choice is yours.

Carefully wash the beets. Trim the stem just before the bulb. Do not slice into the bulb at the stem or root end. Place the beets in a pot and cover with boiling water. Cook for 25 minutes or until the beets are tender.

Lift the beets from the pot and rinse under cold water. Reserve ½ cup liquid. Using your hands, rub away the outside peel. If necessary, use a peeler or knife. Trim away the stem and root ends. Cut the beets into slices and place in a saucepan with the reserved liquid. Add the orange peel, cinnamon and black pepper. Cook until the beets are heated through. Serve immediately, garnished with fresh mint.

Beets are one of the few vegetables that are equally delicious cooked and reheated at a later time.

YIELD: 4 servings

CALORIES	CARBOHYDRATES: 5.7 GM	TOTAL FAT: trace
Per serving: 27	PROTEIN: .9 GM	Saturated fat: 0 GM
Fat: 3%	DIETARY FIBER: 1.0 GM	Monounsaturated fat: 0 GM
Carbohydrates: 86%	SODIUM: 42 MG	
Protein: 11%	CHOLESTEROL: 0 MG	

Pyramid equivalencies: 1 vegetable

Banana Bread Pudding

I generally use a seven-grain bread with nuts for this recipe, although other breads will work. Rye and pumpernickel may be too strongly flavored and some commercial breads are so salty that they do not function well in desserts calling for bread. Only use very ripe bananas. You may also want to serve this as a breakfast or brunch dish.

8 cups (8 slices) whole grain
    bread, torn in 1-inch pieces
½ cup raisins
½ cup sliced almonds
3 medium very ripe bananas,
    peeled
1½ cups fluid nonfat milk

½ cup sherry
1 cup egg whites
½ cup dark brown sugar, firmly
    packed
1 teaspoon vanilla extract
1 teaspoon cinnamon

Preheat oven to 375°F. In a large bowl, mix together the bread, raisins and almonds. Set aside.

In a blender jar, combine the bananas, nonfat milk, sherry, egg whites, brown sugar, vanilla and cinnamon. Process until smooth and creamy. Pour the mixture over the bread and stir until the bread is well coated and evenly mixed.

Spray a shallow 8- or 9-inch square baking dish with nonstick cooking spray. Pour the bread mixture into the pan. Bake at 375°F. for 45 minutes or until an inserted toothpick comes out clean. Serve hot or cold with Orange-Honey Yogurt Creme (recipe follows) on the side.

YIELD: 8 servings

CALORIES
Per serving: 257
Fat: 17%
Carbohydrates: 69%
Protein: 14%

CARBOHYDRATES: 46.7 GM
PROTEIN: 9.5 GM
DIETARY FIBER: 4.8 GM
SODIUM: 257 MG
CHOLESTEROL: 1 MG

TOTAL FAT: 5.2 GM
Saturated fat: .6 GM
Monounsaturated fat: 2.5 GM

Pyramid equivalencies: 1 grain, ⅔ fruit, ¼ dairy, ⅓ protein

Orange-Honey Yogurt Creme

In addition to bread pudding, I like this sauce with fresh strawberries and peaches.

2 cups plain nonfat yogurt
¼ cup dry nonfat milk powder
¼ cup honey

2 tablespoons frozen,
unsweetened orange juice
concentrate

Whisk together all of the ingredients and refrigerate until ready to use. Will keep 4 or 5 days in the refrigerator. Serve as a sauce for desserts.

YIELD: 8 servings

CALORIES
Per serving: 100
Fat: 1%
Carbohydrates: 77%
Protein: 22%

CARBOHYDRATES: 20.7 GM
PROTEIN: 4.4 GM
DIETARY FIBER: trace
SODIUM: 57 MG
CHOLESTEROL: 1 MG

TOTAL FAT: .1 GM
Saturated fat: trace
Monounsaturated fat: trace

Pyramid equivalencies: ½ dairy

12

Herb Garden Magic

FRESH HERBS have a magical way of transforming ordinary fare into aromatic delicacies. An herb can turn the simplest dish into something exotic. Herbs can also produce a warm, earthy allure that is especially appealing in dishes that use little or no oil, fat or salt. Indeed, herbs are a welcome source of flavor in low-fat, low-sodium cookery. This menu celebrates the magical flavors of fresh herbs.

Most American markets now offer a wide selection of fresh herbs year-round. Sometimes, nurseries and garden shops offer small plants that are less expensive than the packets sold in supermarkets. Herbs are easily grown on windowsills and in gardens. Growing conditions vary according to climate. I encourage every cook to also be an herb gardener. Fresh herbs offer a sweet perfume that cannot be equaled by dry herbs. If cooking with fresh herbs is new to you, follow these general principles:

1. For whatever measure of dry herb, plan on using two to three times as much fresh herb.
2. Dry herbs need to cook longer to mellow out the flavor. Sometimes, dry herbs have a slight bitterness that can be lessened by longer cooking. Fresh herbs, on the other hand, offer a sweeter, more aromatic flavor when added at the end of the cooking time.

3. In cooking with herbs, dry or fresh, we generally use only the leaves
   and not the stems. Although the stems often have an equally appealing flavor, some cooks will find the stems have too coarse a texture
   for use in a dish.
4. To store fresh-picked herbs, place in a glass of water as you would put
   flowers in a vase. Lightly sprinkle the leaves with water, loosely cover
   with plastic wrap and refrigerate. You can also wrap the herbs in a wet
   paper towel and place in plastic bag. Again, store in the refrigerator.
5. Fresh herbs can be frozen. When frozen, the leaves of most herbs
   turn black. Certainly, they do not have an attractive appearance, but
   they do not lose their flavor. Frozen herbs can be chopped and used
   in dishes that are cooked or where the color will not be noticed.
6. Fresh herbs can be dried in the home, often producing a superior
   flavor to store-bought varieties. The easiest way to dry herbs is to hang
   them upside down with a string in a dry place. Do not place the herbs
   in direct sunlight. After a month, you will have wonderful whole-leaf
   herbs. Dry herbs are best stored in dark, dry places. Next to the stove
   may be too warm and a refrigerator is too cool and too moist.
7. Herbs vary in intensity of flavor. Dry herbs lose flavor with age. Fresh
   herbs are greatly affected by climatic conditions. Do not be surprised, one year to the next, if your plants yield stronger- or weaker-
   flavored leaves. Even with greenhouse herbs, you can expect
   variations in flavor. Taste the herb before putting it in the pot.

Herb Garden Magic (Menu for 4)

Greens and Balsamic Vinaigrette with Fresh Herbs
Orange-and-Dill-Scented Yogurt Cheese Spread
Orange Roughy with Tarragon and Green Apples
Fragrant Bulgur Pilaf
Jade Vegetables with Lemon and Parmesan
Herb-Scented Honeydew Sorbet with Kiwi

Fresh basil and mint transform common salad greens into sweet, ro-
mantic fare. Greens and Balsamic Vinaigrette with Fresh Herbs is a
popular salad for any season of the year. Orange Roughy with Tarragon
and Green Apples combines an herbal taste with a mild sweet and sour
sauce made with lime, rice vinegar and green apples. The sauce is a rich

complement to the aroma of Fragrant Bulgur Pilaf. Jade Vegetables with Lemon and Parmesan demonstrates how certain vegetables have an herbal-like flavor. To go with the meal, I would suggest a simple whole grain bread or crusty French bread. Orange-and-Dill-Scented Yogurt Cheese is a rich but not overpowering spread for the bread. Herb-Scented Honeydew Sorbet with Kiwi illustrates how herbs can give desserts a delicate glow.

NUTRIENT ANALYSIS FOR HERB GARDEN MAGIC

The nutrient data are for 1 serving of Greens and Balsamic Vinaigrette with Fresh Herbs, Orange-and-Dill-Scented Yogurt Cheese Spread, Orange Roughy with Tarragon and Green Apples, Fragrant Bulgur Pilaf, Jade Vegetables with Lemon and Parmesan, Herb Scented Honeydew Sorbet with Kiwi and a 1-ounce portion of French bread (recipe not included). Diners wanting a larger meal may elect to have a second serving of bread and Yogurt Cheese Spread.

CALORIES	CARBOHYDRATES: 103.0 GM	TOTAL FAT: 15.4 GM
For total meal: 681	PROTEIN: 33.8 GM	Saturated fat: 3.1 GM
Fat: 20%	DIETARY FIBER: 16.9 GM	Monounsaturated fat: 6.2 GM
Carbohydrates: 59%	SODIUM: 395 MG	
Protein: 19%	CHOLESTEROL: 25 MG	
Alcohol: 2%		

Pyramid equivalencies: 3 grains, 2 vegetables, 2½ fruits, ½ dairy, 1 protein

Greens and Balsamic Vinaigrette with Fresh Herbs

Any mix of fresh greens will go with this refreshing vinaigrette. You may want to try one of the premixed salad blends that are now available in markets.

3 cups red leaf lettuce, arugula or oak leaf lettuce, torn in bite-size pieces

2 cups bitter greens (radicchio, Belgian endive, escarole or curly endive), torn in bite-size pieces

3 cups romaine, green leaf or Bibb lettuce, torn in bite-size pieces

1 recipe Balsamic Vinaigrette with Fresh Herbs (recipe follows)

After the greens have been washed and dried with a clean towel or salad spinner, chill at least 1 hour. Toss the greens with the vinaigrette and serve immediately.

YIELD: 4 servings

Nutrient analysis includes the dressing.

CALORIES
Per serving: 86
Fat: 47%
Carbohydrates: 41%
Protein: 12%

CARBOHYDRATES: 8.1 GM
PROTEIN: 2.3 GM
DIETARY FIBER: 4.1 GM
SODIUM: 12 MG
CHOLESTEROL: 0 MG

TOTAL FAT: 4.1 GM
Saturated fat: .5 GM
Monounsaturated fat: 2.5 GM

Pyramid equivalencies: 1 vegetable

Balsamic Vinaigrette with Fresh Herbs

In addition to greens, try this dressing on pasta, potatoes and poached fish or chicken.

¼ cup balsamic vinegar	1 tablespoon water
4 teaspoons frozen, unsweetened apple juice concentrate	4 leaves fresh basil
	1 small sprig fresh mint
1 tablespoon extra-virgin olive oil	1 teaspoon low-sodium Dijon-style mustard
	1 clove garlic

Place all of the ingredients in a blender and process until completely chopped and well blended. Chill 30 minutes before using. Do not make more than 8 hours before serving.

YIELD: 4 servings

CALORIES	CARBOHYDRATES: 5.3 GM	TOTAL FAT: 3.7 GM
Per serving: 54	PROTEIN: .3 GM	Saturated fat: .5 GM
Fat: 60%	DIETARY FIBER: .5 GM	Monounsaturated fat: 2.5 GM
Carbohydrates: 38%	SODIUM: 4 MG	
Protein: 2%	CHOLESTEROL: 0 MG	

Pyramid equivalencies: No equivalencies

Orange-and-Dill-Scented Yogurt Cheese Spread

To make yogurt cheese, do not use a yogurt that has been thickened with gelatin. This spread is an excellent choice when you want a simple spread that doesn't overpower the flavor of the bread.

2 cups plain, nonfat yogurt	2 teaspoons finely grated orange peel
1 teaspoon finely minced fresh dill	

Place a paper coffee filter or cheesecloth in a strainer. Pour the yogurt into the strainer. Set the strainer over a bowl, cover with plastic wrap and refrigerate 6 hours.

Transfer the thickened yogurt to a mixing bowl. Stir in the dill and orange peel. Repeat the process of straining the yogurt. This time, leave the yogurt in the strainer for 24 hours.

The yogurt will now be quite firm. Store in a covered container and refrigerate. Will last 4 days.

YIELD: 8 servings

CALORIES
Per serving: 32
Fat: 3%
Carbohydrates: 57%
Protein: 42%

CARBOHYDRATES: 4.4 GM
PROTEIN: 3.3 GM
DIETARY FIBER: 0 GM
SODIUM: 44 MG
CHOLESTEROL: 1 MG

TOTAL FAT: .1 GM
Saturated fat: .1 GM
Monounsaturated fat: trace

Pyramid equivalencies: ½ dairy

Orange Roughy with Tarragon and Green Apples

A firm fish with full-bodied flavor is best for this dish. In addition to orange roughy, I also use Chilean sea bass and halibut with the sauce.

4 orange roughy fillets
(4 ounces each)
1 green apple, cored and
thinly sliced
¼ cup fresh lime juice
¼ cup rice vinegar
2 tablespoons frozen,
unsweetened apple juice
concentrate

2 teaspoons low-sodium soy
sauce
1 green onion, chopped
2 tablespoons finely minced
fresh tarragon
4 lime wedges, optional
4 sprigs fresh tarragon, optional

Place the fish and apple slices in a skillet. Whisk together the lime juice, vinegar, apple juice concentrate and soy sauce. Pour over the fish. Poach the fish in the mixture at medium temperature for 8 minutes. Keep the pan covered while cooking.

Serve the fish topped with the cooked apple and pan juices. Sprinkle the green onion and fresh minced tarragon over each serving. If desired, garnish with lime wedges and sprigs of fresh tarragon.

YIELD: 4 servings

CALORIES	CARBOHYDRATES: 10.8 GM	TOTAL FAT: 8.2 GM
Per serving: 183	PROTEIN: 16.7 GM	Saturated fat: 2.0 GM
Fat: 40%	DIETARY FIBER: .8 GM	Monounsaturated fat: 3.1 GM
Carbohydrates: 23%	SODIUM: 75 MG	
Protein: 37%	CHOLESTEROL: 23 MG	

Pyramid equivalencies: ½ fruit, 1 protein

Fragrant Bulgur Pilaf

This recipe calls for fine bulgur, like the kind used in tabouli. If you have to get a large-grain, you will need more liquid and will have to cook the bulgur for 10 to 20 minutes.

1 cup boiling water or unsalted, defatted chicken broth	*1 cup fine-grain bulgur*
	1 tablespoon finely minced fresh parsley
1 tablespoon finely grated lemon peel	*1 tablespoon finely minced fresh cilantro*
1 teaspoon low-sodium soy sauce	

Mix together the boiling water, lemon peel and soy sauce. Immediately add the bulgur and stir well. Let stand 20 minutes covered. Stir in the parsley and cilantro. Serve immediately.

YIELD: 4 servings

CALORIES   CARBOHYDRATES: 35.0 GM   TOTAL FAT: .6 GM
Per serving: 162   PROTEIN: 4.6 GM   Saturated fat: trace
Fat: 3%   DIETARY FIBER: 8.0 GM   Monounsaturated fat: .1 GM
Carbohydrates: 86% SODIUM: 45 MG
Protein: 11%   CHOLESTEROL: 0 MG

Pyramid equivalencies: 2 grains

Jade Vegetables with Lemon and Parmesan

The monochromatic mix of broccoli, broccoflower and cauliflower offers an engaging blend of flavor and color.

1¼ cups cauliflower florets   *1 teaspoon finely grated lemon*
1¼ cups broccoflower florets   *   peel*
1¼ cups broccoli florets   *¼ teaspoon white pepper*
* 1 tablespoon finely grated*   *4 sprigs fresh parsley*
*   Parmesan cheese*

Combine the cauliflower and broccoflower in a steamer. Steam 3 minutes. Add the broccoli and steam 2 to 3 minutes longer.

Mix together the cheese, lemon peel and pepper. Sprinkle over the hot vegetables. Garnish with fresh parsley.

YIELD: 4 servings

CALORIES   CARBOHYDRATES: 4.5 GM   TOTAL FAT: .7 GM
Per serving: 30   PROTEIN: 2.8 GM   Saturated fat: .3 GM
Fat: 18%   DIETARY FIBER: 2.3 GM   Monounsaturated fat: .1 GM
Carbohydrates: 50% SODIUM: 48 MG
Protein: 32%   CHOLESTEROL: 1 MG

Pyramid equivalencies: 1 vegetable

Herb-Scented Honeydew Sorbet with Kiwi

Fresh herbs give this sorbet an exotic but subtle flavor. If you can't get rose geranium leaf and lavender, use fresh rosemary.

3 cups honeydew melon, cut into ½-inch cubes	1 teaspoon finely minced fresh rose geranium leaf
¼ cup unsweetened frozen pineapple juice concentrate	½ teaspoon finely minced fresh lavender
2 tablespoons Midori liqueur	1 teaspoon finely minced fresh mint
1 teaspoon fresh lime juice	2 kiwi, peeled
2 teaspoons finely grated lime peel	4 sprigs fresh mint

Combine all of the ingredients, except the kiwi and the sprigs of mint, in a food processor and puree until smooth. Transfer to an ice cream maker and freeze according to the manufacturer's directions.

If you don't have an ice cream maker, pour the melon puree into ice cube trays and freeze. When firm, transfer the frozen melon puree to a food processor and process until creamy. Place the mixture in a bowl or mold and return to the freezer. When ready to serve, let stand 5 to 10 minutes at room temperature before scooping out the sorbet.

While the sorbet is freezing, puree the kiwi. When ready to serve, spoon the sorbet into glasses and drizzle the kiwi puree over the top. Garnish with sprigs of fresh mint.

YIELD: 4 servings

CALORIES	CARBOHYDRATES: 26.0 GM	TOTAL FAT: .6 GM
Per serving: 110	PROTEIN: 1.5 GM	Saturated fat: 0 GM
Fat: 4%	DIETARY FIBER: 1.1 GM	Monounsaturated fat: trace
Carbohydrates: 81%	SODIUM: 17 MG	
Protein: 5%	CHOLESTEROL: 0 MG	
Alcohol: 10%		

Pyramid equivalencies: 2 fruits

13

The Light Side of France

AMERICANS OFTEN mistakenly identify French cooking with rich, heavy meals. Americans conjure up images of rich creams, butters, cheeses, sausages and pâtés. Yes, French cooks do use a lot of rich ingredients, but portions are generally quite small, or at least according to American standards. Recently, much attention has been given to the health attributes of Mediterranean cooking, which includes the cuisine of Provence. Here, the cooking is lighter, by both French and American standards. A warm coastal climate produces a cuisine that focuses strongly on fresh produce and seafood. Provençal cuisine is more likely to feature tomatoes and olive oil than cream and butter.

My version of Provençal cooking uses less oil than is typical of the region. In Provence, cooks walk to the market daily and prepare the meal without all sorts of work- and time-saving gadgets that dominate the American kitchen. The French have a more physically active daily routine, which means they can afford to consume more calories.

THE LIGHT SIDE OF FRANCE (MENU FOR 4)

Two-Squash Soup
Fish with Eggplant, Peppers and Tomatoes
Couscous with Fresh Herbs
Mixed Greens with Tarragon Vinaigrette
Double Plum Compote

Two-Squash Soup is a creme soup without cream. The soup becomes creamy by pureeing vegetables and rice. The French use of a puree to create mock cream probably dates to times when religious rules prohibited dairy products during fast periods, or it may have originated when some ancient cook invented a solution to a milk shortage. Whatever the origin, it's a marvelous way to reduce fat in cooking. Although there is cheese in the soup, using a robust Parmesan enables you to create a deep, cheesy flavor with very little fat.

My version of Fish with Eggplant, Peppers and Tomatoes has less oil than is typical of Provence. I have compensated for the reduction in oil by increasing other flavorful ingredients. By using more wine, the dish is given additional body, one of the functions of oil in cooking. The wine also sweetens the eggplant. By using extra-virgin olive oil, which has a strong flavor, the dish has a fragrant olive flavor with very little oil.

Fish with Eggplant, Peppers and Tomatoes is a good example of how vegetables can be used to extend meat. The eggplant readily absorbs the flavors around it. Even with very little fish, the dish offers hearty portions.

The fish is complemented by Couscous with Fresh Herbs. Couscous, a type of dry pasta that is similar to bulgur, is a popular Provençal dish. The ideal way to prepare couscous is in a couscousière, a specialty pot that is next to impossible to find in the United States. The pot enables you to cook the couscous with steam. However, couscous sold in this country will have instructions that tell you to cook it by pouring boiling liquid over it. Definitely easier, but it will not have the same flavor or texture of traditional couscous. Some package instructions call for the addition of butter or oil. A good strong broth will give flavor without relying on fat. Seasoning with soy sauce instead of salt will also help give the product body so that you will not need the fat.

French diners often follow the entrée with a salad. Salads may range from simple to extravagant, but a homey country meal frequently features a plain salad of only dressed greens. This modest dish refreshes the palate and leaves the diner with a satisfied appetite. Provençal diners often enjoy a blend of bitter greens in their salads. These may include radicchio, Belgian endive, curly endive, escarole and watercress. Lettuce is often incorporated to tame the bitter flavors. Our version of Mixed Greens is dressed with a Tarragon Vinaigrette.

A fruit compote is on every dieter's repertoire of desserts. However, for the French, fresh or cooked fruits, perfumed with liqueur, are a cornerstone of fine dining. This is a culture that prides itself on artistry with fermented and distilled fruits. A simple liqueur-laced compote, made with the finest products, becomes a testament to grand dining. Double Plum Compote is a satisfying finale for the joys of Provençal dining.

A rosé from Provence and mineral water would be excellent choices for a beverage to accompany the meal.

NUTRIENT INFORMATION FOR THE LIGHT SIDE OF FRANCE

Nutrient information for the complete meal is based on 1 serving each of Two-Squash Soup, Fish with Eggplant, Peppers and Tomatoes, Couscous with Fresh Herbs, Mixed Greens with Tarragon Vinaigrette and Double Plum Compote. Persons who want a larger meal may want to include a crispy loaf of French bread.

CALORIES	CARBOHYDRATES: 132.8 GM	TOTAL FAT: 11.7 GM
For total meal: 730	PROTEIN: 32.8 GM	Saturated fat: 2.5 GM
Fat: 14%	DIETARY FIBER: 17.4 GM	Monounsaturated fat: 6.3 GM
Carbohydrates: 69%	SODIUM: 352 MG	
Protein: 17%	CHOLESTEROL: 36 MG	

Pyramid equivalencies: 2 grains, 5 vegetables, 2 fruits, 1 protein

Two-Squash Soup

We call them winter squash and summer squash, implying a seasonal vegetable, but you can buy them everywhere any time of year. Using only winter squash would create a very sweet flavor. Only summer squash would be a little bland. The two together are just great! For the winter squash, you can use banana, acorn or Hubbard squashes. For the summer squash, use yellow crookneck, yellow zucchini or regular green zucchini that has been peeled.

1½ pounds banana squash, peeled, seeded and cubed	1 tablespoon low-sodium soy sauce
2 large onions, coarsely chopped	1 teaspoon ground sage
4 cloves garlic, minced	½ teaspoon ground black pepper
3 cups water	¼ teaspoon ground cinnamon
3 cups sliced yellow crookneck squash	1 cup cooked brown rice
	¼ cup finely minced fresh parsley
	¼ cup freshly grated Parmesan cheese

Combine the banana squash, onions, garlic and water in a saucepan. Simmer covered for 20 minutes. Add the crookneck squash, soy sauce, sage, black pepper and cinnamon. Continue cooking covered for 15 minutes.

Transfer the cooked products with the rice to a blender. Puree until smooth and creamy. If necessary, add more water. Return to the saucepan and heat through.

Serve with the fresh parsley and grated Parmesan sprinkled over each bowl.

YIELD: 8 servings

CALORIES	CARBOHYDRATES: 22.6 GM	TOTAL FAT: 1.5 GM
Per serving: 110	PROTEIN: 4.0 GM	Saturated fat: .7 GM
Fat: 11%	DIETARY FIBER: 3.6 GM	Monounsaturated fat: .3 GM
Carbohydrates: 75%	SODIUM: 128 MG	
Protein: 14%	CHOLESTEROL: 3 MG	

Pyramid equivalencies: 2 vegetables

Fish with Eggplant, Peppers and Tomatoes

For the fish, I would prefer a firm-bodied fish such as swordfish, shark or bass. Because the sauce is boldly flavored, a stronger-tasting fish will work quite well.

1 large eggplant, cut in ½-inch cubes	1 tablespoon finely grated lemon peel
2 large onions, peeled and diced	¼ teaspoon ground black pepper
12 plum tomatoes, diced	2 tablespoons tomato paste, optional
1 large pear, cored and diced	1 tablespoon extra-virgin olive oil
6 cloves garlic, minced	
1 cup dry white wine	¾ pound firm fish, cut in cubes
1 cup water	1 tablespoon finely minced fresh basil
2 bay leaves	
2 green peppers, seeded and diced	

Combine the eggplant, onions, tomatoes, pear, garlic, wine, water and bay leaves in a saucepan. Simmer uncovered for 15 minutes or until the eggplant is tender. If necessary, add more water.

Add the green pepper, lemon peel and black pepper. Cook for 2 minutes. Stir in tomato paste and olive oil and mix until well blended. Add the cubed fish and simmer for 10 minutes. Add the minced basil and serve immediately over Couscous with Fresh Herbs.

YIELD: 4 servings

CALORIES	CARBOHYDRATES: 26.3 GM	TOTAL FAT: 6.1 GM
Per serving: 221	PROTEIN: 18.5 GM	Saturated fat: 1.0 GM
Fat: 23%	DIETARY FIBER: 7.3 GM	Monounsaturated fat: 3.0 GM
Carbohydrates: 45%	SODIUM: 114 MG	
Protein: 32%	CHOLESTEROL: 34 MG	

Pyramid equivalencies: 2 vegetables, 1 protein

Couscous with Fresh Herbs

Couscous is truly one of the most easily prepared grain dishes there is. It is available in most supermarkets, although whole wheat couscous is more likely found in health food stores. If you can't find couscous, use bulgur instead.

2 cups water or unsalted, defatted chicken broth
2 teaspoons low-sodium soy sauce
1 clove garlic, finely minced

2 cups whole wheat couscous
2 tablespoons finely minced fresh parsley
1 tablespoon finely minced fresh chives

In a saucepan, combine the water, soy sauce and garlic. Bring to a boil. Add the couscous and remove from the heat. Let stand for 10 minutes. Add the fresh herbs and fluff the mixture with a fork. Serve immediately.

YIELD: 4 servings

CALORIES
Per serving: 200
Fat: 2%
Carbohydrates: 83%
Protein: 15%

CARBOHYDRATES: 43.2 GM
PROTEIN: 8.6 GM
DIETARY FIBER: 2.2 GM
SODIUM: 94 MG
CHOLESTEROL: 0 MG

TOTAL FAT: .5 GM
Saturated fat: .1 GM
Monounsaturated fat: .1 GM

Pyramid equivalencies: 2 grains

Mixed Greens with Tarragon Vinaigrette

Supermarkets now carry a wide variety of prepackaged mixed greens that make a delicious salad with Tarragon Vinaigrette. I would likely choose a blend that includes curly endive, radicchio and lettuce. Vitamin and mineral content varies with different salad greens. However, the calories, carbohydrates, protein and fat are about the same for all greens. Two cups of greens offer about 20 calories, which are composed almost entirely of carbohydrates.

> 8 cups premixed greens, torn in bite-size pieces, or 4 cups torn romaine lettuce and 1 cup each of radicchio, Belgian endive, curly endive and watercress
>
> 1 recipe Tarragon Vinaigrette (recipe follows)

If you are not buying premixed greens, wash the greens and spin or blot dry. Cover the greens in plastic and chill.

When ready to serve, toss with Tarragon Vinaigrette and serve immediately.

YIELD: 4 servings

CALORIES
Per serving: 72
Fat: 56%
Carbohydrates: 42%
Protein: 2%

CARBOHYDRATES: 10.0 GM
PROTEIN: .4 GM
DIETARY FIBER: 1.2 GM
SODIUM: 12 MG
CHOLESTEROL: 0 MG

TOTAL FAT: 3.7 GM
Saturated fat: .5 GM
Monounsaturated fat: 2.5 GM

Pyramid equivalencies: 1 vegetable

Tarragon Vinaigrette

In addition to greens, this is an excellent dressing for potato salad.

¼ cup champagne vinegar
2 tablespoons water
1 tablespoon frozen, unsweetened apple juice concentrate
2 teaspoons extra-virgin olive oil

2 teaspoons low-sodium Dijon-style mustard (more to taste)
1 clove garlic
2 short sprigs fresh tarragon

Combine all of the ingredients in a blender jar and puree until well blended. Serve immediately or refrigerate for later use. Will keep 2 to 3 days in the refrigerator.

YIELD: 4 servings

CALORIES
Per serving: 52
Fat: 60%
Carbohydrates: 37%
Protein: 3%

CARBOHYDRATES: 5.1 GM
PROTEIN: .3 GM
DIETARY FIBER: .5 GM
SODIUM: 4 MG
CHOLESTEROL: 0 MG

TOTAL FAT: 3.7 GM
Saturated fat: .5 GM
Monounsaturated fat: 2.5 GM

Pyramid equivalencies: No equivalencies

Double Plum Compote

Fruit in cognac is almost a French staple. If you wish to omit the alcohol, use ½ teaspoon vanilla extract in the recipe.

½ cup water
¼ cup frozen, unsweetened
   grape juice concentrate
2 tablespoons lemon juice
½ teaspoon cinnamon
¼ teaspoon whole fennel seed
   (optional)
2 tablespoons brandy or
   cognac (optional)

8 prunes, pitted and halved
4 purple or red plums, pitted
   and quartered
1 cup fresh or frozen blueberries
1 tablespoon grated lemon peel
4 sprigs fresh mint

In a saucepan, combine the water, grape juice concentrate, lemon juice, cinnamon and fennel seed. Bring to a boil and add the cognac. Immediately pour the hot liquid over the prunes and plums. Let stand for 30 minutes.

Add the blueberries and chill 2 hours before serving. Serve in individual cups. Sprinkle the lemon peel over each serving and garnish with a sprig of mint.

YIELD: 4 servings

CALORIES
Per serving: 127
Fat: 4%
Carbohydrates: 91%
Protein: 4%
Alcohol: 1%

CARBOHYDRATES: 30.7 GM
PROTEIN: 1.3 GM
ALCOHOL: .3 GM
DIETARY FIBER: 3.1 GM
SODIUM: 4 MG
CHOLESTEROL: 0 MG

TOTAL FAT: .7 GM
Saturated fat: .1 GM
Monounsaturated fat: .3 GM

Pyramid equivalencies: 2 fruits

14

Pacific Rim Luncheon

GREAT CUISINES are often created by blending cultures. This menu reflects the changing character of the Pacific Southwest, where Mexican, Central American and Asian cultures are mixing to produce an exciting new cuisine. I find deliberately synthesizing different cuisines enables me to create new dishes that are lower in fat, but filled with flavor. Because they are "new" flavors, diners don't have the traditional expectations about how the dishes should taste. A low-fat dish can become the standard for how the dish should be.

PACIFIC RIM LUNCHEON (MENU FOR 4 OR 8)

Golden Vegetable Soup with Crunchy Corn
Pacific Rim Tostada
Mock Sangría
Marinated Tangerines with Mandarin Chocolate Sauce

Additional Recipes:
Baked Tortillas
Black Beans with Garlic
Asian Poached Salmon
Mango Salsa

Pacific Rim Luncheon is a simple meal of three dishes. Most of the preparation and cooking can be done in advance. The menu works well as a light lunch or supper. However, a second serving of Pacific Rim Tostada turns this into a hearty dinner menu. The second tostada increases the calories but still provides a meal that doesn't exceed 10% fat!

The meal begins with Golden Vegetable Soup, a creamy, piquant soup, flavored with a hint of curry. Chewy, roasted corn is a common snack food in Mexico and Central America. In this meal, Crunchy Corn, spicy roasted kernels of corn, is used as a topping over the soup.

In Mexico, a tostada is sometimes described as a salad-sandwich. The word "tostada" literally means "toasted." A tostada refers to a toasted tortilla that is topped with layers of vegetables and meats. A common tostada begins with a flat, crispy tortilla topped with a layer of hot cooked beans, which is then topped with lettuce or cabbage. Tomatoes and cooked chicken are placed on the greens. The tostada is finally topped with a generous serving of raw or cooked salsa. The variety of tostadas is only limited by the cook's imagination. For our Pacific Rim Tostada, the flavors of Mexico take on an Asian flair in an elegant version of rustic fare. The Pacific Rim Tostada is really four recipes that are combined to create the tostada.

Each of these recipes can be appreciated as a dish independent of the tostada. Pacific Rim Tostada begins with Baked Tortillas. Tostadas in Mexico are made just as often with baked tortillas as fried, but in the United States, you generally will find only fried tortillas. Baked Tortillas can be your foundation for creating your own special tostada. Black Beans with Garlic brings an assertive Asian flavor to the beans. Black beans are a popular product in both Mexico and China. This version has a significant reduction in sodium and fat from the traditional preparations. I frequently serve Black Beans with Garlic as a side dish to a wide variety of entrées. Asian Poached Salmon can be served hot or cold. When I make the Pacific Rim Tostadas, I often use leftovers from the night before. Finally, the tostada is topped with an exciting Mango Salsa, bringing a sweet, bold finish to the dish. The Mango Salsa can also be used with grilled chicken and other kinds of fish or seafood.

Mock Sangría is a dry, slightly sweet beverage that subtly enhances the meal. Alcohol-free, this Sangría is also low in calories. Marinated Tangerines served with Mandarin Chocolate Sauce mixes gingery fruit with fat-free chocolate sauce seasoned with the rich aromatic flavor of Chinese five-spice powder. The dessert beautifully concludes a meal that is an exciting blend of simplicity and exotic flavor.

NUTRIENT ANALYSIS FOR PACIFIC RIM LUNCHEON

The nutrient analysis for the complete menu includes 1 serving each of Golden Vegetable Soup, Crunchy Corn, Pacific Rim Tostada and Marinated Tangerines with Mandarin Chocolate Sauce. The analysis also includes 2 servings of Mock Sangría. Persons wanting a heartier meal may elect to have 2 servings of the soup or a second Pacific Rim Tostada. A second helping of either dish will still result in a meal with no more than 10% fat!

CALORIES	CARBOHYDRATES: 126.9 GM	TOTAL FAT: 6.5 GM
For total	PROTEIN: 32.7 GM	Saturated fat: .8 GM
meal: 638	DIETARY FIBER: 15.1 GM	Monounsaturated fat: 1.4 GM
Fat: 8%	SODIUM: 384 MG	
Carbohydrates: 72%	CHOLESTEROL: 27 MG	
Protein: 19%		
Alcohol: 1%		

Pyramid equivalencies: 1½ grains, 2 vegetables, 3 fruits, ¾ dairy, 1 protein

Golden Vegetable Soup

This creamy soup is especially delightful when served with Crunchy Corn, an engaging variation on croutons.

2 medium yellow crookneck squash, coarsely chopped

1 yellow or red bell pepper, seeded and chopped

1 red onion, finely diced

1 large carrot, coarsely chopped

2 cloves garlic, minced

2 cups water

½ cup dry sherry

1 tablespoon frozen, unsweetened orange juice concentrate

2 teaspoons low-sodium soy sauce

1½ teaspoons curry powder

2 cups fluid nonfat milk

½ cup dry nonfat milk powder

¼ teaspoon Tabasco, or more

¼ cup finely minced fresh cilantro

1 recipe Crunchy Corn (recipe follows), optional

Combine the yellow squash, bell pepper, onion, carrot, garlic, water, sherry, juice concentrate, soy sauce and curry powder in a soup pot. Cover the pot with a tight-fitting lid and cook at low temperature for 40 minutes.

Transfer the pot contents to a blender and puree until smooth. Return the puree to the pot.

Whisk together the fluid milk and dry milk. Heat the milk in a microwave to hot but not boiling. Add to the soup and heat through. Stir in the Tabasco and serve topped with cilantro and Crunchy Corn (recipe follows).

YIELD: 8 servings

Nutrient analysis does not include the Crunchy Corn.

CALORIES	CARBOHYDRATES: 12.6 GM	TOTAL FAT: .5 GM
Per serving: 69	PROTEIN: 4.8 GM	Saturated fat: .2 GM
Fat: 6%	DIETARY FIBER: 1.5 GM	Monounsaturated fat: .1 GM
Carbohydrates: 68%	SODIUM: 104 MG	
Protein: 26%	CHOLESTEROL: 2 MG	

Pyramid equivalencies: 1 vegetable, ½ dairy

Crunchy Corn

Crunchy Corn is a tempting alternative to croutons. It adds an intriguing chewy texture to salads and creamy soups.

10 ounces frozen corn,   ½ teaspoon granulated garlic
   thawed   powder
1 teaspoon chili powder   ½ teaspoon ground cumin

Place the corn in a colander and gently press as much moisture from the corn as possible without crushing it. Transfer the corn to a nonstick skillet. Sprinkle with the dry spices. Stir regularly over high heat until the corn is lightly browned and crunchy. May be used immediately or stored in a container with a loose-fitting lid for 2 or 3 days. Do not refrigerate.

YIELD: 8 servings (as a condiment)

CALORIES	CARBOHYDRATES: 7.9 GM	TOTAL FAT: .1 GM
Per serving: 32	PROTEIN: 1.2 GM	Saturated fat: trace
Fat: 3%	DIETARY FIBER: .9 GM	Monounsaturated fat: trace
Carbohydrates: 84%	SODIUM: 5 MG	
Protein: 13%	CHOLESTEROL: 0 MG	

Pyramid equivalencies: ½ grain

Pacific Rim Tostadas

Serve a single tostada for a light lunch or supper. Two tostadas become a hearty, high-protein meal.

1 recipe Baked Tortillas (recipe follows)
1 recipe Black Beans with Garlic (recipe on page 165)
4 cups shredded red cabbage
1 recipe Asian Poached Salmon (recipe on page 166)
1 recipe Mango Salsa (recipe on page 167)
8 sprigs fresh cilantro

All of the component parts of this recipe need to be prepared before you begin assembling the tostadas. The Black Beans with Garlic can be reheated just before serving. The other parts can be served cold or at room temperature.

To make a tostada, place one of the Baked Tortillas on a plate and spread one-eighth of the recipe for Black Beans with Garlic over the tortilla. Sprinkle ½ cup red cabbage over the beans.

Crumble one-eighth recipe of the Asian Poached Salmon over the top of the cabbage. Top the salmon with one-eighth of the recipe for Mango Salsa. Garnish the tostada with a sprig of fresh cilantro.

YIELD: 8 servings

CALORIES
Per serving: 344
Fat: 13%
Carbohydrates: 60%
Protein: 27%

CARBOHYDRATES: 54.3 GM
PROTEIN: 23.9 GM
DIETARY FIBER: 10.2 GM
SODIUM: 233 MG
CHOLESTEROL: 21 MG

TOTAL FAT: 5.3 GM
Saturated fat: .6 GM
Monounsaturated fat: 1.2 GM

Pyramid equivalencies: 1 grain, 1 vegetable, ¼ fruit, 1 protein

Baked Tortillas

This method of baking corn tortillas creates crispy, flat tortillas that are perfect for tostadas.

8 corn tortillas

Place the tortillas (do not overlap) on a baking sheet. Place a second baking sheet on top of the tortillas. Bake in the oven at 375°F. for 25 minutes or until the tortillas are dry and crisp. Since standard baking sheets will only accommodate 6 tortillas, you will need to repeat this process.

The crisp tortillas can be stored for five days in an airtight container. Do not refrigerate.

Use the tortillas for creating the Pacific Rim Tostada or any other tostada.

YIELD: 8 servings

CALORIES
Per serving: 67
Fat: 12%
Carbohydrates: 74%
Protein: 14%

CARBOHYDRATES: 12.8 GM
PROTEIN: 2.1 GM
DIETARY FIBER: 1.0 GM
SODIUM: 53 MG
CHOLESTEROL: 0 MG

TOTAL FAT: 1.1 GM
Saturated fat: .2 GM
Monounsaturated fat: trace

Pyramid equivalencies: 1 grain

Black Beans with Garlic

Don't be intimidated by the large amount of garlic. Slow cooking transforms the garlic into a sweet, mellow flavor. In addition to the Pacific Rim Tostadas, I like to serve these beans with grilled or poached fish and scallops.

1½ cups dry black beans
16 cloves garlic, peeled and chopped
Water or unsalted, defatted chicken broth
½ cup dry sherry
⅓ cup balsamic vinegar

2 tablespoons finely minced fresh ginger
4 teaspoons low-sodium soy sauce
½ teaspoon five-spice powder (or more), optional

Rinse the beans under cold water and check for any pebbles or foreign matter. Combine the beans and garlic in a pot. Cover with enough water or broth to create a level of liquid that is 2 inches above the beans. Bring the liquid to a boil and reduce the heat to low. Cook uncovered until the beans are tender and most of the liquid is evaporated away, about 1½ hours.

Add all of the remaining ingredients and simmer at low temperature for 20 minutes. Transfer 1 cup of the mixture to a blender and process until smooth. Stir the puree back into the pot to thicken the beans. May be served immediately or reheated for later use.

YIELD: 8 servings

CALORIES
Per serving: 140
Fat: 4%
Carbohydrates: 72%
Protein: 24%

CARBOHYDRATES: 26.6 GM
PROTEIN: 8.8 GM
DIETARY FIBER: 6.2 GM
SODIUM: 97 MG
CHOLESTEROL: 0 MG

TOTAL FAT: .6 GM
Saturated fat: trace
Monounsaturated fat: trace

Pyramid equivalencies: ½ protein

Asian Poached Salmon

You can serve Asian Poached Salmon as an entrée one day and then use the leftovers the next day on the Pacific Rim Tostada.

1 *cup dry sherry*
3 *tablespoons fruit-sweetened apricot preserves*
1 *tablespoon finely minced fresh ginger*
2 *cloves garlic, finely minced*

2 *teaspoons low-sodium soy sauce*
1 *pound salmon fillets, boned with skin intact, cut into 4 equal pieces*

Whisk together the sherry and apricot preserves. Pour the mixture into a skillet and add the ginger and garlic. Add enough water to create a depth of ½ inch. Bring the liquid to a boil and cook at high heat until the liquid has been reduced by half.

Add the soy sauce to the liquid. Place the salmon, skin side down, into the liquid. Cover and cook at medium temperature for 7 minutes. Remove the salmon from the pan and increase the temperature to high until the liquid has reduced and thickened. Pour the sauce over the salmon and serve immediately, or chill for later use. May be used hot or cold with the Pacific Rim Tostada.

YIELD: 4 servings

As an entrée by itself, the salmon serves 4 persons. With the Pacific Rim Tostadas, the recipe is enough for 8 tostadas.

CALORIES
Per serving: 190
Fat: 30%
Carbohydrates: 20%
Protein: 50%

CARBOHYDRATES: 9.2 GM
PROTEIN: 23.3 GM
DIETARY FIBER: trace
SODIUM: 135 MG
CHOLESTEROL: 42 MG

TOTAL FAT: 6.4 GM
Saturated fat: 1.2 GM
Monounsaturated fat: 2.2 GM

Pyramid equivalencies: 1 protein

Mango Salsa

In addition to the Pacific Rim Tostada, Mango Salsa is a delicious topping for a full-bodied grilled or poached fish. I also like it with grilled chicken and will sometimes use it as a dressing for a chicken and pasta salad.

1 mango, peeled, pitted and diced
1 large tomato, diced
1 yellow bell pepper, seeded and diced
½ cup diced red onion
1 fresh jalapeño pepper, seeded and minced

2 tablespoons fresh lime juice
1 tablespoon fresh orange juice
1 tablespoon finely minced fresh mint
1 tablespoon finely minced fresh cilantro

Combine all of the ingredients and marinate 30 minutes before serving. Do not make more than 4 hours before serving.

YIELD: **8 servings**

CALORIES
Per serving: 29
Fat: 5%
Carbohydrates: 88%
Protein: 7%

CARBOHYDRATES: 7.4 GM
PROTEIN: .6 GM
DIETARY FIBER: 1.1 GM
SODIUM: 3 MG
CHOLESTEROL: 0 MG

TOTAL FAT: .2 GM
Saturated fat: trace
Monounsaturated fat: trace

Pyramid equivalencies: ½ vegetable, ¼ fruit

Marinated Tangerines

Simple fruit compotes are popular in nearly every cuisine of the world. Fresh ginger offers a hint of the Orient.

8 *tangerines or small oranges*	1 *tablespoon orange-flavored*
¼ *cup frozen orange-pineapple*	*liqueur*
juice concentrate	2 *teaspoons finely minced fresh*
2 *tablespoons water*	*ginger*

Peel the tangerines and pull apart into sections. If necessary, use a knife to trim away the bitter membrane between the peel and the meat of the fruit. If choosing oranges, it is usually easier to peel with a knife so that the white membrane can be cut away.

Place the fruit sections in a bowl with the juice concentrate, water, liqueur and ginger. Refrigerate for 1 hour or more before serving. If desired, serve with the Mandarin Chocolate Sauce (recipe follows).

Spoon Mandarin Chocolate Sauce onto individual serving plates. Arrange the fruit in a pattern over the sauce. You may also serve the dessert by pouring chocolate sauce into a small bowl for dipping. Place the bowl on a tray or platter surrounded by tangerine sections. Keep chilled until ready to serve.

YIELD: 8 servings

Nutrient analysis does not include Mandarin Chocolate Sauce.

CALORIES	CARBOHYDRATES: 13.4 GM	TOTAL FAT: .2 GM
Per serving: 53	PROTEIN: .6 GM	Saturated fat: trace
Fat: 3%	DIETARY FIBER: 1.7 GM	Monounsaturated fat: trace
Carbohydrates: 93%	SODIUM: 3 MG	
Protein: 4%	CHOLESTEROL: 0 MG	

Pyramid equivalencies: 1 fruit

Mandarin Chocolate Sauce

Chocolate originates from Mexico. Five-spice powder gives this version of chocolate sauce an exotic Asian flavor.

2 tablespoons and 2 teaspoons cocoa powder
1/2 teaspoon cinnamon
1/2 teaspoon five-spice powder
1/4 cup hot coffee (or hot water)
2/3 cup chopped, pitted prunes
1 tablespoon blackstrap molasses

2 tablespoons orange-flavored liqueur
1 tablespoon frozen, unsweetened orange-pineapple juice concentrate
1/4 cup dry nonfat milk powder

Dissolve the cocoa, cinnamon and five-spice powder in the hot coffee. Put in a blender jar with the prunes, molasses, liqueur and juice concentrate. Puree until smooth. If necessary, add water to thin to the desired consistency. Add the milk powder and continue processing until completely incorporated. Chill 1 hour before using. Serve with Marinated Tangerines or fresh orange sections or slices of mango.

YIELD: 8 servings

CALORIES
Per serving: 64
Fat: 2%
Carbohydrates: 84%
Protein: 6%
Alcohol: 8%

CARBOHYDRATES: 19.9 GM
PROTEIN: 1.5 GM
DIETARY FIBER: .5 GM
SODIUM: 27 MG
CHOLESTEROL: 4 MG

TOTAL FAT: .2 GM
Saturated fat: trace
Monounsaturated fat: .1 GM

Pyramid equivalencies: 1/4 fruit, 1/8 dairy

Mock Sangría

This is a light, nonalcoholic version of a traditional favorite.

3 cups boiling water
8 bags Red Zinger or other
   hibiscus-flavored tea
1 cup frozen, unsweetened
   berry-flavored juice
   concentrate

8 cups citrus-flavored,
   unsweetened mineral water,
   chilled
2 cups whole strawberries
1 orange, thinly sliced and cut
   in half

Pour the boiling water over the tea bags and steep for 20 minutes. Strain the tea, pressing as much liquid from the bags as possible without rupturing the bags. Discard the bags. Combine the concentrated tea and juice concentrate. Refrigerate until chilled.

Combine the tea and juice mixture with the mineral water in a large pitcher. Add the strawberries and orange slices. Chill 20 minutes before serving. Serve in glasses filled with ice.

YIELD: 16 servings (6 ounces per serving)

CALORIES
Per serving: 38
Fat: 3%
Carbohydrates: 94%
Protein: 3%

CARBOHYDRATES: 9.4 GM
PROTEIN: .3 GM
DIETARY FIBER: .7 GM
SODIUM: 6 MG
CHOLESTEROL: 0 MG

TOTAL FAT: .1 GM
Saturated fat: 0 GM
Monounsaturated fat: trace

Pyramid equivalencies: ½ fruit

15

Bouillabaisse

IF I could choose my last meal on earth, I would want it to include Bouillabaisse. This Provençal classic is a splendid blend of fish, seafood, vegetables and aromatic seasonings that somehow results in a dish that is both homey and exotic.

BOUILLABAISSE (MENU FOR 4)

Bouillabaisse with Rouille and Toast Triangles
Wild Greens with Wine Vinaigrette
Red Fruit Compote

Additional Recipe:
Rich Fish Stock

Bouillabaisse, the signature dish of the French Riviera, is also one of the most famous seafood dishes in the world. Provençal cooks often claim that a true Bouillabaisse must have certain seafood that can only be obtained in that area. This popular notion makes Bouillabaisse one of the most expensive dishes in France. In the United States, it is next to impossible to obtain the Mediterranean seafoods that are considered essential ingredients.

Before you give up on trying to make Bouillabaisse, be aware that cooks from one Riviera town to the next frequently disagree on what seafood should go in an authentic Bouillabaisse. American chefs constantly vary the ingredients based on what are the freshest and most flavorful choices available. The type of seafood used, of course, affects the taste, but what really makes Bouillabaisse so sensational is the aromatic seasonings that flavor the stew. There is no rule etched in stone that Bouillabaisse must be seasoned a certain way, but what most recipes share in common is an exquisite blend of flavors that results in a dish that is both light and rich, subtle, yet bold.

My version of Bouillabaisse uses less fat than is typical of most recipes. I doubt that your dinner guests will notice, because I've taken special steps to be certain the dish retains a genuine robust flavor. This requires extra work. To create richness without fat, you need to make a doubly rich stock. Almost all recipes for Bouillabaisse start with a fish stock. So does mine, except my Rich Fish Stock is made by cooking the fish parts in chicken stock instead of water. The result is an incredibly rich consommé. The flavor is more robust and less fishy tasting than is typical. It also enables you to eliminate ¼ cup of oil from the recipe!

Bouillabaisse should be made with the freshest seafood and fish available. The general formula is that you should have one strongly flavored and the other mildly flavored. One of the fish should be firm and the other delicate. It is typical to have one or two kinds of crusta-ceans in their shell. One or two mollusks may also be included. I find many diners don't like the splashy mess of breaking apart lobster and crab in a soup, so I usually forgo the crustaceans. Since scallops and mussels are personal favorites, I'm likely to include them. My Bouil-labaisse has smaller amounts of fish and seafood than is commonly served in restaurants. Again, I'm trying to cut back on the amount of cholesterol consumed. With the accompanying Toast Triangles, I feel the recipe will fully satisfy 4 hearty eaters. Toast is commonly served floating in the stew, but I generally serve it on the side, letting the diners choose for themselves.

Classic Bouillabaisse is topped with a piquant sauce called Rouille. French cooks make this sauce two different ways. You can make a mayonnaise with egg and oil or you can puree bread with olive oil to create a sauce. The latter is the older, more traditional method and is lower in saturated fat and free of cholesterol. That is the method I will use. I've found you can substitute a small amount of yogurt and reduce the oil content as well. Since the sauce is pungently flavored with cayenne, most diners will never notice the difference in approaches.

When Bouillabaisse is served, it is always the center of attention. You need very little else to complete the meal. A simple green salad served at the same time, or afterward, is an appealing accompaniment. Wild Greens with Wine Vinaigrette has a robust flavor but doesn't overpower the stew. The dressing can be served hot or cold. Although France has its share of rich desserts, Bouillabaisse is rarely served with anything more elaborate than a warm fruit compote. Red Fruit Compote completes the meal with a sufficiently tantalizing sweetness.

This meal colorfully illustrates how French cooks have perfected the art of cooking with wine. Each dish heartily employs wine to create subtle but rich flavors. Although the wine will be cooked, choose a wine for each dish that has suitable drinking appeal. For a wine to serve as a beverage, a rosé is the choice. Mineral water would also be a popular accompanying beverage.

Nutrient Analysis for Bouillabaisse

The nutrient analysis for the complete meal includes 1 serving each of Bouillabaisse, Rouille, Wild Greens with Wine Vinaigrette and Red Fruit Compote. The total includes 2 servings of Toast Triangles (4 pieces). The total does not include wine or any other beverage served with the meal.

CALORIES	CARBOHYDRATES: 133.0 GM	TOTAL FAT: 15.8 GM
For total meal:	PROTEIN: 49.9 GM	Saturated fat: 2.9 GM
875	DIETARY FIBER: 15.6 GM	Monounsaturated fat: 7.2 GM
Fat: 16%	SODIUM: 854 MG	
Carbohydrates: 61%	CHOLESTEROL: 78 MG	
Protein: 23%		

Pyramid equivalencies: 2¼ grains, 4 vegetables, 2 fruits, 1½ protein

Rich Fish Stock

Cooking fish in chicken broth results in a rich, full-bodied stock without a strong fishy flavor. Starting with a homemade chicken or turkey stock is ideal, but this is one time a canned product will work nicely.

3 cups unsalted, defatted
　　chicken or turkey stock
1 cup dry white wine
1 cup water
½ pound fish trimmings
1 large yellow or white onion,
　　coarsely chopped

1 large carrot
4 cloves garlic, peeled
1 whole bay leaf
2 whole cloves
3 or 4 whole peppercorns

Combine all of the ingredients in a pot and simmer at low temperature for 1½ hours. Remove the pot from the heat and strain the stock, discarding all but the liquid. Skim off any fat. Measure the liquid and add enough water to yield a total of 6 cups. Use for preparing Bouillabaisse or other fish stews and soups.

CALORIES
Per serving: 40
Fat: 0%
Carbohydrates: 98%
Protein: 2%

CARBOHYDRATES: 10.0 GM
PROTEIN: .2 GM
DIETARY FIBER: 0 GM
SODIUM: 4 MG
CHOLESTEROL: 0 MG

TOTAL FAT: trace
Saturated fat: 0 GM
Monounsaturated fat: 0 GM

Pyramid equivalencies: No equivalencies

Bouillabaisse

Accompanied by toast, Bouillabaisse is truly a meal in one dish. Before beginning the dish, read the introduction to this chapter.

6 cups Rich Fish Stock (previous recipe)

2 cups wine

1 tablespoon Pernod

1 tablespoon low-sodium soy sauce

4 large potatoes, peeled and cubed

2 large carrots, cut in ½-inch rounds

1 leek, washed well and coarsely chopped

4 shallots, chopped

4 cloves garlic, finely minced

2 teaspoons finely minced fresh rosemary

2 teaspoons finely grated fresh orange peel

¼ teaspoon ground fennel seed

½ teaspoon crushed saffron

8 plum tomatoes, finely chopped

1 celery stalk, diced

½ pound firm, flavorful fish, cut in 1-inch cubes

½ pound delicate, mildly flavored fish, cut in 1-inch cubes

16 mussels, washed with beard trimmed away

½ pound bay scallops or sea scallops cut in half

3 tablespoons finely minced fresh parsley

In a large pot, combine the stock, wine, Pernod and soy sauce and bring to a boil. Add the potatoes, carrots, leek, shallots, garlic, rosemary, orange peel, fennel seed and saffron. When the liquid returns to a boil, reduce the heat to medium and cook until the potatoes are nearly tender, about 12 minutes. Remove from the heat and stir in the tomatoes and celery. Cover the pot and let stand for 3 hours or overnight in the refrigerator.

Remove 1 cup of the potatoes and liquid from the pot and puree until smooth. Set aside. Bring the pot of cooked vegetables to a boil. Reduce the heat to medium and add the firm fish. Cook for 3 minutes. Add the mild fish and cook for 2 minutes. Add the mussels and cook until the shells start to open. Stir in the potato puree and scallops. Continue cooking for 5 minutes. Mix in the fresh parsley and serve immediately.

Serve the Bouillabaisse in large bowls. Drizzle the Rouille over each bowl and place the Toast Triangles on the side.

YIELD: 4 servings

Nutrient analysis does not include Rouille or the Toast Triangles.

CALORIES	CARBOHYDRATES: 53.9 GM	TOTAL FAT: 3.7 GM
Per serving: 440	PROTEIN: 40.9 GM	Saturated fat: 1.3 GM
Fat: 8%	DIETARY FIBER: 4.4 GM	Monounsaturated fat: .8 GM
Carbohydrates: 52%	SODIUM: 514 MG	
Protein: 40%	CHOLESTEROL: 85 MG	

Pyramid equivalencies: 3 vegetables, 1½ protein

Rouille

This very spicy sauce is a bewitching addition to Bouillabaisse.

1 slice French bread or whole wheat bread
4 teaspoons extra-virgin olive oil
1 tablespoon plain nonfat yogurt
1 tablespoon fluid nonfat milk
1 teaspoon fresh lemon juice
3 cloves garlic
1½ teaspoons cayenne pepper
⅛ teaspoon white pepper

Trim the crust from the bread and discard. Tear the bread into chunks and combine with all of the other ingredients in a blender. Puree until completely smooth. Refrigerate until ready to serve. Use as a topping for Bouillabaisse, other fish dishes or soups.

YIELD: 4 servings

CALORIES	CARBOHYDRATES: 4.5 GM	TOTAL FAT: 4.9 GM
Per serving: 65	PROTEIN: 1.1 GM	Saturated fat: .7 GM
Fat: 66%	DIETARY FIBER: .2 GM	Monounsaturated fat: 3.3 GM
Carbohydrates: 27%	SODIUM: 44 MG	
Protein: 7%	CHOLESTEROL: 0 MG	

Pyramid equivalencies: ¼ grain

Toast Triangles

Toast Triangles are served traditionally floating on a bowl of Bouillabaisse. You may elect to serve it on the side and as an accompaniment to the salad.

> 8 *slices whole wheat bread*   *Salt-free lemon-herb seasoning*
> *Nonstick cooking spray*   *blend*
> *made with extra-virgin*   *Paprika*
> *olive oil*

   Trim the crust from each slice and cut in half, diagonally, creating 2 triangles. Arrange the triangles on a cookie sheet, without overlapping. Place the cookie sheet under a preheated broiler. Leave under the broiler for 45 seconds and check to see if it has lightly browned. If necessary, leave the bread under the broiler for a few seconds more.

   Remove the tray and turn the bread triangles over. Lightly spray the bread with the olive-oil-based nonstick spray. Generously sprinkle the bread with the seasoning blend. Follow with a light sprinkling of paprika. Return the bread to the broiler. Toast for 45 seconds or until the bread is lightly browned. Serve hot with Bouillabaisse.

YIELD: 8 servings, 2 triangles per serving

CALORIES	CARBOHYDRATES: 11.3 GM	TOTAL FAT: 1.4 GM
Per serving: 63	PROTEIN: 2.4 GM	Saturated fat: .1 GM
Fat: 19%	DIETARY FIBER: 2.7 GM	Monounsaturated fat: .2 GM
Carbohydrates: 67%	SODIUM: 156 MG	
Protein: 14%	CHOLESTEROL: 0 MG	

Pyramid equivalencies: 2 grains

Wild Greens with Wine Vinaigrette

Although it's titled "wild greens," I assume you will more likely use the domesticated varieties. I've tried wild dandelion greens, but I find them quite tough and bitter. Domesticated dandelion, chicory and watercress have a marvelous pungent flavor that will be "wild" enough to satisfy most palates.

2 cups romaine lettuce, torn in bite-size pieces
2 cups oak leaf or red leaf lettuce, torn in bite-size pieces
2 cups dandelion greens, escarole or spinach, torn in bite-size pieces

2 cups curly chicory or watercress, torn in bite-size pieces
1 recipe Wine Vinaigrette (recipe follows)
Freshly ground black pepper

After the greens have been washed and drained, toss with the Vinaigrette and serve immediately. Sprinkle each salad serving with freshly ground pepper.

YIELD: 4 servings

CALORIES
Per serving: 61
Fat: 54%
Carbohydrates: 35%
Protein: 11%

CARBOHYDRATES: 5.5 GM
PROTEIN: 1.9 GM
DIETARY FIBER: 2.0 GM
SODIUM: 24 MG
CHOLESTEROL: 0 MG

TOTAL FAT: 3.7 GM
Saturated fat: .5 GM
Monounsaturated fat: 2.5 GM

Pyramid equivalencies: 1 vegetable

Wine Vinaigrette

This simple vinaigrette is delicious hot or cold.

½ cup dry white wine
1 tablespoon water
1 clove garlic, finely minced
1 tablespoon frozen, unsweetened apple juice concentrate
1 tablespoon extra-virgin olive oil

1 teaspoon unsalted Dijon-style mustard
1 tablespoon finely minced fresh tarragon, or 1 teaspoon dry

In a small saucepan, stir together the wine, water and garlic. Simmer at a low boil for 2 to 3 minutes. Remove from the heat, whisk in the remaining ingredients and pour into a measuring cup. If necessary, add enough water to yield ½ cup of dressing. Use immediately or chill for later use.

YIELD: 4 servings

CALORIES
Per serving: 43
Fat: 76%
Carbohydrates: 22%
Protein: 2%

CARBOHYDRATES: 2.3 GM
PROTEIN: .2 GM
DIETARY FIBER: trace
SODIUM: 3 MG
CHOLESTEROL: 0 MG

TOTAL FAT: 3.4 GM
Saturated fat: .5 GM
Monounsaturated fat: 2.5 GM

Pyramid equivalencies: No equivalencies

Red Fruit Compote

This spicy compote is appealing any time of year, hot or cold. Any sweet, red dessert wine can be used instead of the port.

½ cup port
¼ cup water
¼ cup frozen raspberry- or cherry-flavored juice concentrate
½ teaspoon ground cinnamon
¼ teaspoon ground cloves

⅛ teaspoon cayenne pepper
½ cup dried cranberries, cherries or strawberries
8 whole pitted dates
1 red apple, cored and sliced
1 cup fresh or frozen pitted cherries

Combine the port, water, juice concentrate, cinnamon, cloves and cayenne pepper in a saucepan. Heat to almost boiling and add the dry fruits and apple. Reduce to low and cook 15 minutes covered. Add the cherries and heat through. Serve the compote hot or, if you prefer, chill and serve cold.

YIELD: 4 servings

CALORIES
Per serving: 183
Fat: 3%
Carbohydrates: 94%
Protein: 3%

CARBOHYDRATES: 46.7 GM
PROTEIN: 1.4 GM
DIETARY FIBER: 3.7 GM
SODIUM: 37.2 MG
CHOLESTEROL: 0 MG

TOTAL FAT: .7 GM
Saturated fat: .1 GM
Monounsaturated fat: .1 GM

Pyramid equivalencies: 2 fruits

16

Country Comforts

Sometimes the simplest foods make the best meals. Ordinary ingredients and easy preparations can yield extraordinary flavor. This menu will remind you of the comforting dishes of a farmhouse kitchen. You may think country cooking is synonymous with high-fat cookery, but this dinner demonstrates even delicious "comfort" foods can be healthy.

Country Comforts (Menu for 4)

Red Cabbage and Red Bean Soup
Pork Tenderloin with Apple-Vegetable Mélange
Mashed Potatoes with Herbs and Parmesan
Pumpkin Gingerbread with Fancy Warm Preserves

Additional Recipes:
Red Cabbage and Red Bean Soup with Turkey Sausage
Turkey Medallions with Apple-Vegetable Mélange

A rustic soup is synonymous with comfort cuisine. Red Cabbage and Red Bean Soup is packed with good nutrition and hearty flavors. This

181

humble dish can serve as an appetizer or a main course. A variation of the soup, Red Cabbage and Red Bean Soup with Turkey Sausage, is a marvelous one-pot meal.

Many cooks still do not associate pork with low-fat cooking. Pork tenderloin is the leanest cut of pork, deriving 27% of its calories from fat. No, it is not as lean as fish, seafood or breast of chicken or turkey. But pork tenderloin does have less fat than the dark meat of chicken or turkey and has less fat than lamb and many cuts of beef.

In this meal, fresh herbs are used to create a simple earthy flavor that effectively produces a hearty taste without using fat. Pork Tenderloin with Apple-Vegetable Mélange is perfumed with the sweet, aromatic flavor of fresh fennel and the familiar earthiness of sage. Wine, used in the way many cooks would use butter or oil, also contributes to the illusion of richness. For those who don't eat pork, Turkey Medallions with Apple-Vegetable Mélange is a good substitute.

Potatoes are a perfect canvas for exploring the flavor hues of many herbs. Mashed Potatoes with Herbs and Parmesan again demonstrates how fresh herbs create a sense of richness without relying on butter or cream.

Gingerbread has been a delight of bakers for several centuries. Long before diners started counting calories, gingerbread frequently was prepared with little or no fat. This version contains pumpkin, which keeps the cake moist. The Pumpkin Gingerbread has a healthy dose of beta-carotene. Fancy Warm Preserves turns the bread into a company dessert.

NUTRIENT INFORMATION FOR COUNTRY COMFORTS

Persons seeking a heartier meal may elect to add bread to the menu. Nutrient information for the complete meal includes 1 serving each of Red Cabbage and Red Bean Soup, Pork Tenderloin with Apple-Vegetable Mélange, Mashed Potatoes with Herbs and Parmesan and Gingerbread with Fancy Warm Preserves.

CALORIES	CARBOHYDRATES: 131.0 GM	TOTAL FAT: 10.0 GM
For total meal: 732	PROTEIN: 37.6 GM	Saturated fat: 2.9 GM
Fat: 11%	DIETARY FIBER: 11.7 GM	Monounsaturated fat: 3.6 GM
Carbohydrates: 69%	SODIUM: 646 MG	
Protein: 20%	CHOLESTEROL: 54.5 MG	

Pyramid equivalencies: 2 grains, 3½ vegetables, 1 fruit, 1¼ proteins

Red Cabbage and
Red Bean Soup

I chose red cabbage and red beans because I like the intense color. Feel
free to substitute green cabbage and white beans.

4 cups unsalted, defatted
  chicken, turkey or beef broth
  or water
2 large red onions, diced
6 cloves garlic, minced
2 teaspoons low-sodium soy
  sauce
1 bay leaf, crushed
½ teaspoon black pepper
¼ teaspoon allspice
¼ teaspoon dry thyme
⅛ teaspoon liquid smoke
  flavoring

1 parsnip, diced
1 carrot, diced
1 stalk celery with leaves, diced
1 small head of red cabbage,
  coarsely chopped
1½ cups cooked kidney beans or
  other red beans
1 cup unsalted tomato puree
2 tablespoons finely minced
  fresh parsley
8 lemon wedges

Bring the broth to a boil. Add the onions, garlic, soy sauce, bay leaf,
black pepper, allspice, thyme and liquid smoke. Cover the pot and
reduce to low heat. Simmer 20 minutes.

Add the parsnip, carrot and celery. Cover again and cook at low heat
for 30 minutes.

Add the cabbage and beans. Increase the heat and simmer uncovered until the cabbage is tender. Stir in the tomato puree and heat
through. Serve the soup hot with sprinkled parsley and lemon wedges
on the side.

YIELD: 8 servings

CALORIES	CARBOHYDRATES: 24.5 GM	TOTAL FAT: .5 GM
Per serving: 120	PROTEIN: 6.3 GM	Saturated fat: .1 GM
Fat: 4%	DIETARY FIBER: 6.0 GM	Monounsaturated fat: .1 GM
Carbohydrates: 76%	SODIUM: 72 MG	
Protein: 20%	CHOLESTEROL: 0 MG	

Pyramid equivalencies: 1½ vegetables, ¼ protein

Red Cabbage and Red Bean Soup with Turkey Sausage

Adding Spicy Turkey Sausage to the previous recipe turns the soup into a rich, hearty main course. To the previous recipe, simply add ½ recipe of the Spicy Turkey Sausage (pages 60–63).

YIELD: 8 servings

CALORIES	CARBOHYDRATES: 25.8 GM	TOTAL FAT: 1.0 GM
Per serving: 193	PROTEIN: 20.6 GM	Saturated fat: .3 GM
Fat: 5%	DIETARY FIBER: 6.2 GM	Monounsaturated fat: .2 GM
Carbohydrates: 53%	SODIUM: 167 MG	
Protein: 42%	CHOLESTEROL: 35 MG	

Pyramid equivalencies: 1½ vegetables, ½ protein

Pork Tenderloin with Apple-Vegetable Mélange

If you don't like fennel, simply omit or replace it with a stalk of diced celery and a pinch of ground cloves.

- ¾ pound pork tenderloin, trimmed of fat
- ¾ cup dry sherry
- 1 tablespoon Dijon-style mustard
- 1 tablespoon frozen, unsweetened apple juice concentrate
- 2 teaspoons low-sodium soy sauce
- ½ cup all-purpose flour
- 1½ teaspoons dry crushed sage
- ½ teaspoon black pepper
- 2 red apples, cored and sliced
- 1 large carrot, cut in thin rounds
- 1 bulb fresh fennel, coarsely chopped
- ½ cup diced red onion
  Fennel leaf or parsley for garnish

Slice the pork tenderloin crosswise in 8 pieces. With a mallet, gently pound each piece into rounds no more than ⅛ inch thick. Place the rounds in a bowl with the dry sherry, mustard, apple juice concentrate and soy sauce. Marinate for 1 hour, stirring occasionally.

Whisk together the flour, sage and black pepper. Remove the pork from the marinade, draining carefully and reserving the liquid. Dredge each slice of pork in the flour mixture, coating each side.

Spray a nonstick skillet with nonstick cooking spray. Place the skillet over a medium-high heat. Brown the tenderloin slices on each side, 3 or 4 minutes per side. Immediately transfer the meat to a plate. Pour the reserved marinade into the hot skillet, scraping down the sides to dissolve the browned flour. Immediately add the apples, carrot, fennel and onion. If necessary, add enough water to the pan to cover the bottom with liquid. Simmer 2 minutes. Place the pork slices over the apple mixture. Simmer uncovered for 8 minutes. Check regularly to verify the pan has enough liquid.

Serve the pork and apple-vegetable mélange garnished with sprigs of fresh fennel leaf or parsley.

YIELD: 4 servings

CALORIES
Per serving: 225
Fat: 16%
Carbohydrates: 48%
Protein: 36%

CARBOHYDRATES: 28.6 GM
PROTEIN: 21.2 GM
DIETARY FIBER: 1.7 GM
SODIUM: 158 MG
CHOLESTEROL: 59 MG

TOTAL FAT: 4.3 GM
Saturated fat: 1.1 GM
Monounsaturated fat: 1.8 GM

Pyramid equivalencies: 1 vegetable, ½ fruit, 1 protein

Turkey Medallions with Apple-Vegetable Mélange

Instead of Pork Tenderloin, turkey breast can be substituted. The flavor will not be quite as rich but still very appealing.

Slice 1 pound raw turkey breast into very thin slices, no more than 2 inches across. With a mallet, pound each piece to a thickness no greater than ⅛ inch. Proceed as in the previous recipe with the pork.

YIELD: 8 servings

CALORIES
Per serving: 209
Fat: 13%
Carbohydrates: 51%
Protein: 36%

CARBOHYDRATES: 28.9 GM
PROTEIN: 20.2 GM
DIETARY FIBER: 3.5 GM
SODIUM: 176 MG
CHOLESTEROL: 35 MG

TOTAL FAT: 3.3 GM
Saturated fat: .9 GM
Monounsaturated fat: 1.1 GM

Pyramid equivalencies: 1 vegetable, ½ fruit, 1 protein

Mashed Potatoes with Herbs and Parmesan

Fresh herbs are best, but you can substitute dry herbs, using one-third as much. Many other herbs also work well with potatoes. Consider tarragon (fresh or dry), chives, caraway leaf or even celery leaves.

4 large potatoes, peeled and cubed

2 cloves garlic, minced

¼ cup plain nonfat yogurt

¼ cup fluid nonfat milk

1 tablespoon unsalted Dijon-style mustard

2 green onions, finely diced

3 tablespoons freshly grated Parmesan cheese

3 tablespoons finely minced fresh parsley

1 tablespoon finely minced fresh dill

¼ teaspoon black pepper

Combine the potatoes and garlic in a pot. Cover with water and simmer until tender.

Meanwhile, stir together the yogurt, nonfat milk and mustard. When the potatoes are done, drain and add the yogurt mixture. Mash the potatoes using a hand masher or electric mixer. When the potatoes are smooth, stir in the remaining ingredients and mix well. Serve immediately.

YIELD: 4 servings

CALORIES	CARBOHYDRATES: 30.2 GM	TOTAL FAT: 2.2 GM
Per serving: 165	PROTEIN: 6.6 GM	Saturated fat: 1.3 GM
Fat: 12%	DIETARY FIBER: 1.7 GM	Monounsaturated fat: .6 GM
Carbohydrates: 72%	SODIUM: 145 MG	Polyunsaturated fat: .1 GM
Protein: 16%	CHOLESTEROL: 5 MG	

Pyramid equivalencies: 2 vegetables, ½ dairy

Pumpkin Gingerbread

This Gingerbread is delicious served warm or at room temperature. I like to spread warm Gingerbread with Fancy Warm Preserves or toast the slices under a broiler, then top with a thin slice of cheddar cheese.

1½ cups whole wheat flour	⅛ teaspoon cayenne pepper
½ cup cornstarch	½ cup brown sugar dissolved in
1¼ teaspoons baking powder	1 cup water
1 teaspoon baking soda	1 cup canned pumpkin
2 teaspoons ginger	½ cup dark molasses
1 teaspoon cinnamon	2 egg whites
⅛ teaspoon allspice	2 tablespoons dark sesame oil

Preheat oven to 350°F. Sift together the flour, cornstarch, baking powder, baking soda and spices and set aside.

Beat together the brown sugar dissolved in water, pumpkin, molasses, egg whites and oil until smooth and creamy. Beat in dry ingredients and mix well.

Spray an 8-inch loaf pan with nonstick cooking spray. Pour batter into pan and bake at 350°F. for 45 minutes or until an inserted toothpick comes out clean.

YIELD: 10 servings

CALORIES		
Per serving: 188	CARBOHYDRATES: 38.1 GM	TOTAL FAT: 3.0 GM
Fat: 14%	PROTEIN: 3.1 GM	Saturated fat: .4 GM
Carbohydrates: 79%	DIETARY FIBER: 2.3 GM	Monounsaturated fat: 1.1 GM
Protein: 7%	SODIUM: 111 MG	
	CHOLESTEROL: 0 MG	

Pyramid equivalencies: 2 grains

Fancy Warm Preserves

Ordinary preserves become a gourmet delight with just a few additions. Use as a spread for the Gingerbread or date bread or as a topping for nonfat frozen yogurt.

½ cup fruit-sweetened peach or apricot preserves

2 tablespoons water

1 tablespoon rum or ¼ teaspoon rum extract

¼ teaspoon cinnamon

Whisk together all the ingredients and gently warm in a saucepan or heat in a microwave. Orange marmalade can be substituted for the peach or apricot preserves.

YIELD: 10 servings

CALORIES		
Per serving: 34	CARBOHYDRATES: 9.6 GM	TOTAL FAT: 0 GM
Fat: 0%	PROTEIN: 0 GM	Saturated fat: 0 GM
Carbohydrates: 100%	DIETARY FIBER: trace	Monounsaturated fat: 0 GM
Protein: 0%	SODIUM: 0 MG	
	CHOLESTEROL: 0 MG	

Pyramid equivalencies: ½ fruit

17

Meaty Vegetables—The Asian Way

THIS HEARTY meal is a salute to the ingenious ways that Asian cooks use small quantities of meat to flavor vegetable dishes. The menu is a fascinating mix of formal banquet fare and casual family dishes. The flavors and culinary techniques are rooted in the traditions of China, Vietnam and Thailand, with a bow to contemporary American cooking.

MEATY VEGETABLES—THE ASIAN WAY (MENU FOR 4)

Vietnamese Lettuce Rolls with Curry Peanut Sauce
Szechwan Hash
Kale in Ginger Sauce
Dry Shrimp and Snow Pea Soup
Oven-Steamed Brown Rice
Marsala-Poached Pears with Apricots

Additional Recipe:
Szechwan Marinade

Although there are many exclusively vegetarian groups, Asia is largely a population of meat eaters. As a continent, Asian meals feature more dishes with meat than would be typical of a Western menu. Formal, special-occasion menus are strongly oriented toward meat dishes, featuring something from the land (red meats), something from the air (poultry) and something from the sea (fish and seafood). However, everyday family dining focuses on vegetables with meats as a seasoning. And the family dishes generally use less fat and oil in the preparation.

Asians have mastered the art and science of giving vegetables a "meaty" flavor. The most famous technique is the use of soy sauce. This salty, fermented sauce simulates the robust flavor of browned meat. The source of the flavor is due largely to the process of fermentation, and soybeans furnish a unique meatiness. High in protein and high in fat, soybeans are commonly processed to create tofu (bean curd), a cheese-like product that serves as a meat extender or substitute. Although higher in fat than many commonly eaten meat products, tofu has no cholesterol and very little saturated fat. It also is a strong source of calcium and iron. Tofu is not the only way Asians have for extending meat. Dried mushrooms, dried fish or seafood, fermented or pickled condiments and nuts (especially peanuts) are often mixed in dishes to create "meatiness."

Asian cuisine is generally very high in sodium. Salt is usually in the form of fermented products such as soy sauce, fish sauce and a variety of pickled condiments. Soy sauce and other salty products help give Asian dishes a more "meaty" flavor. Unfortunately, there are health risks with high sodium consumption. For this Asian menu, I have created recipes that have about one-quarter the amount of sodium that would be typical. You will be aware of a definite difference in saltiness. I have also reduced the amount of oil used in the preparations; this change, however, is much less noticeable.

Vietnamese Lettuce Rolls frequent Southeast Asian banquet tables. My version is typical of what you will find in Vietnamese restaurants in this country. A lettuce roll is sort of a salad wrapped up in lettuce leaves that can be served as an appetizer or as part of the meal. Some restaurants present the ingredients and have you make your own. Common fillings for these "lettuce crepes" include rice noodles, bits of fresh vegetables and slivers of beef, pork or chicken. Two or three different sauces may be served with the roll. I like a peanut sauce, which gives the Vietnamese Lettuce Rolls a more robust flavor. To reduce the sodium content of the sauce, I seasoned my version with curry to create a heartier flavor. In addition to the Curry Peanut Sauce, you may want to offer one of the dipping sauces featured in chapter 20, " Asian Nouvelle."

Szechwan Hash is the name I give a delightful Szechwan dish that in China is known as Pock Marked Ma's Tofu. The dish is said to be named for the wife of a famous Chengtu chef. The Chinese often give dishes a playful and sometimes sarcastic name. Although named after a restaurateur, I doubt that most establishments would want to use that name on their menus. The hashlike appearance of the dish is why I call it Szechwan Hash. You can call it what you like!

There isn't much beef in Szechwan Hash, but the combination of tofu, dried mushrooms and water chestnuts gives the dish an amazingly meaty texture and flavor. The dish is spicy. When I created the Szechwan Marinade to flavor the meat, I decided to use less pepper than is typical. Given that I have also reduced the use of oil and salt, I think my reduction in hot spices offers a more balanced flavor. You can adjust the "heat" to your taste.

Cooking with garlic and ginger is a large part of many different Asian cuisines. Kale in Ginger Sauce mixes those flavors with a tart green apple. Tart fruits are often used in the seasoning of Thai dishes. It also helps provide flavor without relying on salt or fat.

Soup has a different role in cuisines of Asia than is typical of the West. Soup will likely be served at every meal of the day, including breakfast. It is also served as a snack or instead of a beverage. The soup may be served any time during the meal; it may function as a palate refresher between courses or even conclude the meal. Hot brothy soups fill you up and satisfy the appetite. If we ate soup as the Asians do, we would probably be less inclined to eat other high-calorie dishes. For this dinner, I created Dry Shrimp and Snow Pea Soup. The base of the soup uses dry shrimp powder and water. Large supermarkets and Asian or Latin American specialty stores usually carry shrimp powder. Most packets of the powder are made from ground, dry shrimp without any other ingredients. I use that instead of shrimp paste because I find the paste may include high amounts of salt and MSG. Dry Shrimp and Snow Pea Soup has a slightly hot and sour flavor, common in Southeast Asia. Use whatever vegetables you like in creating the soup.

More brown rice is eaten in the United States than any other country of the world. I like brown rice, but it is considered gauche in most parts of the world. White rice lacks the fiber of brown rice but still offers many important nutrients. You will not rot in Bad Nutrition Hell if you eat white rice. Oven-Steamed Brown Rice is my favorite way of preparing plain brown rice. Plain rice with this menu balances the spicy flavors of the other dishes.

Few Asian countries offer desserts with meals. Sweets are more likely eaten apart from the meal at another time of day. Very special banquets may include dessert. Fruit, however, is always present. It may be raw or cooked. Marsala-Poached Pears with Apricots is elegant enough for a banquet and simple enough for family fare.

NUTRIENT ANALYSIS FOR MEATY VEGETABLES MENU

The nutrient analysis for the complete meal includes 1 serving each of Vietnamese Lettuce Rolls, Curry Peanut Sauce, Szechwan Hash, Kale in Ginger Sauce, Oven-Steamed Brown Rice and Marsala-Poached Pears with Apricots. It also includes 2 servings of Dry Shrimp and Snow Pea Soup.

CALORIES	CARBOHYDRATES: 185.0 GM	TOTAL FAT: 20.0 GM
For total meal: 1,094	PROTEIN: 60.0 GM	Saturated fat: 4.5 GM
Fat: 15%	DIETARY FIBER: 17.1 GM	Monounsaturated fat: 8.6 GM
Carbohydrates: 64%	SODIUM: 811 MG	
Protein: 21%	CHOLESTEROL: 82 MG	

Pyramid equivalencies: 2½ grains, 4½ vegetables, 2⅔ fruits, 1¾ proteins

Vietnamese Lettuce Rolls

These are commonly served as an appetizer at multicourse Vietnamese parties.

*4 ounces dry rice sticks or
  other Asian noodles*
4 green onions
*4 large green leaf lettuce
  leaves*
*½ chicken breast, poached and
  cut in slivers*

*4 stalks canned hearts of palm,
  rinsed in cold water*
2 sprigs fresh mint, chopped
2 sprigs fresh cilantro, chopped
*1 recipe Curry Peanut Sauce
  (recipe follows)*

Prepare the noodles according to package instructions for cooking in water. Drain the noodles and set aside.

Take the green onions and cut away the white part. Cut the white portions in thin slivers lengthwise. Set aside. Take the green stems and plunge in boiling water. Remove immediately and dip into cold water. Drain and set aside.

Just below the center of each lettuce leaf, place a portion of the rice noodles, slivered onion, chicken, hearts of palm, mint and cilantro. Roll the lettuce into a cylindrical shape. Tie a blanched green onion stem around the center of each lettuce roll to prevent unrolling. Trim the edges of each roll to create an attractive appearance.

Place the rolls on individual plates, allowing each diner to dip the roll in the Curry Peanut Sauce or to spoon the sauce over the top.

YIELD: 4 servings

Nutrient analysis does not include the sauce

CALORIES	CARBOHYDRATES: 35.1 GM	TOTAL FAT: 1.4 GM
Per serving: 197	PROTEIN: 12.4 GM	Saturated fat .3 GM
Fat: 6%	DIETARY FIBER: 1.4 GM	Monounsaturated fat: .3 GM
Carbohydrates: 70%	SODIUM: 145 MG	
Protein: 24%	CHOLESTEROL: 18 MG	

Pyramid equivalencies: 1 grain, 1 vegetable, ¼ protein

Curry Peanut Sauce

A staple of Southeast Asian cuisine, peanut sauce can be prepared quickly.

¼ cup water

2 tablespoons pure, unsalted peanut butter

2 tablespoons frozen, unsweetened apple juice concentrate

1½ teaspoons low-sodium soy sauce

½ to 1 teaspoon curry powder

¼ teaspoon dry ground ginger

¼ teaspoon liquid hot pepper sauce

Whisk together all of the ingredients in a small saucepan. Cover tightly and simmer at low temperature for 8 minutes.

Serve warm or at room temperature as a sauce for the Vietnamese Lettuce Rolls. Also serve as a sauce for plain raw or steamed vegetables and as a dipping sauce with the dishes featured in chapter 20, "Asian Nouvelle."

YIELD: 4 servings

CALORIES
Per serving: 65
Fat: 54%
Carbohydrates: 30%
Protein: 16%

CARBOHYDRATES: 5.3 GM
PROTEIN: 2.8 GM
DIETARY FIBER: 1.0 GM
SODIUM: 70 MG
CHOLESTEROL: 0 MG

TOTAL FAT: 4.4 GM
Saturated fat: .7 GM
Monounsaturated fat: 2.1 GM

Pyramid equivalencies: ⅛ fruit

Szechwan Hash

This is a hearty, stick-to-the-ribs Chinese dish.

½ pound extra-lean ground beef
1 recipe Szechwan Marinade (recipe follows)
¼ cup dried mushrooms or 1 cup sliced fresh mushrooms
1 cup boiling water
⅓ cup dry sherry
6 cloves finely minced garlic

2 tablespoons finely minced fresh ginger
½ cup sliced water chestnuts
12 ounces drained firm tofu
4 green onions, finely minced
1½ teaspoons cornstarch dissolved in 1 tablespoon cold water
4 small sprigs of fresh cilantro

Stir together the ground beef and Szechwan Marinade. Let stand 30 minutes.

Meanwhile, place the dried mushrooms in a small bowl with the boiling water. Let soak for 20 minutes or until they are soft.

Drain the liquid from the mushrooms into a wok or skillet. Cut the softened mushrooms into slivers and discard any tough, woody bits. Set the mushrooms aside. Add the sherry, garlic and ginger to the mushroom water in the wok. If using a skillet, add enough water to just cover the bottom of the pan. Bring the mixture to a boil, reduce the temperature slightly and simmer 1 minute.

Add the ground meat mixture to the wok, stir continually and cook for 1 minute. Use a spoon to break up any large clumps of meat. Add the mushrooms and water chestnuts and continue stirring and cooking for 1 minute.

Add the tofu and additional water, if necessary. Stir the mixture, reduce the heat and simmer covered at moderate temperature for 2 to 3 minutes.

Stir in the green onions and if necessary more liquid. If desired, thicken the mixture with the cornstarch. Garnish with sprigs of cilantro.

YIELD: 4 servings

CALORIES	CARBOHYDRATES: 25.1 GM	TOTAL FAT: 11.1 GM
Per serving: 311	PROTEIN: 32.7 GM	Saturated fat: 2.3 GM
Fat: 30%	DIETARY FIBER: 1.8 GM	Monounsaturated fat: 3.2 GM
Carbohydrates: 30%	SODIUM: 351 MG	
Protein: 40%	CHOLESTEROL: 36 MG	

Pyramid equivalencies: ½ vegetable, 1½ proteins

Szechwan Marinade

Traditional Szechwan cooking might have even greater amounts of peppercorns and pepper flakes. You may want to adjust the amounts to your personal taste.

⅓ cup dry sherry
2 tablespoons balsamic vinegar
3 tablespoons unsalted tomato paste
5 teaspoons low-sodium soy sauce

2 teaspoons brown sugar
1 teaspoon blackstrap molasses
1 teaspoon dark roasted sesame oil
1 teaspoon ground Szechwan peppercorns
½ teaspoon red pepper flakes

Whisk together all of the ingredients and refrigerate until ready to use. In addition to using as a marinade for the ground beef in Szechwan Hash, also use as a sauce or marinade for spicy grilled meats.

YIELD: 4 servings

CALORIES
Per serving: 44
Fat: 23%
Carbohydrates: 67%
Protein: 10%

CARBOHYDRATES: 8.4 GM
PROTEIN: 1.2 GM
DIETARY FIBER: .7 GM
SODIUM: 315 MG
CHOLESTEROL: 0 MG

TOTAL FAT: 1.2 GM
Saturated fat: .2 GM
Monounsaturated fat: .5 GM

Pyramid equivalencies: No equivalencies

Kale in Ginger Sauce

Cabbage, rapini, spinach and mustard greens, in addition to kale, are delicious when prepared in this manner.

⅓ cup water
3 tablespoons frozen, unsweetened apple juice concentrate
2 tablespoons plain rice vinegar
1 teaspoon low-sodium soy sauce
1 small green or red apple, cored and sliced

2 green onions, chopped
1 tablespoon finely minced fresh ginger
2 cloves garlic, finely minced
6 cups freshly chopped kale, stems discarded
2 teaspoons cornstarch dissolved in 1 tablespoon water
2 teaspoons sesame seeds

In a large skillet, combine the water, juice concentrate, vinegar and soy sauce and bring to a boil. Immediately add the apple, onions, ginger and garlic and reduce the heat to low. If necessary, add more water, or enough to just cover the bottom of the pan. Cover and simmer for 4 minutes.

Increase the heat and add the chopped kale and toss thoroughly with the sauce. Continue cooking and stirring the kale until the leaves have wilted and turned dark green. Lift the kale and apple from the pan and transfer to a warm dish. Quickly stir the dissolved cornstarch into the sauce. Continue stirring until the liquid has thickened. Pour the sauce over the kale and toss. Serve immediately with the sesame seeds sprinkled over the top.

YIELD: 4 servings

CALORIES	CARBOHYDRATES: 17.6 GM	TOTAL FAT: 1.3 GM
Per serving: 85	PROTEIN: 2.3 GM	Saturated fat: .1 GM
Fat: 12%	DIETARY FIBER: 3.5 GM	Monounsaturated fat: trace
Carbohydrates: 78%	SODIUM: 66 MG	
Protein: 10%	CHOLESTEROL: 0 MG	

Pyramid equivalencies: 1 vegetable, ½ fruit

Dry Shrimp and Snow Pea Soup

Ground dry shrimp is a common ingredient in many Asian cuisines, as well as the cuisines of Mexico and Central America. You will likely find the product in the spice or international foods section of your market. It is also readily available in ethnic markets. If you can't find the shrimp powder, substitute unsalted fish broth for the water.

6 cups water

2 tablespoons dry ground shrimp powder

4 teaspoons balsamic vinegar or other vinegar

1 tablespoon low-sodium soy sauce

2 teaspoons brown sugar

¼ to ½ teaspoon coconut extract

¼ teaspoon hot pepper sauce (Tabasco)

2 cloves garlic, finely minced

1 small carrot, sliced thinly in rounds

1 small kohlrabi, halved and sliced thinly

1 3-inch piece daikon, sliced thinly

1 cup snow peas, trimmed

2 green onions, diced

In a pot, combine the water, dry shrimp powder, vinegar, soy sauce, brown sugar, coconut extract, hot sauce and garlic and bring to a boil. Add the carrot and kohlrabi and after the liquid returns to a boil, reduce the heat to moderate and cook for 3 minutes. Add the daikon and cook for 1 minute. Add the snow peas and cook for another minute. Serve immediately with the diced green onion sprinkled over each serving.

YIELD: 8 servings

CALORIES	CARBOHYDRATES: 4.3 GM	TOTAL FAT: .2 GM
Per serving: 27	PROTEIN: 2.4 GM	Saturated fat: trace
Fat: 5%	DIETARY FIBER: 1.0 GM	Monounsaturated fat: trace
Carbohydrates: 61%	SODIUM: 87 MG	
Protein: 34%	CHOLESTEROL: 14 MG	

Pyramid equivalencies: 1 vegetable

Oven-Steamed Brown Rice

Oven steaming is especially effective for preparing brown rice.

1½ cups brown rice   *2¾ cups boiling water*

Place the rice in a small ovenproof baking dish. Pour the boiling water over the rice and stir. Cover the dish with a tight-fitting lid or foil and immediately place in the oven. Bake at 350°F. for 50 minutes. Stir the rice before serving.

YIELD: 4 servings

CALORIES	CARBOHYDRATES: 37.3 GM	TOTAL FAT: .9 GM
Per serving: 174	PROTEIN: 3.7 GM	Saturated fat: .1 GM
Fat: 5%	DIETARY FIBER: 2.5 GM	Monounsaturated fat: .3 GM
Carbohydrates: 86%	SODIUM: 0 MG	
Protein: 9%	CHOLESTEROL: 0 MG	

Pyramid equivalencies: 1½ grains

Marsala-Poached Pears with Apricots

This dessert develops a sweeter, more aromatic flavor when it is made 1 or 2 days ahead.

4 *ripe but firm Bosc pears*	1 *tablespoon finely grated*
1 *cup Marsala*	*orange peel*
½ *cup fruit-sweetened apricot*	1 *tablespoon finely minced fresh*
preserves	*ginger*
¼ *cup water*	½ *cup chopped, dried apricots*

Peel the pears. Cut a thin slice from the bottom of each pear. Starting from the bottom, with a corer or small knife, hollow out each pear. Leave the stem end of the pear intact. Be careful not to puncture the walls of the pear.

In a small saucepan, stir together the Marsala, preserves, water, orange peel and ginger. Bring to a boil and immediately add the pears. If necessary, add enough water to just cover the pears. Reduce the heat to low and simmer for 20 minutes or until the pears are tender.

Remove the pan from the heat. Immediately take ½ cup of the hot poaching liquid and pour over the dried apricots in a small bowl. Allow the pears to cool in the remaining liquid. The pears and apricots will develop a more intense flavor if left to marinate overnight in the refrigerator. Drain the pears, reserving the poaching liquid. Gently press the chopped apricots into the core of each pear.

Serve the pears hot or cold with some of the poaching liquid poured over each pear.

YIELD: 4 servings

CALORIES   CARBOHYDRATES: 56.1 GM   TOTAL FAT: .6 GM
Per serving: 208   PROTEIN: 1.2 GM   Saturated fat: trace
Fat: 2%   DIETARY FIBER: 4.9 GM   Monounsaturated fat: .2 GM
Carbohydrates: 96%   SODIUM: 5 MG
Protein: 2%   CHOLESTEROL: 0 MG

Pyramid equivalencies: 2 fruits

18

Currying Favors

WHEN AMERICANS think of Indian cuisine, they think of curry. And when they think of curry, they think of a yellow blend of spices sold under the name "curry powder." Indian cuisine and curry have a lot more to contribute than just the flavor from that jar of spices. India offers a diverse and complex cuisine with a massive array of spices that from ancient times has had immense impact on the culinary habits of the rest of the world. It is, after all, Indian spices that motivated Christopher Columbus to set sail 500 years ago. American cooks may now discover that Indian spices offer marvelous choices for infusing flavor into dishes in which fat and salt have been taken away. Indian cuisine is anything but bland. This menu illustrates how Indian spices can be used effectively in low-fat cooking.

CURRYING FAVORS (MENU FOR 4)

Kitsch-ery
Chicken Curry
Lamb and Vegetable Kabob
Steamed Green Beans
Cucumber Raita
Chapati
Pineapple Chutney
Fresh Mint and Cilantro Chutney
After Dinner Treats

Additional Recipes:
Roasted Curry Powder
Quick Curry Powder
Enhanced Curry Powder
Garam Masala
Spiced Lentils
Fragrant Basmati Rice
Mulligatawny Soup
Yogurt Marinade
Raita Dressing

"Curry" is the Anglicized version of the South Indian word "kari," which means "sauce." An Englishman, returning from India, had his Indian servants prepare a blend of spices used in some of his favorite sauces. Back home, the spice mix became the rage of Victorian kitchens and the rest is history. In India, a blend of spices is called "masala" and "curry" denotes a sauce. But in the Western world, most diners think of curry as anything that has a flavor similar to what is in that little jar of yellow spices. Commercial curry powder is a blend of many spices, including the familiar flavors of cinnamon, black pepper, nutmeg, cloves and anise. Less familiar inclusions are coriander and cumin seeds, which also appear in chili powder blends. Curry powder is likely to contain a few spices that most cooks never use, except in curry powder. These include fenugreek, cardamom and turmeric. The latter spice is what gives curry powder its distinct yellow color. I've found that when I season with any of these less familiar spices, someone is apt to say, "It tastes like curry."

Indian cooks wouldn't think of using a premixed blend of spices to season their dishes. They might use all of the spices that are contained in a jar of curry powder, but they would vary the proportions, depending on the flavor they want to achieve. Curry dishes in America tend to taste a lot alike. In India, the variety is endless. Indians take their spices very seriously. Traditionally, Indian cooks buy whole spices, then roast them before grinding into a powder. This creates a richer, more robust and aromatic flavor. Electric spice grinders (coffee grinders) make this easy to do in the American kitchen. Because many cookbooks (including this one) call for the convenience of prepared curry powder, I've included recipes for homemade curry powder. Roasted Curry Powder uses whole spices that are to be roasted just before grinding. To appreciate its robust flavor, you should use it within a few days. Quick Curry

Powder utilizes spices already ground and commonly found in super-markets. Enhanced Curry Powder shows how you can take a commercially prepared curry powder and doctor it up a bit. As spices age, they tend to become bland or bitter. Adding a sweet spice such as cinnamon is one of the ways you can enliven the flavor of a curry powder. I've also included a recipe for Garam Masala, a sweet, peppery blend of spices that is used in Indian cuisine much the same way that Americans sprinkle black pepper on their food. It can be purchased commercially already mixed, but I think you will find the flavor especially delightful when made from freshly roasted spices.

When Columbus went searching for spices, European cuisine, at least among the wealthy classes, utilized far more spices than it now does. At that time, the style of seasoning was much closer to the profuse spicing that typifies contemporary Indian cooking. Some historians believe that heavy spicing was used to cover up tainted food.

When spices are used liberally, it is easier to create a balanced flavor if a high amount of fat or oil is also used. Compared to most countries of the world, Indians use far more fat and spices. More than half the calories in traditional Indian fare comes from fat. Fat mellows and synthesizes the flavors of the spices. To reduce the fat in Indian dishes, it is generally necessary to also reduce the amount of spices. Instead of frying spices to mellow them out, I usually cook the spices in wine or some other liquid. Adding the spices early in the cooking also helps.

My version of Chicken Curry uses both of these techniques. Curried chicken, in some form or another, has been popular in England and America since the middle of the Victorian period. Mulligatawny Soup has been on American menus for the same amount of time. Originally, this soup was made from leftover curried chicken. That's how I make mine.

Lamb and Vegetable Kabobs are spiced in a way that is typical of India and many Arab countries. Are they Indian or Arab? Because of centuries of Indian and Arab spice trading, it's impossible to know the origins for certain. Both Indian and Arab culinary traditions frequently utilize a Yogurt Marinade to flavor and tenderize meats. I like serving Lamb and Vegetable Kabob because it's a great way to make a little bit of meat seem like a lot.

One of India's most significant contributions to international cuisine is an endless repertoire of innovative rice and bean dishes. Poverty and vegetarian philosophies have turned simple grain and legume cookery into an art form. One of India's most famous dishes is a blend of rice, lentils and spices cooked together until the mixture becomes a creamy paste. Vegetables, fruits and nuts may be added to the blend and clarified butter or yogurt is frequently a topping. After mother's milk, this is often the first food given to infants. This is a popular dish among all classes and part of the cuisine of every country where India has had a major influence, including Pakistan, Afghanistan, Ethiopia and various Middle Eastern countries. The dish is called kedgeree, which may also be spelled khichari, khichdee, khichhari, khichri, kichree, kitchdi, kitcheri, kitchree, kitchri, koushari or koushry. For this book, I decided to add a new spelling, Kitsch-ery. In my version of Kitsch-ery, the rice and lentils are cooked separately and then assembled together with a yogurt topping. By itself, I call the rice Fragrant Rice because it uses the highly aromatic basmati rice. Most of the spices are cooked with the lentils. The Spiced Lentils can also be served as a separate dish.

It is nearly impossible to create authentic, traditional Indian cuisine that is low in fat, because frying is the dominant cooking method. However, some vegetable dishes are prepared by a type of steaming technique, although clarified butter will likely be added. Steamed Green Beans features a water-based method without the added fat.

Spicy foods require a complementary balance of mild foods. Indian cuisine offers a variety of such dishes that are now popular all over the world. Yogurt is a cool contrast to fiery dishes. Indians adore raitas, yogurt-based salads with fresh fruits or vegetables. Cucumber Raita is popular in many countries. The Raita Dressing can be used for other salads as well. Plain bread will also soothe the palate. Chapati is a humble whole wheat griddle bread, similar to pita, that is a frequent Indian accompaniment. Chutneys, a kind of piquant sweet and sour relish, are a tantalizing condiment that balance an Indian meal. Pineapple Chutney is a cooked chutney, the kind that most Americans know. Chutney can also be raw, sort of like a finely minced salsa. Fresh Mint and Cilantro Chutney represents that variety.

In addition to desserts, Indians often serve dried fruits and nuts at the conclusion of a meal. Cardamom seeds are offered as a kind of after-dinner mint. For this feast of Indian flavors, I decided to forgo a dessert and offer a simple plate of After Dinner Treats to serve as a palate refresher.

Currying Favors is a feast of many flavors. If you prepared all of the dishes on the menu, you will have a grand meal. You can omit some of the dishes and still have plenty of food. The nutrient analysis is provided for a variety of combinations: a vegetarian menu, a curried chicken dinner, a dinner with lamb and a grand feast with all the dishes.

NUTRIENT ANALYSIS FOR CURRYING FAVORS VEGETARIAN

Analysis includes 1 serving of Kitsch-ery, Steamed Green Beans, Cucumber Raita, Pineapple Chutney, Fresh Mint and Cilantro Chutney and After Dinner Treats. The total for the meal also includes two servings of Chapati.

CALORIES	CARBOHYDRATES: 151.0 GM	TOTAL FAT: 10.1 GM
For total	PROTEIN: 31.9 GM	Saturated fat: 1.2 GM
meal: 765	DIETARY FIBER: 18.3 GM	Monounsaturated fat: 5.4 GM
Fat: 11%	SODIUM: 332 MG	
Carbohydrates: 74%	CHOLESTEROL: 3 MG	
Protein: 15%		

Pyramid equivalencies: 3¼ grains, 2½ vegetables, 2 fruits, ¾ dairy, ½ protein

NUTRIENT ANALYSIS FOR CURRYING FAVORS CHICKEN

The nutrient analysis for this menu includes all of the dishes for the vegetarian menu and the Chicken Curry.

CALORIES	CARBOHYDRATES: 174.0 GM	TOTAL FAT: 14.1 GM
For total	PROTEIN: 62.7 GM	Saturated fat: 2.2 GM
meal: 1,007	DIETARY FIBER: 22.0 GM	Monounsaturated fat: 6.6 GM
Fat: 12%	SODIUM: 568 MG	
Carbohydrates: 65%	CHOLESTEROL: 76 MG	
Protein: 23%		

Pyramid equivalencies: 3¼ grains, 4½ vegetables, 2¼ fruits, 1 dairy, 1½ proteins

NUTRIENT ANALYSIS FOR CURRYING FAVORS LAMB

The nutrient analysis for this menu includes all of the dishes for the vegetarian menu and the Lamb and Vegetable Kabob.

CALORIES   CARBOHYDRATES: 160.0 GM   TOTAL FAT: 16.5 GM
For total   PROTEIN: 58.6 GM   Saturated fat: 3.7 GM
   meal: 966   DIETARY FIBER: 20.5 GM   Monounsaturated fat: 5.4 GM
Fat: 14%   SODIUM: 426 MG
Carbohydrates: 63%   CHOLESTEROL: 83 MG
Protein: 23%

Pyramid equivalencies: 3¼ grains, 4½ vegetables, 2 fruits, 1 dairy, 1½ proteins

NUTRIENT ANALYSIS FOR CURRYING FAVORS FEAST

The nutrient analysis for this menu includes all of the dishes for the vegetarian menu and the Chicken Curry and Lamb and Vegetable Kabob.

CALORIES   CARBOHYDRATES: 183.0 GM   TOTAL FAT: 20.4 GM
For total   PROTEIN: 89.4 GM   Saturated fat: 4.7 GM
   meal: 1,209   DIETARY FIBER: 24.2 GM   Monounsaturated fat: 6.6 GM
Fat: 14%   SODIUM: 661 MG
Carbohydrates: 58%   CHOLESTEROL: 156 MG
Protein: 28%

Pyramid equivalencies: 3¼ grains, 6½ vegetables, 2¼ fruits, 1 dairy, 2½ proteins

Roasted Curry Powder

Roasting whole spices, then grinding them, results in a richly aromatic flavor that far surpasses commercially prepared ground spices. The sooner the spices are used after roasting and grinding, the better the flavor will be.

      3 tablespoons coriander seeds   *1 teaspoon mustard seeds*
      1 3-inch cinnamon stick   *1 tablespoon ground turmeric*
      1 tablespoon cumin seeds   *1 tablespoon ground ginger*
      2 teaspoons fenugreek seeds   *½ teaspoon cayenne pepper*
      1 teaspoon cardamom seeds   *½ teaspoon ground nutmeg*
      6 whole cloves

Combine the coriander seeds, cinnamon stick, cumin seeds, fenugreek seeds, cardamom seeds, cloves and mustard seeds in a nonstick frying pan. Turn the pan to high heat and gently slide back and forth, constantly moving the seeds in the pan. Roast the seeds about 2 minutes or until they just begin to change color.

Transfer the roasted seeds to a spice or clean coffee grinder and grind to a powder. Mix with the remaining spices and transfer to a dry, airtight container. Store in a dry, dark place until ready to use.

Used in cooking, spices add negligible calories and nutrients.

Quick Curry Powder

Using common ground spices, this curry powder can be mixed together quickly. Use in the same way you would use commercially prepared curry powders.

3 tablespoons ground coriander	¼ teaspoon ground cloves
1 tablespoon ground ginger	¼ teaspoon ground nutmeg
1 tablespoon ground cumin	¼ teaspoon cayenne pepper
1 teaspoon ground cinnamon	¼ teaspoon ground black pepper
¼ teaspoon ground fennel or anise	¼ teaspoon ground turmeric

Blend together all of the spices and transfer to a dry, airtight container. Store in a dry, dark place until ready to use.

Used in cooking, spices add negligible calories and nutrients.

Enhanced Curry Powder

When a commercially prepared curry powder seems too bitter, which usually means too much turmeric, add ginger and cinnamon to mellow it out. If the powder is a little flat, I may also add some cayenne pepper.

> 3 tablespoons commercially prepared curry powder
> 1 teaspoon ground ginger
>
> ½ teaspoon ground cinnamon
> ¼ teaspoon cayenne pepper, optional

Blend together all of the ingredients and transfer to a dry, airtight container. Store in a dry, dark place until ready to use. Omit the cayenne pepper if the curry powder is already quite piquant.

Used in cooking, spices add negligible calories and nutrients.

Garam Masala

This spice blend brings a faintly sweet, peppery flavor to foods. This can be used in the same way black pepper is typically sprinkled over dishes.

> 1 three-inch cinnamon stick
> 2 tablespoons whole cumin seeds
> 2 tablespoons whole black peppercorns
>
> 2 tablespoons whole coriander seeds
> 1 tablespoon whole cardamom seeds
> 1 tablespoon whole cloves

Combine all of the ingredients in a nonstick frying pan. Turn the pan to high heat and gently slide back and forth, constantly moving the seeds in the pan. Roast the seeds about 2 minutes or until they just begin to change color.

Transfer the roasted seeds to a spice or clean coffee grinder and grind to a powder. Transfer to a dry, airtight container. Store in a dry, dark place until ready to use.

Used in cooking, spices add negligible calories and nutrients.

Kitsch-ery

Rice and lentils cooked together to form a porridgelike consistency is a classic dish of India. In this contemporary version, the two products are cooked separately, maintaining distinctly individual textures and flavors. Both can be served as independent dishes or mounded together to form a fascinating vegetarian entrée.

> *1 recipe Spiced Lentils (recipe follows)*
> *1 recipe Fragrant Basmati Rice (recipe follows)*
>
> *1 cup plain nonfat yogurt*
> *4 sprigs fresh cilantro*

Prepare the Spiced Lentils and Fragrant Basmati Rice as directed in the recipes that follow. Mound the rice on a large platter. Use a spoon to create a large cavity in the middle of the rice. Fill the center with the Spiced Lentils. Spoon the yogurt over the lentils and decorate with sprigs of cilantro. Serve immediately while hot.

YIELD: 4 servings

CALORIES
Per serving: 366
Fat: 11%
Carbohydrates: 71%
Protein: 18%

CARBOHYDRATES: 69.2 GM
PROTEIN: 18.0 GM
DIETARY FIBER: 8.0 GM
SODIUM: 169 MG
CHOLESTEROL: 1 MG

TOTAL FAT: 4.7 GM
Saturated fat: .5 GM
Monounsaturated fat: 2.8 GM

Pyramid equivalencies: 1¼ grains, ½ vegetable, ½ fruit, ½ dairy, ½ protein

Spiced Lentils

This protein-rich dish is delicious by itself or as part of Kitsch-ery (previous recipe). The dry spices can be replaced by 2 teaspoons of one of the homemade curry powders introduced at the beginning of the chapter.

¼ cup cold water	½ teaspoon ground cumin
1 large yellow onion, peeled and diced	¼ teaspoon ground cinnamon
1 cup chopped fresh mushrooms	¼ teaspoon ground cloves
4 cloves garlic, finely minced	¼ teaspoon ground turmeric
2 teaspoons low-sodium soy sauce	¼ teaspoon ground black pepper
½ teaspoon ground coriander seed	2 cups boiling water
	1 cup dry lentils
	2 tablespoons finely minced fresh parsley, mint or cilantro

Combine the cold water, onion, mushrooms, garlic, soy sauce and all of the dry spices in a nonstick saucepan. Cover with a tight-fitting lid and cook at low temperature for 20 minutes.

Meanwhile, pour the boiling water over the lentils and let stand. When the onion mixture has cooked for 20 minutes, add the lentils in water. Stirring regularly, continue cooking at low temperature until most of the liquid has evaporated and the lentils are tender. Serve immediately with the fresh herb sprinkled over the lentils.

YIELD: 4 servings

CALORIES	CARBOHYDRATES: 25.5 GM	TOTAL FAT: .2 GM
Per serving: 132	PROTEIN: 9.4 GM	Saturated fat: trace
Fat: 2%	DIETARY FIBER: 5.9 GM	Monounsaturated fat: trace
Carbohydrates: 72%	SODIUM: 119 MG	
Protein: 26%	CHOLESTEROL: 0 MG	

Pyramid equivalencies: ½ vegetable, ½ protein

Fragrant Basmati Rice

Use this dish to create Kitsch-ery (recipe on page 209) or as a singular accompaniment to the Chicken Curry or Lamb and Vegetable Kabobs.

2 teaspoons brown sugar	1 tablespoon finely grated fresh
2½ cups water	orange peel
1¼ cups Wehani or brown	¼ cup sliced almonds
basmati rice	2 tablespoons finely minced
½ cup dry, diced apricots	fresh cilantro or parsley

Preheat oven to 375°F. In a saucepan, dissolve the brown sugar in the water. Bring the water to a boil. Add the rice, dry apricots and orange peel. When the water has returned to a boil, transfer the mixture to a baking dish. Cover tightly and bake for 45 minutes.

Stir in the sliced almonds, garnish with the minced cilantro or parsley and serve hot. Vegetables and meats can also be cooked in the casserole with the rice and lentils. The dish makes a superb filling for stuffing vegetables.

YIELD: 4 servings

CALORIES	CARBOHYDRATES: 29.3 GM	TOTAL FAT: 4.4 GM
Per serving: 202	PROTEIN: 5.4 GM	Saturated fat: .4 GM
Fat: 18%	DIETARY FIBER: 2.1 GM	Monounsaturated fat: 2.8 GM
Carbohydrates: 72%	SODIUM: 8 MG	
Protein: 10%	CHOLESTEROL: 0 MG	

Pyramid equivalencies: 1¼ grains, ½ fruit

Chicken Curry

The dry spices can be replaced by 2 teaspoons of one of the homemade curry powders featured in the beginning of the chapter.

½ cup dry sherry
1 tablespoon low-sodium soy sauce
1½ cups chopped onions
2 cloves garlic, finely minced
2 teaspoons finely minced fresh ginger
¾ teaspoon ground cumin
¾ teaspoon ground coriander
½ teaspoon ground cayenne pepper
½ teaspoon ground turmeric
¼ teaspoon ground fennel seed
1 green apple, cored and chopped

4 chicken breast halves, bone intact, skin and fat removed
1 green or red bell pepper, seeded and chopped
2 cups carrots, sliced in ¼-inch-thick rounds
1 or more tablespoons unsalted tomato paste
2 teaspoons fresh lime juice
1 teaspoon Garam Masala (recipe on page 208)
½ cup plain nonfat yogurt
2 tablespoons finely chopped fresh cilantro

Pour the wine and soy sauce into a nonstick skillet. Add enough water to just cover the bottom of the pan. Add the onions, garlic, fresh ginger, cumin, coriander, cayenne, turmeric and fennel seed. Cover with a tight-fitting lid and cook at low temperature for 20 minutes.

Stir the onion mixture and arrange the chicken breasts over the top. Pour the apple, bell pepper and carrot slices over the chicken. If necessary, add enough water to create a depth of ¼ inch. Cover the pot and cook at moderate temperature for 15 minutes. Remove the lid, turn the chicken pieces, stir in the tomato paste, lime juice and Garam Masala and continue cooking until the chicken is tender and the sauce has thickened, about 10 minutes. If necessary, add more water while the chicken is cooking. When the chicken is done, if the sauce is quite thin, stir in a little more tomato paste.

To serve, arrange the chicken on a heated serving platter or individual plates. Pour the sauce and vegetables over and around the chicken breasts. Whisk the yogurt until it is smooth and creamy. Drizzle the yogurt over the top of the sauce. Immediately sprinkle with the fresh cilantro and serve. Accompany the chicken with plain or spiced rice.

YIELD: 4 servings

CALORIES	CARBOHYDRATES: 22.4 GM	TOTAL FAT: 3.9 GM
Per serving: 242	PROTEIN: 30.8 GM	Saturated fat: 1.0 GM
Fat: 14%	DIETARY FIBER: 3.7 GM	Monounsaturated fat: 1.2 GM
Carbohydrates: 36%	SODIUM: 236 MG	
Protein: 50%	CHOLESTEROL: 74 MG	

Pyramid equivalencies: 2 vegetables, ¼ fruit, ¼ dairy, 1 protein

Mulligatawny Soup

This Anglo-Indian soup is made from leftover Chicken Curry.

½ recipe cooked Chicken Curry
(previous recipe)
5 cups unsalted, defatted
chicken broth (divided use)
1 cup cooked brown basmati
rice (or other cooked rice)
1 teaspoon Garam Masala
(recipe on page 208)

¼ cup freshly chopped cilantro
or parsley
1 green apple, freshly diced, or 1
not fully ripened peach or 1
nectarine, optional

Remove the chicken breasts from the prepared Chicken Curry. Dice the meat, discard the bone and return the meat to the Chicken Curry mixture. Transfer the Chicken Curry to a large pot, add 3 cups of the chicken broth and heat through.

Meanwhile, place the rice in a blender jar with the remaining 2 cups of the chicken broth. Puree until smooth and creamy. Stir the puree into the pot to thicken the soup. Taste the soup to determine if you want to add more Garam Masala. Refrigerate the soup for later use or heat through and serve immediately.

Garnish each bowl with freshly chopped cilantro and, if desired, freshly diced fruit.

YIELD: 8 servings

CALORIES   CARBOHYDRATES: 15.5 GM   TOTAL FAT: 1.0 GM

Per serving: 109   PROTEIN: 10.1 GM   Saturated fat: .3 GM

Fat: 8%   DIETARY FIBER: 1.2 GM   Monounsaturated fat: .3 GM

Carbohydrates: 56%   SODIUM: 84 MG

Protein: 36%   CHOLESTEROL: 18 MG

Pyramid equivalencies: ¼ grain, ¼ vegetable, ¼ fruit, ⅛ protein

Lamb and Vegetable Kabob

This can be prepared on your barbecue or under the broiler.

1 *pound boneless leg of lamb, trimmed of fat, cut in 1½-inch cubes*

1 *recipe Yogurt Marinade (recipe follows)*

1 *head cauliflower, cut into large florets*

2 *carrots, cut in 1½-inch-thick rounds*

2 *tablespoons finely minced fresh mint or cilantro*

½ *teaspoon Garam Masala (recipe on page 208)*

In a small bowl, toss the lamb with the Yogurt Marinade and refrigerate for 4 hours. Stir occasionally.

Meanwhile, steam the cauliflower and carrots for 4 or 5 minutes or until just tender but still quite crisp. When the lamb has marinated for 3 hours, add the vegetables to the marinade.

Prepare a barbecue and let the coals reach the white state or turn a stove broiler to the highest heat. Thread chunks of lamb onto skewers alternately with cauliflower and carrot pieces. If using a broiler, place the skewers over a large flat baking dish so that the ends of the skewers hang over the edge of the pan. The meat and vegetables should not touch the bottom of the pan. Pour enough water in the pan to just cover the bottom. Broil the Kabob about 3 inches from the heat. Rotate the skewers every 3 or 4 minutes and cook until it is done to your taste. Sprinkle the fresh herb and Garam Masala over each skewer before serving.

YIELD: 4 servings

CALORIES   CARBOHYDRATES: 9.0 GM   TOTAL FAT: 6.3 GM
Per serving: 201   PROTEIN: 26.7 GM   Saturated fat: 2.5 GM
Fat: 29%   DIETARY FIBER: 2.2 GM   Monounsaturated fat: .2 GM
Carbohydrates: 18%   SODIUM: 93 MG
Protein: 53%   CHOLESTEROL: 81 MG

Pyramid equivalencies: 2 vegetables, 1 protein, ⅛ dairy

Yogurt Marinade

This marinade will bring a subtle, robust flavor to lamb, beef or chicken.

⅓ *cup plain nonfat yogurt*
1 *teaspoon ground cumin*
1 *teaspoon low-sodium soy sauce*
1 *teaspoon brown sugar*
1 *scallion, finely minced*

2 *tablespoons finely minced fresh cilantro*
2 *tablespoons finely minced fresh ginger*
1 *clove garlic, finely minced*

Whisk together all of the ingredients and refrigerate until ready to use. Do not make more than 24 hours ahead. Use with the Lamb and Vegetable Kabob (previous recipe).

YIELD: 4 servings

CALORIES   CARBOHYDRATES: 3.6 GM   TOTAL FAT: .2 GM
Per serving: 20   PROTEIN: 1.3 GM   Saturated fat: trace
Fat: 8%   DIETARY FIBER: .3 GM   Monounsaturated fat: trace
Carbohydrates: 67%   SODIUM: 16 MG
Protein: 25%   CHOLESTEROL: trace

Pyramid equivalencies: ⅛ dairy

Steamed Green Beans

The Indian way of steaming is different from the Chinese and Japanese approaches.

3 cups fresh green beans, cut   ½ teaspoon crushed fennel seed
   in 1-inch pieces   ⅛ teaspoon cayenne pepper
1 medium red onion, peeled   ½ cup plain nonfat yogurt
   and sliced into rings   2 teaspoons fresh lemon juice
1 tablespoon finely minced   ½ teaspoon paprika
   fresh ginger
1 teaspoon low-sodium soy
   sauce

Combine the beans, onion, ginger, soy sauce, fennel seed and cayenne in a saucepan. Add enough water to create a depth of ¼ inch. Cover the pan and simmer at low heat for 10 minutes. Check the pan occasionally to verify there is still liquid. If necessary, add more water and cook longer to get the beans tender. When the dish is complete, there should be very little liquid left. If necessary, increase the heat to evaporate the water. Serve the beans hot.

Whisk the yogurt to make it smooth and creamy. Transfer to a small serving bowl. Stir together the lemon juice and paprika. Drizzle the mixture over the yogurt. Serve the yogurt on the side as a sauce for the beans.

YIELD: 4 servings

CALORIES	CARBOHYDRATES: 10.9 GM	TOTAL FAT: .4 GM
Per serving: 56	PROTEIN: 3.5 GM	Saturated fat: .1 GM
Fat: 6%	DIETARY FIBER: 1.8 GM	Monounsaturated fat: .1 GM
Carbohydrates: 71%	SODIUM: 68 MG	
Protein: 23%	CHOLESTEROL: 1 MG	

Pyramid equivalencies: 1 vegetable, ¼ dairy

Cucumber Raita

This salad can also be made with raw zucchini, jicama and green apples.

1 large cucumber, peeled and
  diced
1 large tomato, diced

2 green onions, finely diced
1 recipe Raita Dressing (recipe
  follows)

Stir together the cucumber, tomato and onion. Let stand 10 minutes. Toss with the Raita Dressing and serve immediately.

YIELD: 4 servings

CALORIES	CARBOHYDRATES: 7.2 GM	TOTAL FAT: .2 GM
Per serving: 41	PROTEIN: 3.1 GM	Saturated fat: trace
Fat: 5%	DIETARY FIBER: 1.3 GM	Monounsaturated fat: trace
Carbohydrates: 66%	SODIUM: 39 MG	
Protein: 29%	CHOLESTEROL: 1 MG	

Pyramid equivalencies: 1 vegetable, ¼ dairy

Raita Dressing

In addition to being a salad dressing, this is delicious as a sauce for poached salmon.

½ cup plain nonfat yogurt
2 tablespoons dry nonfat milk
  powder
1½ teaspoons fresh lime juice
1 teaspoon finely minced fresh
  dill

1 teaspoon finely minced fresh
  mint
¼ teaspoon ground cumin
⅛ teaspoon liquid hot pepper
  sauce

Whisk together the yogurt and milk powder. Stir in the remaining ingredients and chill 1 hour before tossing with the salad.

YIELD: 4 servings

CALORIES	CARBOHYDRATES: 3.5 GM	TOTAL FAT: .1 GM
Per serving: 24	PROTEIN: 2.4 GM	Saturated fat: trace
Fat: 3%	DIETARY FIBER: trace	Monounsaturated fat: trace
Carbohydrates: 58%	SODIUM: 35 MG	
Protein: 39%	CHOLESTEROL: 1 MG	

Pyramid equivalencies: ¼ dairy

Chapati

This simple bread is baked in a skillet and served immediately. Its simple flavor is a pleasing contrast to other spicy, aromatic dishes.

1 cup whole wheat flour   *¼ to ½ cup water*

Sift the flour into a bowl. Remove ¼ cup of the flour and set aside. Make a well in the center of the flour and pour in ¼ cup of the water. Using your hands, mix together the flour and water. Vigorously knead the mixture so that it can be formed into a ball. If the dough is crumbly, add a little more water. You want the dough to be firm and smooth but not pasty.

Spread the remaining ¼ cup flour on a clean surface. Continually knead the flour for 10 minutes or until the dough is smooth and elastic. Re-form the dough into a ball and cover with a clean, damp towel. Let stand at room temperature for 30 minutes.

Divide the dough into 8 equal parts and form into individual balls. On a floured surface, roll each ball into a round, flat cake, about 5 inches in diameter. Cover the chapatis with waxed paper or a towel after each one is formed.

Heat a nonstick skillet or griddle at high temperature. When water immediately sizzles when dropped on the surface, you are ready to begin. Place a chapati on the surface. Use a spatula at the edge of the chapati to continually move it over the surface. Cook for about 1 minute or until the top begins to darken. Turn the chapati and continue cooking for another minute. Wearing a kitchen glove, or wrapping a clean towel around your hand, gently press down on the bread. Lift your hand and the bread will puff up. Use the spatula to slide the chapati onto a plate. Continue the process until complete. Because the chapatis taste best when warm, serve immediately.

YIELD: 8 servings

CALORIES	CARBOHYDRATES: 10.6 GM	TOTAL FAT: .3 GM
Per serving: 50	PROTEIN: 2.0 GM	Saturated fat: .1 GM
Fat: 4%	DIETARY FIBER: 1.9 GM	Monounsaturated fat: trace
Carbohydrates: 81%	SODIUM: 1 MG	
Protein: 15%	CHOLESTEROL: 0 MG	

Pyramid equivalencies: 1 grain

Pineapple Chutney

This cooked chutney is a tantalizing condiment for meats, curries and rice.

1 cup fresh pineapple, cut in
1-inch cubes
½ cup diced red onion
¼ cup frozen, unsweetened
apple juice concentrate
¼ cup apple cider vinegar
¼ cup raisins

1 tablespoon finely minced fresh
ginger
1 tablespoon brown sugar
1 teaspoon low-sodium soy sauce
2 cloves garlic, finely minced

Combine all of the ingredients in a saucepan and simmer at low temperature for 10 minutes or until the mixture has thickened. Store in the refrigerator until ready to use. Serve as a condiment, hot or cold.

YIELD: 4 servings

CALORIES   CARBOHYDRATES: 25.5 GM   TOTAL FAT: .3 GM
Per serving: 100   PROTEIN: 1.0 GM   Saturated fat: trace
Fat: 3%   DIETARY FIBER: 1.3 GM   Monounsaturated fat: trace
Carbohydrates: 93%   SODIUM: 50 MG
Protein: 4%   CHOLESTEROL: 0 MG

Pyramid equivalencies: 1 fruit

Fresh Mint and Cilantro Chutney

In India, raw chutneys are just as popular as cooked varieties.

- ¼ cup fresh lime juice
- ¼ cup water
- 1 cup fresh cilantro leaves
- 1 cup fresh mint leaves
- 2 green onions, diced
- 1 tablespoon finely minced fresh ginger
- ¼ teaspoon black pepper
- 1 teaspoon brown sugar
- 1 serrano chile, seeded and diced

Combine all of the ingredients in a blender and puree until smooth. Serve as condiment for curries, rice or grilled foods.

YIELD: 4 servings

CALORIES   CARBOHYDRATES: 3.7 GM   TOTAL FAT: trace
Per serving: 13   PROTEIN: .4 GM   Saturated fat: trace
Fat: 2%   DIETARY FIBER: .1 GM   Monounsaturated fat: trace
Carbohydrates: 87%   SODIUM: 3 MG
Protein: 11%   CHOLESTEROL: 0 MG

Pyramid equivalencies: No equivalencies

After Dinner Treats

This is the Indian version of after-dinner mints.

>   *8 whole dates*   *4 whole cardamom pods*
>   *8 whole almonds, shelled*

   Arrange 2 dates, 2 almonds and a cardamom pod on small individual plates. Set a plate for each diner at the conclusion of a meal.

YIELD: 4 servings

CALORIES   CARBOHYDRATES: 13.9 GM   TOTAL FAT: 3.9 GM
Per serving: 90   PROTEIN: 1.8 GM   Saturated fat: .4 GM
Fat: 36%   DIETARY FIBER: 2.1 GM   Monounsaturated fat: 2.4 GM
Carbohydrates: 56%   SODIUM: 1 MG
Protein: 8%   CHOLESTEROL: 0 MG

Pyramid equivalencies: ½ fruit

19

Farmhouse
Favorites

MEMORIES OF my mother's farmhouse kitchen were the starting place for this menu. Mom's cooking was simple fare that was rarely seasoned with anything more than a little salt, pepper or butter. Although her dishes were often bland, she made certain that there was plenty to eat and a balance of foods. Mom would laugh at hearing that her weekly meat loaf inspired an elaborate Fruit-Crusted Meat Loaf. Her version didn't have much more than ground beef, saltine crackers and ketchup.

FARMHOUSE FAVORITES (MENU FOR 4)

Fruit-Crusted Meat Loaf
Brussels Sprouts with Caraway Sauce
Two Bean Medley
Green Corn Spoon Bread
Banana Sesame Bread

Additional Recipes:
Orchard Yams
Fruit Crust and Topping

Every late summer and fall, my mother would can or freeze bushel baskets of peaches, pears and plums. It was always a mad rush to complete the task. You had to wait for the fruit to ripen fully, then quickly put it away before the fruit spoiled. I doubt that I'll ever take the time to do my own canning, but I do long for the wonderful, sweet aromas of the season. Somehow memories of Mom's meat loaf and canned peaches came together to inspire Fruit-Crusted Meat Loaf.

Fruit-Crusted Meat Loaf has many of the same flavors as the Mexican meat concoction picadillo. And like that dish, it has a lot of ingredients and takes a while to make. I've tried to simplify the process by creating steps that can be made ahead. The meat loaf is multilayered, with a central filling of yam and apple. This filling can be served as a dish by itself, which I call Orchard Yams. Double the filling recipe and you have two separate dishes. Likewise, the fruit topping that crusts the meat loaf can be prepared as a separate dish. Double the recipe for Fruit Crust and Topping and you have a topping for meat loaf, pancakes or frozen yogurt.

My mother always put everything on the table at once. Even when entertaining, there were never separate courses, except for dessert. Although that isn't how I usually entertain, I decided to present Farmhouse Favorites in my mother's style. She usually served salads only in the summertime. Other months, we would have a second vegetable side dish. Brussels sprouts were much too exotic a vegetable for my mother's taste, but they are something I've learned to enjoy. Brussels Sprouts with Caraway Sauce can be served hot or cold, as a salad or a side dish. Green beans were the favorite vegetable in our family. My Two Bean Medley mixes green and yellow beans with a red sauce. My mother wanted me to be an art teacher. I'm sure she would claim that my penchant for colorful dishes comes from my days in art class. Green Corn Spoon Bread, however, doesn't refer to its color. In earlier times, dried corn, hominy and cornmeal dishes were the most common preparations of corn. Fresh corn was called "green corn." Green Corn Spoon Bread mixes fresh corn and dry corn in a variation on an historical American dish. The meal concludes with Banana Sesame Bread, a mildly sweet bread that serves well as a dessert and as an accompaniment to salads and slightly sweet entrées. I also like it toasted for breakfast.

My mother always made more than enough. Tonight's dinner was tomorrow's lunch. This menu was designed for 4, but I created recipes to assure leftover meat loaf and banana bread. That's how Mom did it.

NUTRIENT INFORMATION FOR FARMHOUSE FAVORITES

The nutrient information includes 1 serving each of Fruit-Crusted Meat Loaf, Brussels Sprouts with Caraway Sauce, Two Bean Medley, Green Corn Spoon Bread and Banana Sesame Bread.

CALORIES	CARBOHYDRATES: 168.9 GM	TOTAL FAT: 10.0 GM
For the total	PROTEIN: 44.3 GM	Saturated fat: 1.8 GM
meal: 892	DIETARY FIBER: 15.4 GM	Monounsaturated fat: 3.6 GM
Fat: 10%	SODIUM: 695 MG	
Carbohydrates: 71%	CHOLESTEROL: 42 MG	
Protein: 19%		

Pyramid equivalencies: 4 grains, 3 vegetables, 1 fruit, ⅔ dairy, 1⅓ proteins

Fruit-Crusted Meat Loaf

This is a layered loaf, beginning with a base of richly flavored meat, a filling of yams, another layer of meat and a final fruit topping. The yams and fruit topping can be prepared 1 to 2 days ahead.

1 recipe Orchard Yams (recipe on page 226)
1 recipe Fruit Crust and Topping (recipe on page 227)
½ small red apple, diced
½ small peach, diced
½ cup diced red onion
½ cup diced red bell pepper
¼ cup finely diced celery
4 cloves garlic, finely minced
⅓ cup unsalted, defatted chicken broth or water
1 tablespoon low-sodium soy sauce
1 tablespoon crushed dry sage
¼ teaspoon black pepper
¼ teaspoon cayenne pepper
¼ teaspoon allspice
¼ teaspoon ground nutmeg
⅓ cup tomato puree
3 tablespoons frozen, unsweetened apple juice concentrate
2 tablespoons apple cider vinegar
2 egg whites
¾ pound extra-lean ground beef
¾ pound ground turkey breast
1½ cups whole wheat bread crumbs (or more)

Prepare the recipes for Orchard Yams and Fruit Crust and Topping before beginning the loaf. These components need to cool enough for you to handle.

For the loaf, combine the diced apple, peach, onion, pepper, celery and garlic with the broth. Simmer at moderate temperature until the vegetables are tender but crisp. Just before removing the fruit and vegetable mixture from the heat, stir in the soy sauce, sage, black pepper, cayenne pepper, allspice and nutmeg. Meanwhile, in a large bowl, blend together the tomato puree, apple juice concentrate, vinegar and egg whites. Add the ground beef and turkey breast and mix well. Add the vegetable and fruit mixture and stir until well incorporated. Slowly add the bread crumbs, ½ cup at a time, mixing until each batch is thoroughly incorporated. The loaf should be moist but not sticky. Use the crumbs to create the right texture.

Spray a 9-by-5-inch loaf pan with nonstick cooking spray. Spread half of the mixture over the bottom of the pan. Evenly distribute one recipe of Orchard Yams over the meat mixture. Spread the remaining half of the meat mixture over the yams. Using a spatula, gently press the meat mixture into the yam layer.

Strain the Fruit Crust and Topping, separating the fruit slices from the cooking liquid. Arrange the fruit slices over the meat loaf. Spoon a little of the liquid over the top of the fruit. Set the remaining juice aside.

Bake the loaf at 350°F. for 45 minutes. Meanwhile, cook the remaining liquid from the fruit until it is a thick syrup. After the loaf has baked for 45 minutes, pour the syrup over the top and bake for 15 minutes more. Remove the loaf from the oven and let stand 10 to 15 minutes before serving.

YIELD: 8 servings

CALORIES	CARBOHYDRATES: 62.4 GM	TOTAL FAT: 4.4 GM
Per serving: 360	PROTEIN: 21.9 GM	Saturated fat: 1.0 GM
Fat: 10%	DIETARY FIBER: 3.8 GM	Monounsaturated fat: 1.9 GM
Carbohydrates: 67%	SODIUM: 180 MG	
Protein: 23%	CHOLESTEROL: 40 MG	

Pyramid equivalencies: 1 grain, ½ fruit, ⅔ vegetable, 1 protein

Orchard Yams

I usually double this recipe. I serve it one day as a vegetable dish and a couple of days later as the filling in Fruit-Crusted Meat Loaf (previous recipe). This recipe is the amount needed for the meat loaf recipe.

1 apple, cored and sliced	*1 teaspoon ground cinnamon*
1 large yam or sweet potato, peeled and cut in ¾-inch cubes	*¼ cup raisins*
	¼ cup blanched slivered almonds
1 tablespoon fruit-sweetened peach preserves	

Place the apple slices and yam cubes on a steamer rack. Steam in a pot, using as little water as possible. When the yams are tender, usually about 8 minutes, remove from the heat and immediately transfer to a bowl.

In a separate small bowl, stir together the peach preserves, cinnamon and 2 tablespoons of the water from the steamer. Immediately toss with the hot yams. Stir in the raisins and almond slivers. Serve immediately or allow to cool a few minutes for filling in Fruit-Crusted Meat Loaf (previous recipe).

Nutrient information is based on 4 servings as a side dish. As a filling in the meat loaf, it serves 8 persons.

YIELD: 4 servings

CALORIES	CARBOHYDRATES: 34.8 GM	TOTAL FAT: 4.0 GM
Per serving: 175	PROTEIN: 2.7 GM	Saturated fat: .4 GM
Fat: 19%	DIETARY FIBER: 1.9 GM	Monounsaturated fat: 2.4 GM
Carbohydrates: 75%	SODIUM: 7 MG	
Protein: 6%	CHOLESTEROL: 0 MG	

Pyramid equivalencies: 1 vegetable, ⅔ fruit

Fruit Crust and Topping

This recipe was created as topping for the Fruit-Crusted Meat Loaf. It also happens to be delicious on frozen yogurt, pancakes and gingerbread.

½ cup dry sherry
⅓ cup fruit-sweetened peach
  preserves
⅓ cup water

¼ teaspoon powdered ginger
½ small red apple, cut in slices
½ small peach, cut in slices

Stir together the sherry, preserves, water and ginger in a small pan. Bring the mixture to a boil and add the fruit slices. Reduce the temperature to low and simmer 5 minutes or until the fruit is tender but not mushy. Use as a topping for Fruit-Crusted Meat Loaf or other dish. May be reheated for later use or served cold.

Nutrient information is based on 4 servings as a topping for pancakes or other dish. As a topping for the meat loaf, it serves 8 persons.

YIELD: 4 servings

CALORIES
Per serving: 74
Fat: 1%
Carbohydrates: 98%
Protein: 1%

CARBOHYDRATES: 21.2 GM
PROTEIN: .2 GM
DIETARY FIBER: .6 GM
SODIUM: 55 MG
CHOLESTEROL: 0 MG

TOTAL FAT: .1 GM
Saturated fat: trace
Monounsaturated fat: trace

Pyramid equivalencies: 1 fruit

Brussels Sprouts with Caraway Sauce

This simple dish can be served as a salad or a side dish.

2½ cups fresh Brussels sprouts   *1 recipe Caraway Sauce (recipe*
      Water for steaming   *follows)*

   Wash and trim the ends of the Brussels sprouts. Fill a pot suitable for steaming with ½ inch water. Set a steamer basket in the pot and fill with the sprouts. Cover and steam for 8 minutes or until the sprouts are tender. Toss with the Caraway Sauce, which, like the sprouts, can be served warm or cold.

YIELD: 4 servings

CALORIES   CARBOHYDRATES: 9.5 GM   TOTAL FAT: .7 GM
Per serving: 44   PROTEIN: 2.4 GM   Saturated fat: .1 GM
Fat: 11%   DIETARY FIBER: 3.4 GM   Monounsaturated fat: .1 GM
Carbohydrates: 71%   SODIUM: 18 MG
Protein: 18%   CHOLESTEROL: 0 MG

Pyramid equivalencies: 1 vegetable

Caraway Sauce

This tangy sauce can be used with almost any member of the cabbage family, Jerusalem artichoke hearts, green beans, turnips and even potatoes.

1 tablespoon frozen, unsweetened orange juice concentrate	*2 tablespoons unsalted Dijon-style mustard*
1 tablespoon fresh lemon juice	*1 tablespoon water*
	2 teaspoons caraway seeds

Whisk together all of the ingredients and refrigerate until ready to use. May be served cold or warm as a sauce for vegetables.

YIELD: 4 servings

CALORIES	CARBOHYDRATES: 2.7 GM	TOTAL FAT: .3 GM
Per serving: 14	PROTEIN: .4 GM	Saturated fat: trace
Fat: 16%	DIETARY FIBER: .1 GM	Monounsaturated fat: .1 GM
Carbohydrates: 72%	SODIUM: 1 MG	
Protein: 12%	CHOLESTEROL: 0 MG	

Pyramid equivalencies: No equivalencies

Two Bean Medley

Green beans and wax beans give this dish a showy appearance. Of course, it can be made with just one variety of bean if you like.

1 red onion, peeled, quartered and thinly sliced	*1 tablespoon capers, rinsed and drained*
4 plum tomatoes, coarsely chopped	*½ pound yellow wax beans, trimmed and cut in 1½-inch pieces*
2 cloves garlic, minced	
½ cup unsalted, defatted chicken stock or water	*½ pound green beans, trimmed and cut in 1½-inch pieces*
¼ teaspoon ground black pepper	*2 teaspoons finely minced fresh marjoram or oregano*

Combine the onion, tomatoes, garlic, stock, and black pepper in pot. Cover tightly and simmer at low temperature for 20 minutes. Add the beans and capers, cover and continue cooking for 15 minutes or until the beans are tender but crisp. Stir in the fresh herb and serve immediately.

YIELD: 4 servings

CALORIES	CARBOHYDRATES: 11.4 GM	TOTAL FAT: .5 GM
Per serving: 54	PROTEIN: 3.1 GM	Saturated fat: .1 GM
Fat: 8%	DIETARY FIBER: 2.5 GM	Monounsaturated fat: .1 GM
Carbohydrates: 72%	SODIUM: 143 MG	
Protein: 20%	CHOLESTEROL: 0 MG	

Pyramid equivalencies: 1¼ vegetables

Green Corn Spoon Bread

This dish, in some form or another, has been around since the founding of the colonies.

1 cup diced yellow onion	1 cup yellow cornmeal
1 cup frozen corn kernels	2 tablespoons brown sugar
¼ cup dry sherry	½ teaspoon baking soda
5 egg whites (3 egg whites in one bowl and 2 in another)	¼ teaspoon ground black pepper
	¼ teaspoon cayenne pepper
1 cup plain nonfat yogurt	1¼ cups boiling water
½ cup fluid nonfat milk	

Place the onion, corn and sherry in a nonstick skillet over moderate heat. Stir continually until the onion and corn are lightly browned and most of the moisture has evaporated. Set aside.

In a medium bowl, whisk together 2 of the egg whites, yogurt and nonfat milk. Add the onion and corn kernels and mix well. Set aside.

In a large bowl, stir together the cornmeal, brown sugar, baking soda, black pepper and cayenne pepper. Pour the boiling water over the cornmeal and stir vigorously until it is evenly blended. Add the onion and yogurt and mix well. Set aside.

Beat the 3 remaining egg whites until soft peaks form. Fold the egg whites into the batter. Immediately transfer the mixture to a 9-inch square baking dish sprayed with nonstick cooking spray. Bake at 375°F. for 30 minutes. It should be set, but soft and moist inside. If necessary, bake for a few minutes more.

YIELD: 4 servings

CALORIES
Per serving: 248
Fat: 3%
Carbohydrates: 76%
Protein: 21%

CARBOHYDRATES: 48.2 GM
PROTEIN: 13.3 GM
DIETARY FIBER: 3.4 GM
SODIUM: 238 MG
CHOLESTEROL: 2 MG

TOTAL FAT: .8 GM
Saturated fat: .2 GM
Monounsaturated fat: .1 GM

Pyramid equivalencies: 2 grains, ¼ vegetable, ⅔ dairy, ⅓ protein

Banana Sesame Bread

This versatile bread is sweet enough to be a dessert, but not so sweet that it detracts as an accompaniment to other dishes.

1 cup unbleached all-purpose flour
½ cup whole wheat flour
1 teaspoon baking soda
½ teaspoon baking powder
½ teaspoon cinnamon
2 large ripe bananas
1 tablespoon finely grated orange peel
1 cup brown sugar, firmly packed

¼ cup plain nonfat yogurt
2 egg whites
2 tablespoons water
1 tablespoon dark sesame oil
1 tablespoon canola oil
½ teaspoon banana extract
1 to 2 tablespoons fresh orange juice
1 tablespoon sesame seeds

Sift together and mix well the white flour, whole wheat flour, baking soda, baking powder and cinnamon. Set aside.

Mash until smooth or puree the bananas. Add the grated orange peel and set aside.

With a mixer or food processor blend until smooth and creamy the brown sugar, yogurt, egg whites, water, sesame oil, canola oil and banana extract. Mix in the flour mixture. When smooth and fully incorporated, mix in the banana puree. When thoroughly mixed, pour into a small loaf pan sprayed with nonstick cooking spray. Bake at 350°F. for 30 minutes or until an inserted toothpick comes out clean.

Immediately after taking the bread from the oven, loosen the edges of the bread with a spatula and remove the loaf from the pan. While the bread is still very hot, brush the top of the bread with the orange juice and sprinkle the sesame seeds over the moist surface. Before serving, let stand for 30 minutes; if not for immediate use, after 30 minutes of cooling, wrap in plastic and refrigerate until ready to serve. Will keep 3 or 4 days in the refrigerator.

YIELD: 10 servings

CALORIES	CARBOHYDRATES: 36.9 GM	TOTAL FAT: 3.6 GM
Per serving: 186	PROTEIN: 3.5 GM	Saturated fat: .4 GM
Fat: 17%	DIETARY FIBER: 2.3 GM	Monounsaturated fat: 1.5 GM
Carbohydrates: 76%	SODIUM: 115 MG	
Protein: 7%	CHOLESTEROL: trace	

Pyramid equivalencies: 1 grain, ½ fruit, ½ extra

20

Asian Nouvelle

VIETNAMESE COOKING is sometimes described as the "nouvelle" cuisine of Asia. Compared to other Asian countries, Vietnamese menus feature fewer fried foods and offer more vegetables, including raw vegetables. In fact, Vietnam is listed as having the highest per capita consumption of vegetables of any country in the world. Thailand, Laos and Cambodia also have their share of wonderful light dishes. This menu is a collection of inspirations from Southeast Asian cuisine that offers a bounty of healthy, delicious dishes for the American table.

ASIAN NOUVELLE (MENU FOR 4)

Asparagus with Orange-Sesame Marinade
Shrimp and Green Papaya Salad with Spicy Lime Dressing
Velvet Corn Soup with Hearts of Palm
Southeast Asian Fondue with Assorted Dipping Sauces
Vietnamese Vegetable Platter
Braised Bananas

Additional Recipes:
Asian Poaching Broth
New Saigon Dipping Sauce
Buddhist Dipping Sauce
Fragrant Dipping Sauce

In Vietnam, asparagus is referred to as "Asian bamboo." I like to serve Asparagus with Orange-Sesame Marinade at a variety of meals, not just Asian ones. It can serve as an appetizer, salad or side dish. The dressing is delicious on other vegetables as well. Shrimp and Green Papaya Salad with Spicy Lime Dressing is a variation on a popular Thai salad. It's often quite piquant, so I've toned my version down a bit. You may want to add or subtract chiles according to your palate. Corn soup is popular in many Asian countries and is a good example of how an American dish was assimilated into their cuisines. Velvet Corn Soup with Hearts of Palm incorporates a popular tropical product. In the soup, I replaced traditional canned creamed corn with frozen corn kernels to cut back on the saltiness of the soup. Otherwise, the dish is very much like what you would find in many Asian countries.

Southeast Asian Fondue is the centerpiece of the meal. Following the tradition of the hot pot, Southeast Asian Fondue is more than food, it is a family gathering. Each guest cooks his or her own meat in a pot of Asian Poaching Broth placed in the center of the table. Unlike the hot pot of China and Japan, the broth is used exclusively for meat. The vegetables are served raw on the side. Diners cook the meats in the broth, then place them on the Vietnamese Vegetable Platter. Using chopsticks, the guests dip their meats and vegetables in a variety of dipping sauces. New Saigon Dipping Sauce, Buddhist Dipping Sauce and Fragrant Dipping Sauce are names I gave to the sauces created for this meal. Asian desserts are usually restricted to fruits. Braised Bananas epitomizes the tropical flavor that is so important to Southeast Asian cuisine.

NUTRIENT ANALYSIS FOR THE ASIAN NOUVELLE

The nutrient information for the complete meal includes 1 serving each of Asparagus with Orange-Sesame Marinade, Shrimp and Green Papaya Salad with Spicy Lime Dressing, Velvet Corn Soup with Hearts of Palm, Southeast Asian Fondue, Vietnamese Vegetable Platter and Braised Bananas. The information also includes 1 serving each of New Saigon Dipping Sauce, Buddhist Dipping Sauce and Fragrant Dipping Sauce. It is highly unlikely that your diners will consume that much dipping sauce. The sauces are also excellent over plain rice. If you want more food at the table, you could include rice or offer a second serving of the soup.

CALORIES
For total
  meal: 894
Fat: 12%
Carbohydrates: 64%
Protein: 24%

CARBOHYDRATES: 155.0 GM
PROTEIN: 56.8 GM
DIETARY FIBER: 12.7 GM
SODIUM: 1,072 MG
CHOLESTEROL: 113 MG

TOTAL FAT: 12.2 GM
Saturated fat: 2.3 GM
Monounsaturated fat: 4.0 GM

Pyramid equivalencies: 2½ grains, 4¼ vegetables, 2½ fruits, 1¼ proteins

Asparagus with Orange-Sesame Marinade

This easily prepared dish is ideal as an appetizer, salad or side dish.

1 pound fresh asparagus
1 recipe Orange-Sesame
  Marinade (recipe follows)

¼ cup finely chopped fresh red
  bell pepper

Place the tip ends of the asparagus against a straight edge. Cut the asparagus at the base end so that all the spears will be the same length and any tough portions of the stalk will have been cut away.

Steam the asparagus standing upright. This is easily done by wrapping foil over the bunch of asparagus at the tip ends. The foil will hold the asparagus together when you stand the stalks upright in a pot. Add water to the pot to the depth of ¾ inch. Cover the pot and steam for 6 to 8 minutes, depending on the thickness of the stalks. Remove from the heat and immediately rinse in cold water.

Lay the asparagus in a shallow dish. Cover with the Orange-Sesame Marinade. Marinate 30 minutes to 1 hour before serving, but no longer than that. Serve garnished with finely chopped red pepper.

YIELD: 4 servings

CALORIES
Per serving: 59
Fat: 20%
Carbohydrates: 62%
Protein: 18%

CARBOHYDRATES: 10.6 GM
PROTEIN: 3.0 GM
DIETARY FIBER: 1.3 GM
SODIUM: 92 MG
CHOLESTEROL: 0 MG

TOTAL FAT: 1.5 GM
Saturated fat: .2 GM
Monounsaturated fat: .5 GM

Pyramid equivalencies: 1 vegetable, ¼ fruit

Orange-Sesame Marinade

This tantalizing dressing takes only a couple of minutes to prepare.

¼ cup water
¼ cup plain rice vinegar
3 tablespoons frozen,
unsweetened orange juice
concentrate
2 teaspoons low-sodium soy
sauce

1 teaspoon dark roasted sesame
oil
1 clove garlic, finely minced
¼ teaspoon red chile flakes or
more to taste

To prepare the marinade, simply whisk together all of the ingredients. It will keep several days in refrigerator. Use as a marinade or sauce for steamed vegetables, a salad dressing or as a marinade for fish and chicken.

YIELD: 4 servings

CALORIES
Per serving: 36
Fat: 28%
Carbohydrates: 65%
Protein: 7%

CARBOHYDRATES: 6.4 GM
PROTEIN: .6 GM
DIETARY FIBER: .2 GM
SODIUM: 87 MG
CHOLESTEROL: 0 MG

TOTAL FAT: 1.2 GM
Saturated fat: .2 GM
Monounsaturated fat: .5 GM

Pyramid equivalencies: ¼ fruit

Shrimp and Green Papaya Salad with Spicy Lime Dressing

It's best to use a not fully ripened papaya, but don't use one that is hard as a rock, either.

¼ *pound fresh green beans, cut in 1-inch pieces*
2 *cups green papaya, peeled, seeded and cut in 1-inch cubes*
¼ *pound cooked bay shrimp*
1 *recipe Spicy Lime Dressing (recipe follows)*

3 *cups shredded green leaf lettuce*
3 *cups shredded napa cabbage*
2 *tablespoons unsalted peanuts, crushed*
2 *plum tomatoes, quartered*

Place the beans on a steamer rack above ½ inch boiling water. Steam for 3 or 4 minutes or until the beans are bright green but still crisp. Immediately rinse the beans under cold water. Toss together the beans, papaya, shrimp and Spicy Lime Dressing. Let stand 20 minutes.

Mix together the lettuce and cabbage and arrange on individual serving plates. Using a slotted spoon, mound the papaya mixture onto each plate. Pour the remaining juices over the greens. Sprinkle the crushed peanuts over the salad. Garnish each plate with tomato wedges and serve immediately.

YIELD: 4 servings

CALORIES
Per serving: 131
Fat: 16%
Carbohydrates: 57%
Protein: 27%

CARBOHYDRATES: 20.3 GM
PROTEIN: 9.8 GM
DIETARY FIBER: 3.4 GM
SODIUM: 239 MG
CHOLESTEROL: 55 MG

TOTAL FAT: 2.6 GM
Saturated fat: .4 GM
Monounsaturated fat: 1.0 GM

Pyramid equivalencies: 1½ vegetables, 1 fruit, ¼ protein

Spicy Lime Dressing

Use as much fresh chile as you dare! The dressing has a pleasant flavor without the chiles as well.

⅓ cup fresh lime juice
1 clove garlic, finely minced
1 or 2 fresh serrano chiles, seeded and finely minced

4 teaspoons dark brown sugar
1 tablespoon low-sodium soy sauce
1 tablespoon water

Combine all of the ingredients in a small bowl and refrigerate until ready to serve. Remember to wash your hands and utensils after handling the chiles. They can definitely offer a sting. The dressing tends to get hotter as time passes, but the papaya and greens will mute much of the heat.

YIELD: 4 servings

CALORIES	CARBOHYDRATES: 7.1 GM	TOTAL FAT: trace
Per serving: 27	PROTEIN: .6 GM	Saturated fat: trace
Fat: 1%	DIETARY FIBER: 0 GM	Monounsaturated fat: trace
Carbohydrates: 92%	SODIUM: 130 MG	
Protein: 7%	CHOLESTEROL: 0 MG	

Pyramid equivalencies: No equivalencies

Velvet Corn Soup with Hearts of Palm

Although Asian, this hearty soup combines well with the cuisines of many cultures.

¼ cup dry white wine
2 cloves garlic, finely minced
4 cups unsalted, defatted chicken broth
1 pound frozen, unsalted corn kernels, thawed

2 teaspoons brown sugar
1 teaspoon low-sodium soy sauce
1 fourteen-ounce can hearts of palm
1 egg white
8 leaves fresh cilantro
Freshly ground black pepper

Combine the wine, garlic and 1 cup of the broth in a soup pot. Cover and simmer at moderate temperature for 5 minutes.

Meanwhile, set aside 1 cup of the corn kernels. Combine the remaining kernels and broth in a blender jar. Add the brown sugar and soy sauce and puree until smooth and creamy. Transfer the corn puree to the soup pot mixture. Stir in the cup of whole kernels and continue cooking at moderate temperature for 8 minutes.

Rinse the hearts of palm under cold water. Slice in ½-inch-thick rounds and add to the corn mixture. Cook for 5 minutes. Stir in the egg white and continue cooking for 30 seconds. Remove from the heat and pour into individual bowls. Garnish each bowl with a cilantro leaf and a sprinkling of freshly ground pepper.

YIELD: 8 servings

CALORIES	CARBOHYDRATES: 27.7 GM	TOTAL FAT: .1 GM
Per serving: 121	PROTEIN: 6.3 GM	Saturated fat: trace
Fat: 1%	DIETARY FIBER: 1.2 GM	Monounsaturated fat: trace
Carbohydrates: 81%	SODIUM: 166 MG	
Protein: 18%	CHOLESTEROL: 0 MG	

Pyramid equivalencies: 1 grain, ¼ vegetable

Southeast Asian Fondue

Fondue creates a casual dining experience that is perfect for bringing people together.

> ¼ *pound top round beef, sliced*
> *paper thin*
> ¼ *pound shark or other firm-*
> *bodied fish, sliced paper*
> *thin*

> ¼ *pound sea scallops, halved*
> ¼ *pound lobster slipper tails, cut*
> *in chunks*
> 1 *recipe Asian Poaching Broth*
> *(recipe follows)*

Attractively arrange the beef, fish and seafood on a platter. On the stove, bring the poaching broth to a boil. Transfer the broth to a fondue pot, Mongolian hot pot or electric skillet. Place the pot in the center of the table. Using chopsticks or tongs, have each guest cook their pieces of meat in the broth. Serve the fondue-cooked meats with the Vietnamese Vegetable Platter and dipping sauces (recipes this chapter).

YIELD: 4 servings

CALORIES	CARBOHYDRATES: 3.4 GM	TOTAL FAT: 2.8 GM
Per serving: 140	PROTEIN: 24.3 GM	Saturated fat: .8 GM
Fat: 19%	DIETARY FIBER: trace	Monounsaturated fat: 1.0 GM
Carbohydrates: 10%	SODIUM: 195 MG	
Protein: 71%	CHOLESTEROL: 57 MG	

Pyramid equivalencies: 1 protein

Asian Poaching Broth

This broth will enhance the flavor of fish, chicken or vegetable dishes.

½ cup dry sherry
3 tablespoons rice vinegar
2 shallots, finely minced
2 cloves garlic, finely minced
2 teaspoons low-sodium soy sauce

2 teaspoons unsalted tomato paste
2 teaspoons brown sugar
½ teaspoon coconut extract
2 cups unsalted, defatted chicken broth

Combine the sherry, vinegar, shallots and garlic in a pot. Cover tightly and simmer at moderate temperature for 8 minutes. Stir in the remaining ingredients and set aside until ready to use. Cook until nearly boiling, when you are ready to transfer it to the fondue pot for Southeast Asian Fondue. Use the leftover broth for soups, sauces or poaching liquid for fish or vegetables.

YIELD: 4 servings

CALORIES
Per serving: 41
Fat: 1%
Carbohydrates: 70%
Protein: 29%

CARBOHYDRATES: 8.4 GM
PROTEIN: 3.4 GM
DIETARY FIBER: .1 GM
SODIUM: 100 MG
CHOLESTEROL: 0 MG

TOTAL FAT: trace
Saturated fat: trace
Monounsaturated fat: trace

Pyramid equivalencies: No equivalencies

Vietnamese Vegetable Platter

Southeast Asia is famous for plates of raw foods accompanied by dipping sauces and meats.

6 ounces dry linguine or rice
sticks
4 cups shredded romaine
lettuce
1 large tomato, cut in 8
wedges
1 cup fresh mint leaves

1 cup fresh cilantro leaves
1 medium cucumber, peeled and
thinly sliced
1 cup fresh pineapple chunks
1 cup fresh bean sprouts
2 stalks bok choy, sliced

Prepare whatever pasta you like according to instructions for cooking in water. Rinse the pasta in cold water. Divide the lettuce between 4 individual serving plates. Mound the pasta in the center of each plate. Arrange all of the remaining ingredients on the plates and serve with the dipping sauces and Southeast Asian Fondue (recipes this chapter).

YIELD: 4 servings

CALORIES
Per serving: 215
Fat: 5%
Carbohydrates: 79%
Protein: 16%

CARBOHYDRATES: 43.8 GM
PROTEIN: 9.1 GM
DIETARY FIBER: 4.7 GM
SODIUM: 15 MG
CHOLESTEROL: 0 MG

TOTAL FAT: 1.3 GM
Saturated fat: .2 GM
Monounsaturated fat: .1 GM

Pyramid equivalencies: 1½ grains, 1½ vegetables, ¼ fruit

New Saigon Dipping Sauce

This simple sauce has an amazing robust flavor.

2 tablespoons rice vinegar
2 tablespoons water
1 tablespoon tomato paste
1 tablespoon low-sodium soy
   sauce
1 tablespoon fresh lime juice
1 teaspoon dark roasted
   sesame oil

1 fillet anchovy
2 cloves garlic, minced
¼ to 1 teaspoon hot red pepper
   flakes
2 green onions, finely minced

Combine all of the ingredients, except the green onions, in a blender and process until well blended. Refrigerate until ready to use. Use within 2 days. Just before serving, add the green onions. Use as a sauce for vegetables, meats and rice.

YIELD: 4 servings

CALORIES
Per serving: 23
Fat: 45%
Carbohydrates: 39%
Protein: 16%

CARBOHYDRATES: 2.5 GM
PROTEIN: 1.0 GM
DIETARY FIBER: .2 GM
SODIUM: 169 MG
CHOLESTEROL: 0 MG

TOTAL FAT: 1.3 GM
Saturated fat: .2 GM
Monounsaturated fat: .5 GM

Pyramid equivalencies: No equivalencies

Buddhist Dipping Sauce

Although delicious on meats, Buddhist sauces were originally created for vegetarian dishes.

2 tablespoons unseasoned rice vinegar	1 tablespoon unsalted tomato paste
4 teaspoons brown sugar	1 tablespoon water
1 tablespoon low-sodium soy sauce	1 clove garlic, finely minced
1 tablespoon pure, unsalted peanut butter	1/4 teaspoon liquid hot pepper sauce (Tabasco)

Whisk together all of the ingredients until smooth and well blended. Refrigerate until ready to use. Will keep several days. Use as a sauce for vegetables, meats and rice.

YIELD: 4 servings

CALORIES
Per serving: 49
Fat: 36%
Carbohydrates: 50%
Protein: 14%

CARBOHYDRATES: 6.8 GM
PROTEIN: 1.8 GM
DIETARY FIBER: .6 GM
SODIUM: 135 MG
CHOLESTEROL: 0 MG

TOTAL FAT: 2.2 GM
Saturated fat: .3 GM
Monounsaturated fat: 1.1 GM

Pyramid equivalencies: No equivalencies

Fragrant Dipping Sauce

This is an aromatic sweet and sour sauce.

1/4 cup unseasoned rice vinegar	1/2 teaspoon five-spice powder
2 tablespoons blackstrap molasses	1/4 teaspoon liquid hot pepper sauce (Tabasco)
2 tablespoons brown sugar	1/8 teaspoon ground coriander seed
1 teaspoon low-sodium soy sauce	1/8 teaspoon cumin seed
1 tablespoon unsalted tomato paste	1/8 teaspoon dry ground ginger

Whisk together all of the ingredients until smooth and well blended. Refrigerate until ready to use. Will keep several days. Use as a sauce for vegetables, grilled meats and rice.

YIELD: 4 servings

CALORIES	CARBOHYDRATES: 14.0 GM	TOTAL FAT: .1 GM
Per serving: 56	PROTEIN: .3 GM	Saturated fat: trace
Fat: 1%	DIETARY FIBER: .2 GM	Monounsaturated fat: trace
Carbohydrates: 97%	SODIUM: 58 MG	
Protein: 2%	CHOLESTEROL: 0 MG	

Pyramid equivalencies: No equivalencies

Braised Bananas

For a less sweet dish, try this with plantain.

2 bananas
¼ cup water
¼ cup frozen, unsweetened
    orange juice concentrate
2 tablespoons fresh lime juice

1 tablespoon brown sugar
¼ teaspoon ground cinnamon
¼ teaspoon ground ginger
4 sprigs fresh mint

Peel and quarter the bananas, cutting in half lengthwise and cross-wise. In a skillet, whisk together the water, juice concentrate, lime juice, brown sugar, cinnamon and ginger. If necessary, add enough water to cover the bottom of the pan. Turn the heat to high, and when the mixture begins to bubble, add the banana slices. Cook for 3 minutes, then turn the bananas. If necessary, add more water. Cook 2 or 3 minutes or until the bananas are tender and the sauce has thickened. Serve immediately garnished with fresh mint.

YIELD: 4 servings

CALORIES
Per serving: 96
Fat: 3%
Carbohydrates: 93%
Protein: 4%

CARBOHYDRATES: 24.4 GM
PROTEIN: 1.1 GM
DIETARY FIBER: 1.1 GM
SODIUM: 3 MG
CHOLESTEROL: 0 MG

TOTAL FAT: .3 GM
Saturated fat: .1 GM
Monounsaturated fat: trace

Pyramid equivalencies: 1 fruit

21

Spicy Garden

THIS IS a meal for people who want a lively bunch of vegetables. Frequently, vegetables are treated as delicate creatures, to be mildly seasoned, so as not to detract from the hearty, flavorful main course. All too often this means the vegetables are bland and boring. Why should vegetables always play second fiddle? I created this meal to show that vegetables respond beautifully to bold, piquant and aromatic flavors. After all, the Jolly Green Giant is no wimp! Spicy seasonings are a great way to bring flavor to dishes without relying on fat. Consider that Americans most commonly season vegetables with salt, butter, oil, cream or cheese, all of which need to be restricted on a health-conscious diet. This spicy vegetarian menu offers an array of zesty seasoning alternatives.

SPICY GARDEN (MENU FOR 4)

Spinach and Red Bean Salad with Spicy Mint Vinaigrette
Spaghetti Squash with Broccoli, Peanuts and Fresh Ginger Sauce
Cornbread with Onion and Jalapeño and Orange-Chile Marmalade
Banana Yogurt Creme

Additional Recipes:
Spicy Mint-Yogurt Dressing
Basic Yogurt Cheese

Contrasts in color, flavor and texture always add interest to a dish. Beyond allure, contrasts are sometimes essential for creating palatability. Piquant seasonings, such as mustard, horseradish, ginger, black pepper and fresh and dried chiles, often require a cooling flavor to balance the effect of the heat. Cool, soothing contrasts include fresh herbs, sweet aromatic fruits, milk and yogurt. In addition to a cooling balance, hot spices can be tamed by the use of starches, such as breads, pasta, grains, beans, potatoes, yams and squash. The Spicy Garden menu finds a satisfying balance between "fire" and "ice."

Spinach and Red Bean Salad with Spicy Mint Vinaigrette is a tantalizing plate of contrasts. Deep green spinach is complemented by the maroon and scarlet tones of the beans and tomatoes. Spinach and red beans also offer appealing differences in texture. The "fire" in the salad comes from allspice and red pepper flakes. An abundance of fresh mint leaves offers a calming counterbalance. For the diner who wants a lower-fat dressing, a Spicy Mint-Yogurt Dressing substitutes beautifully. Apart from culinary appeal, spinach, beans and tomato offer the diner a bounty of nutrients.

Fresh ginger can be surprisingly "hot." I've had ginger that had more fire than jalapeño peppers. Of course, ginger can also be quite mild. Variables in growing climate and freshness are the main factors behind differences in heat. A Fresh Ginger Sauce turns Spaghetti Squash with Broccoli and Peanuts into a lively vegetable entrée. So much has recently been written about the immune-boosting qualities of both squash and broccoli, I felt a little guilty creating a recipe that paired the two together. I thought you might think I was trying to slip you a dose of mega-vitamins. Apart from their nutritional attributes, the faintly sweet squash and the "cabbagy" aroma of the broccoli are earthy foils for the snappy ginger sauce. Again, lively contrasts in color and texture strengthen the appeal of the dish. A garnish of crushed peanuts beautifully illustrates how nuts, although high in fat, can be used in small quantities to create the illusion of a rich dish.

Cornbread laced with chile peppers has become a staple of southwestern cookery. However, I enjoy Cornbread with Onion and Jalapeño with many different cuisines. In a vegetarian meal, the cornbread becomes a complete protein when teamed with bean dishes. Instead of topping the bread with butter, I like to use Orange-Chile Marmalade, an enticing spread that's delicious on other breads as well.

In Indian and Middle Eastern cuisines, yogurt dishes are commonly featured as a soothing balance to spicy fare. Starting with Basic Yogurt Cheese, Banana Yogurt Creme is a cooling finale with an incredibly rich taste.

NUTRIENT ANALYSIS FOR SPICY GARDEN (MENU FOR 4)

Nutrient information is for 1 serving each of Spinach and Red Bean Salad with Spicy Mint Vinaigrette, Spaghetti Squash with Broccoli, Peanuts and Fresh Ginger Sauce, Cornbread with Onion and Jalapeño, Orange-Chile Marmalade and Banana Yogurt Creme.

CALORIES
For total meal:
691
Fat: 15%
Carbohydrates: 71%
Protein: 14%

CARBOHYDRATES: 130.3 GM
PROTEIN: 26.9 GM
DIETARY FIBER: 13.0 GM
SODIUM: 442 MG
CHOLESTEROL: 2.7 MG

TOTAL FAT: 12.7 GM
Saturated fat: 2.1 GM
Monounsaturated fat: 7.0 GM

Pyramid equivalencies: 2 grains, 4 vegetables, 2 fruits, 1 dairy, ¼ protein

Spinach and Red Bean Salad with Spicy Mint Vinaigrette

This spicy salad will please the diner with a hearty appetite. Although you can use canned beans, cooking dry beans will produce a tastier salad.

1 large bunch fresh spinach, carefully washed and stemmed
1 recipe Spicy Mint Vinaigrette (recipe follows)

8 plum tomatoes, quartered
1 small red onion, peeled and cut into rings
1½ cups cooked kidney beans or other large red beans

Toss the spinach in Spicy Mint Vinaigrette, coating well. Add the remaining ingredients and toss again. Serve immediately.

YIELD: 4 servings

CALORIES	CARBOHYDRATES: 23.4 GM	TOTAL FAT: 3.9 GM
Per serving: 149	PROTEIN: 8.2 GM	Saturated fat: .6 GM
Fat: 22%	DIETARY FIBER: 7.8 GM	Monounsaturated fat: 2.5 GM
Carbohydrates: 58%	SODIUM: 58 MG	
Protein: 20%	CHOLESTEROL: 0 MG	

Pyramid equivalencies: 1½ vegetables, ¼ protein

Spicy Mint Vinaigrette

In addition to the Spinach and Red Bean Salad, this is a refreshing dressing for a potato or pasta salad.

½ cup fresh mint leaves
¼ cup fresh lemon juice
1 tablespoon frozen, unsweetened apple juice concentrate
2 tablespoons water

1 tablespoon extra-virgin olive oil
2 cloves garlic
¼ teaspoon allspice
¼ teaspoon hot red pepper flakes (or more to taste)

In a blender jar, combine all the ingredients. Process until smooth. Refrigerate until ready to serve. Do not make more than 3 hours before using.

YIELD: 4 servings

CALORIES	CARBOHYDRATES: 3.9 GM	TOTAL FAT: 3.4 GM
Per serving: 44	PROTEIN: .3 GM	Saturated fat: .5 GM
Fat: 64%	DIETARY FIBER: .2 GM	Monounsaturated fat: 2.5 GM
Carbohydrates: 33%	SODIUM: 4 MG	
Protein: 3%	CHOLESTEROL: 0 MG	

Pyramid equivalencies: No equivalencies

Spicy Mint-Yogurt Dressing

This version of a spicy mint dressing replaces oil with nonfat yogurt. The flavor is very different, but still delicious.

In the previous recipe, Spicy Mint Vinaigrette, omit the olive oil and water. Reduce the lemon juice to 2 tablespoons and add ½ cup plain nonfat yogurt. Add the other ingredients and process in the blender as directed. Use immediately.

YIELD: 4 servings

CALORIES
Per serving: 28
Fat: 3%
Carbohydrates: 72%
Protein: 25%

CARBOHYDRATES: 5.4 GM
PROTEIN: 1.9 GM
DIETARY FIBER: .1 GM
SODIUM: 26 MG
CHOLESTEROL: .5 MG

TOTAL FAT: .1 GM
Saturated fat: trace
Monounsaturated fat: trace

Pyramid equivalencies: No equivalencies

Spaghetti Squash with Broccoli, Peanuts and Fresh Ginger Sauce

Peanuts and ginger turn ordinary vegetables into zesty, exciting fare.

½ medium spaghetti squash
1 recipe Fresh Ginger Sauce
(recipe follows)
4 cups broccoli florets

2 green onions, finely chopped
2 tablespoons dry roasted,
unsalted peanuts, crushed

Remove the seeds from the squash and cut in 3-inch squares. Place in a steamer with ½ inch water. Steam covered for 8 to 10 minutes or until tender. Meanwhile, prepare the Fresh Ginger Sauce.

When the squash is cooked, remove from the steamer and begin steaming the broccoli. The broccoli should take about 2 minutes to cook. While the broccoli is cooking take a fork and scrape the strands of squash from the rind.

Place the strands of squash on serving plates. Arrange the broccoli around the squash and pour the warm ginger sauce over the vegetables. Sprinkle the chopped green onion and crushed peanuts over the top.

YIELD: 4 servings

CALORIES	CARBOHYDRATES: 23.0 GM	TOTAL FAT: 2.6 GM
Per serving: 117	PROTEIN: 5.2 GM	Saturated fat: .3 GM
Fat: 17%	DIETARY FIBER: 2.8 GM	Monounsaturated fat: .9 GM
Carbohydrates: 68%	SODIUM: 184 MG	
Protein: 15%	CHOLESTEROL: 0 MG	

Pyramid equivalencies: 2½ vegetables

Fresh Ginger Sauce

This is delicious as a sauce for vegetables or as a marinade for beef, chicken or fish.

⅔ cup dry sherry
1 tablespoon finely minced fresh ginger
2 cloves garlic, finely minced

2 tablespoons frozen, unsweetened apple juice concentrate
1 tablespoon low-sodium soy sauce

Combine all of the ingredients. If using as a sauce, simmer covered for 5 minutes. Cooking is not necessary if using as a marinade. However, after marinating a meat, you may wish to cook the marinade, turning it into a sauce for the dish.

YIELD: 4 servings

CALORIES
Per serving: 27
Fat: 1%
Carbohydrates: 90%
Protein: 9%

CARBOHYDRATES: 7.6 GM
PROTEIN: .7 GM
DIETARY FIBER: trace
SODIUM: 132 MG
CHOLESTEROL: 0 MG

TOTAL FAT: .1 GM
Saturated fat: trace
Monounsaturated fat: trace

Pyramid equivalencies: No equivalencies

Cornbread with Onion and Jalapeño

This hearty bread is also delicious with soup.

1¼ cups whole wheat flour
1 cup yellow cornmeal
1 tablespoon baking powder
1¼ cups fluid nonfat milk
¼ cup honey
2 egg whites
3 tablespoons extra-virgin olive oil

2 teaspoons low-sodium soy sauce
3 tablespoons finely diced canned jalapeño peppers
¼ cup finely chopped red onion
2 tablespoons finely minced fresh cilantro or celery leaves

Preheat oven to 375°F. Sift together the flour, cornmeal and baking powder. Set aside.

Whisk together the milk, honey, egg whites, olive oil and soy sauce. Add the flour mixture and stir until thoroughly blended. Stir in the pepper, onion and cilantro.

Spray a 9-inch square baking pan with nonstick cooking spray. Pour the batter into the pan and bake at 375°F. for 20 minutes or until an inserted toothpick comes out clean.

Serve hot with Orange-Chile Marmalade (recipe follows).

YIELD: 9 servings

CALORIES	CARBOHYDRATES: 32.4 GM	TOTAL FAT: 5.4 GM
Per serving: 193	PROTEIN: 5.6 GM	Saturated fat: .8 GM
Fat: 24%	DIETARY FIBER: .7 GM	Monounsaturated fat: 3.3 GM
Carbohydrates: 64%	SODIUM: 111 MG	
Protein: 12%	CHOLESTEROL: .7 MG	

Pyramid equivalencies: 2 grains

Orange-Chile Marmalade

This spicy spread is delicious on cornbread and other hearty breads. It also makes an exciting glaze for broiled chicken breasts.

¼ cup dry sherry
½ cup finely diced red onion
½ teaspoon ground cumin
½ teaspoon ground cinnamon

1 ten-ounce jar fruit-sweetened orange marmalade
¼ teaspoon liquid hot pepper sauce (or more to taste)

In a small nonstick pan, combine the sherry, onion, cumin and cinnamon. Cook at high heat, stirring regularly, until most of the liquid is gone. Remove from the heat.

Whisk together the cooked onions, marmalade and hot pepper sauce. If desired, add more pepper sauce to taste. Transfer to a glass jar and refrigerate until ready to use. Serve warm or at room temperature.

YIELD: 24 servings, 1 tablespoon each

CALORIES	CARBOHYDRATES: 10.4 GM	TOTAL FAT: trace
Per serving: 37	PROTEIN: trace	Saturated fat: trace
Fat: 0%	DIETARY FIBER: .1 GM	Monounsaturated fat: trace
Carbohydrates: 99%	SODIUM: trace	
Protein: 1%	CHOLESTEROL: 0 MG	

Pyramid equivalencies: ½ fruit

Banana Yogurt Creme

Although this dish is very low in fat, most diners will find it an incredibly rich dessert.

1 recipe Basic Yogurt Cheese (recipe follows)
3 large, very ripe bananas, peeled and sliced
3 tablespoons frozen unsweetened pineapple juice concentrate
1 tablespoon fresh lemon juice
¼ teaspoon ground nutmeg or cardamom
1 tablespoon finely grated fresh lemon peel

Prepare the Basic Yogurt Cheese at least 6 hours before it is needed. Combine the bananas, juice concentrate and lemon juice in a blender and puree until completely smooth. Remove from the blender and whisk together with the Yogurt Cheese. Do not use the blender to mix the bananas and Yogurt Cheese. Transfer the mixture to individual serving dishes. Top with a sprinkle of nutmeg or cardamom. Garnish with the fresh lemon peel.

YIELD: 4 servings

CALORIES	CARBOHYDRATES: 41.4 GM	TOTAL FAT: .8 GM
Per serving: 195	PROTEIN: 7.9 GM	Saturated fat: .4 GM
Fat: 3%	DIETARY FIBER: 1.6 GM	Monounsaturated fat: .3 GM
Carbohydrates: 82%	SODIUM: 89 MG	
Protein: 15%	CHOLESTEROL: 2 MG	

Pyramid equivalencies: 1½ fruits, 1 dairy

Basic Yogurt Cheese

To make yogurt cheese, do not use a yogurt that has been thickened with gelatin. Yogurt Cheese is excellent as a spread for muffins and bagels or as an accompaniment to fruit. It is also delicious mixed with fresh herbs and used as a topping for baked potatoes.

2 cups plain nonfat yogurt

Place a paper coffee filter or cheesecloth in a strainer. Pour the yogurt into the strainer. Set the strainer over a bowl, cover with plastic wrap and refrigerate 6 hours or overnight.

The whey will drain out, leaving a thickened yogurt, similar to the texture of cream cheese. The longer it sits, the denser it will get. Do not leave in the strainer more than 48 hours. Store in a covered container and refrigerate.

YIELD: 8 servings (as a spread)

CALORIES	CARBOHYDRATES: 4.4 GM	TOTAL FAT: .1 GM
Per serving: 32	PROTEIN: 3.3 GM	Saturated fat: .1 GM
Fat: 3%	DIETARY FIBER: 0 GM	Monounsaturated fat: trace
Carbohydrates: 55%	SODIUM: 44 MG	
Protein: 42%	CHOLESTEROL: 1 MG	

Pyramid equivalencies: ½ dairy

22

Riviera Picnic

ONE OF summertime's great pleasures is an evening at an outdoor concert. It can be the Philharmonic at the Bowl or the community orchestra crammed into the old bandstand in the center of the park. The evening's pleasure is the same. The acoustics are often imperfect, the musicians may have to swat insects attracted to bright lights and the seating is rarely comfortable, but somehow music under the stars joyfully reminds us that the arts and nature are really one. Part of the evening's fun is the picnic beforehand. When I lived in Los Angeles, I worked one summer in a gourmet shop that featured picnic dinners that you could take to the Hollywood Bowl. A variety of baskets were sold, each with a different theme. These were no ordinary baskets. Some of the most luxurious and expensive dinners I've prepared went into those baskets. Riviera Picnic is a basket I recently created for an outing to San Diego's Old Globe Theatre. It's an elegant meal that happens to be meatless, but if you don't mention it, I doubt that anyone will notice.

RIVIERA PICNIC (MENU FOR 8)

Cucumber Soup with Tomato Caviar
Open-Face Artichoke Sandwich with Roasted Vegetable Spread
Potato Salad with Two Dressings
Almond Cake with Golden Fruit Mélange

Additional Recipes:
Whole Wheat Pasta with Roasted Vegetable Spread
Mustard Vinaigrette
Creamy Pimento Dressing
Passover Almond Cake

In Mediterranean countries, a traditional summer soup is chilled yogurt soup topped with caviar. Mediterranean countries also have a tradition of "mock caviar," thought to have originated among peasants who couldn't afford the expensive roe. Poor man's caviar is often made with eggplant and bits of other vegetables. My Cucumber Soup, which is a creamy yogurt-based soup, is topped with a spicy relish I call Tomato Caviar. Roasted Vegetable Spread, which goes on the Open-Face Artichoke Sandwich, is actually more like the "mock caviars" that we associate with Mediterranean countries. Any leftover Spread can be used for Whole Wheat Pasta with Roasted Vegetable Spread.

Potato Salad with Two Dressings tastes incredibly rich but is still under 20% fat. While the potatoes are hot, the salad is tossed with Mustard Vinaigrette, which infuses the potatoes with intense flavor. Later, the salad is topped with Creamy Pimento Dressing, which adds a subtle richness and attractive color.

Almond desserts are hugely popular in the Mediterranean region. My version of Almond Cake lowers the fat from the nuts by using a mix of oatmeal and bread crumbs. For Passover, the cake can be easily adapted for use as Passover Almond Cake. Golden Fruit Mélange tops the cake with a blaze of sunny color.

Iced tea, mineral water or champagne are obvious considerations as a picnic beverage. Iced Mocha Royale (page 34) would make a delicious dessert beverage.

NUTRIENT ANALYSIS FOR RIVIERA PICNIC

The nutrient analysis includes 1 serving each of Cucumber Soup with Tomato Caviar, Open-Face Artichoke Sandwich with Roasted Vegetable Spread, Potato Salad with Two Dressings and Almond Cake with Golden Fruit Mélange. No beverages are included in the total for the meal.

CALORIES	CARBOHYDRATES: 128.4 GM	TOTAL FAT: 13.4 GM
For total meal: 702	PROTEIN: 25.5 GM	Saturated fat: 2.2 GM
Fat: 16%	DIETARY FIBER: 12.1 GM	Monounsaturated fat: 6.7 GM
Carbohydrates: 70%	SODIUM: 672 MG	
Protein: 14%	CHOLESTEROL: 7 MG	

Pyramid equivalencies: 2⅓ grains, 4 vegetables, 1 fruit, 2⅓ dairy

Cucumber Soup with Tomato Caviar

A mix of cool and spicy makes this soup an appealing dish of contrasts.

3 large cucumbers
⅔ cup loosely packed fresh celery leaves
¼ cup loosely packed fresh mint leaves
2 cloves fresh garlic
1 green onion, coarsely chopped
2 tablespoons fresh lemon juice

3 tablespoons finely grated fresh lemon peel (1½ lemons)
2 cups liquid nonfat milk
3 cups plain nonfat yogurt
1 recipe Tomato Caviar (recipe follows)
8 small sprigs fresh cilantro or parsley

Peel the cucumbers, cut in half lengthwise and scoop out the seeds. Coarsely chop the cucumber and place in a blender or food processor. Add the celery leaves and mint leaves, garlic, green onion, lemon juice, lemon peel and milk. Puree until smooth and creamy. Transfer the mixture to a bowl and whisk in the yogurt. Refrigerate for at least 1 hour, but no more than 8 hours.

When ready to serve, pour the chilled soup into goblets. Spoon Tomato Caviar on top of each serving and garnish with cilantro or parsley.

YIELD: 8 servings

Nutrient analysis includes the Tomato Caviar.

CALORIES	CARBOHYDRATES: 18.3 GM	TOTAL FAT: .6 GM
Per serving: 117	PROTEIN: 8.2 GM	Saturated fat: .2 GM
Fat: 5%	DIETARY FIBER: 2.2 GM	Monounsaturated fat: .1 GM
Carbohydrates: 66%	SODIUM: 107 MG	
Protein: 29%	CHOLESTEROL: 3 MG	

Pyramid equivalencies: 1 vegetable, 1 dairy

Tomato Caviar

This spicy topping is a tantalizing contrast to the cool cucumber soup. Also use as a condiment for grilled fish or chicken.

2 tablespoons fruit-sweetened orange marmalade
2 tablespoons fresh lemon juice
½ teaspoon ground cumin
¼ teaspoon curry powder

2 medium tomatoes, finely chopped
¼ cup finely minced red onion
¼ teaspoon Tabasco (or more to taste)

Whisk together the marmalade, lemon juice, cumin and curry. Stir in the tomatoes, onion and hot pepper sauce. Taste and add more hot sauce if desired. Do not make more than 4 hours before serving.

YIELD: 8 servings

CALORIES	CARBOHYDRATES: 4.3 GM	TOTAL FAT: .1 GM
Per serving: 18	PROTEIN: .4 GM	Saturated fat: trace
Fat: 5%	DIETARY FIBER: .3 GM	Monounsaturated fat: trace
Carbohydrates: 87%	SODIUM: 3 MG	
Protein: 8%	CHOLESTEROL: 0 MG	

Pyramid equivalencies: ⅓ vegetable

Open-Face Artichoke Sandwich with Roasted Vegetable Spread

For this sandwich, the garnishes are incidental. What is really important is matching a hearty bread with the robust flavor of the Roasted Vegetable Spread. For the bread, I personally like to use thick slices of Italian whole wheat bread.

1 *package (9 ounces) frozen*
   artichoke hearts
½ *cup extra-dry sherry*
¼ *cup water*
1 *tablespoon freshly grated*
   lemon peel
8 *thick slices Italian whole*
   wheat bread (or other bread
   of choice)

1 *cup Roasted Vegetable Spread*
   (recipe follows)
2 *ounces feta cheese,*
   crumbled
4 *Roma tomatoes, sliced*
   Fresh basil leaves

Place the frozen artichoke hearts in a small pan with the dry sherry, water and lemon peel. Simmer until tender. Drain the liquid from the artichoke hearts, reserving for use in soups or sauces. Set aside the artichoke hearts.

To create the open-face sandwiches, thickly spread each slice with the Roasted Vegetable Spread, then sprinkle with the crumbled cheese. Arrange the artichoke hearts, tomato slices and basil leaves on each piece of bread. Serve immediately.

YIELD: 8 slices

CALORIES	CARBOHYDRATES: 30.1 GM	TOTAL FAT: 6.5 GM
Per serving: 195	PROTEIN: 6.9 GM	Saturated fat: 1.2 GM
Fat: 28%	DIETARY FIBER: 6.7 GM	Monounsaturated fat: 2.6 GM
Carbohydrates: 59%	SODIUM: 450 MG	
Protein: 13%	CHOLESTEROL: 3.2 MG	

Pyramid equivalencies: 2 grains, 1 vegetable, ⅛ dairy

Roasted Vegetable Spread

Roasting the vegetables produces a remarkable intensity of flavor. I have also made this spread by simply simmering the ingredients in dry sherry. The result was tasty, but for me not as appealing as roasting. Persons wanting to cut their calories may elect to omit the olive oil and use only additional nonfat yogurt.

1 medium eggplant	2 tablespoons plain nonfat
1 red onion	yogurt
1 bulb garlic	1 tablespoon capers, drained
1 large red bell pepper	and rinsed
2 tablespoons broth or water	1 tablespoon finely chopped
2 tablespoons extra-virgin	fresh basil
olive oil	1/4 teaspoon Tabasco

Do not peel the eggplant, onion or garlic. Slice the eggplant in half lengthwise. Place on a nonstick baking sheet. Also place the onion, with outer dry skin intact, and the whole bulb of garlic on the baking sheet. Bake at 325°F. for 45 minutes. Hereafter, check every 15 minutes. Remove each item when it has become soft to the touch. All the vegetables should be soft in 1 to 2 hours.

Set each vegetable aside to cool for 30 minutes; do not wait too long to peel it. The release of natural sugars makes the vegetables slightly sticky. Thus, it is more difficult to remove the outer skin when they are cool.

You may also roast the pepper in the oven, but I personally prefer roasting it over a flame. With metal tongs, hold the pepper directly over the flame of a gas range, constantly rotating it until the pepper is blackened. Immediately wrap in a clean towel. After 20 minutes, remove the towel, pull the blackened skin away and discard. Rinse under cold water. Open the pepper and remove the seeds.

Combine the roasted eggplant, onion, garlic and red pepper in a food processor. Add 2 tablespoons broth or water. (The liquid from cooking the artichoke hearts in the above recipe is excellent.) Also add the olive oil and yogurt. Puree until smooth. Stir in the capers, fresh basil and Tabasco. Use as a spread for bread, filling for boiled eggs (yolk discarded) or dip for vegetables or crackers.

YIELD: 2 cups, 16 servings

CALORIES	CARBOHYDRATES: 3.5 GM	TOTAL FAT: 3.5 GM
Per serving: 46	PROTEIN: .8 GM	Saturated fat: .5 GM
Fat: 65%	DIETARY FIBER: .6 GM	Monounsaturated fat: 2.5 GM
Carbohydrates: 29%	SODIUM: 72 MG	
Protein: 6%	CHOLESTEROL: trace	

Pyramid equivalencies: ¼ vegetable

Whole Wheat Pasta with Roasted Vegetable Spread

There will be Roasted Vegetable Spread left over after making the Open-Face Artichoke Sandwiches. You can use it as a spread for almost any sandwich or heat it up and toss it with pasta. Its robust flavor goes well with whole wheat pasta. If you want to add bits of chopped vegetables, chicken or fish, that's fine, but I confess I usually have it plain with just the pasta.

Allow ⅓ cup Roasted Vegetable Spread for each 2-ounce serving of dry pasta. You may wish to add 1 to 3 tablespoons of water to the Spread. Simply heat the Spread in a microwave or saucepan. Prepare the pasta according to package directions, omitting oil and salt. Toss the Spread with the cooked pasta and enjoy!

Nutrient analysis is for ⅓ cup Roasted Vegetable Spread and Whole Wheat Pasta made from 2 ounces of dry pasta.

CALORIES	CARBOHYDRATES: 48.3 GM	TOTAL FAT: 9.3 GM
Per serving: 343	PROTEIN: 13.1 GM	Saturated fat: 1.5 GM
Fat: 25%	DIETARY FIBER: 9.1 GM	Monounsaturated fat: 7.7 GM
Carbohydrates: 59%	SODIUM: 232 MG	
Protein: 16%	CHOLESTEROL: trace	

Pyramid equivalencies: 2 grains, ¾ vegetable

Potato Salad with Two Dressings

This elegant potato salad offers interesting contrasts in flavor and texture.

6 large potatoes, peeled and cut in 1-inch cubes
1 cup finely diced red onion
1 small green bell pepper, finely diced
4 cloves garlic, finely minced
1 recipe Mustard Vinaigrette (recipe follows)

¼ cup finely minced fresh parsley
1 tablespoon finely minced fresh tarragon
1 recipe Creamy Pimento Dressing (recipe on page 264)
8 radicchio leaves for garnish

Place the potatoes on a steamer rack and steam covered for 10 minutes or until tender. Immediately transfer the hot potatoes to a mixing bowl and toss with the onion, bell pepper and garlic. Toss the potato mixture with the Mustard Vinaigrette. Let cool to room temperature, then cover and refrigerate.

Just before serving, toss with the parsley and tarragon. Drizzle the Creamy Pimento Dressing over the entire salad or over each individual portion. Garnish with radicchio leaves.

YIELD: 8 servings

CALORIES	CARBOHYDRATES: 29.5 GM	TOTAL FAT: 3.1 GM
Per serving: 150	PROTEIN: 4.7 GM	Saturated fat: .5 GM
Fat: 17%	DIETARY FIBER: 2.0 GM	Monounsaturated fat: 2.1 GM
Carbohydrates: 72%	SODIUM: 42 MG	
Protein: 11%	CHOLESTEROL: 1 MG	

Pyramid equivalencies: 2 vegetables, ¼ dairy

Mustard Vinaigrette

This tart dressing is delicious on hot vegetables, especially potatoes, carrots and other root vegetables.

⅓ cup red wine vinegar
1 tablespoon olive oil
2 tablespoons low-sodium, Dijon-style mustard

2 tablespoons water
¼ teaspoon ground black pepper (or more)

Whisk together all of the ingredients and use immediately or refrigerate in a glass container for later use.

YIELD: 8 servings

CALORIES
Per serving: 20
Fat: 79%
Carbohydrates: 17%
Protein: 4%

CARBOHYDRATES: .9 GM
PROTEIN: .2 GM
DIETARY FIBER: trace
SODIUM: 65 MG
CHOLESTEROL: 0 MG

TOTAL FAT: 1.9 GM
Saturated fat: .2 GM
Monounsaturated fat: 1.3 GM

Pyramid equivalencies: No equivalencies

Creamy Pimento Dressing

In addition to potato salad, this is an attractive dressing for chilled poached salmon or cold pasta.

⅔ cup plain nonfat yogurt
1 tablespoon dry nonfat milk powder
2 tablespoons red wine vinegar
4 teaspoons low-sodium, Dijon-style mustard
2 teaspoons extra-virgin olive oil

2 teaspoons frozen, unsweetened apple juice concentrate
1 teaspoon unsalted tomato paste
¼ cup chopped pimentos (not packed in oil)
¼ teaspoon Tabasco

Whisk together the yogurt and dry milk powder. Add the vinegar, mustard, olive oil, juice concentrate and tomato paste. Stir until thoroughly blended. Add the pimento and stir until evenly mixed. Add the Tabasco and mix well. Refrigerate until ready to use.

YIELD: 8 servings

CALORIES
Per serving: 34
Fat: 27%
Carbohydrates: 53%
Protein: 20%

CARBOHYDRATES: 5.7 GM
PROTEIN: 2.1 GM
DIETARY FIBER: trace
SODIUM: 33 MG
CHOLESTEROL: 1 MG

TOTAL FAT: 1.3 GM
Saturated fat: .2 GM
Monounsaturated fat: .8 GM

Pyramid equivalencies: ¼ dairy

Almond Cake

This light cake has the flavor of a rich almond pastry.

2 slices multigrain bread
⅓ cup sliced almonds
⅓ cup raw oatmeal
1 cup brown sugar, firmly
  packed
1 cup egg whites
1 tablespoon grated lemon peel

1 teaspoon almond extract
3 tablespoons water
2 tablespoons fruit-sweetened
  peach preserves
1 tablespoon sliced almonds for
  garnish

Preheat oven to 350°F. Place the bread in a food processor and pulse until the bread is ground. Transfer from the processor to a mixing bowl.

Place the almonds and oatmeal in the processor and pulse until ground. Transfer to the bowl with bread crumbs. Stir in the brown sugar, breaking up any lumps.

Rinse the processor container. Pour the egg whites into the processor and run continuously until the whites are thick and creamy. Add the lemon peel and almond extract.

Empty the egg white mixture into the bowl with the dry ingredients.

Fold mixture until blended. Spray a 9-inch springform pan or nonstick round cake pan with nonstick cooking spray. Pour the batter into the pan. Bake at 350°F. for 40 minutes, or until the cake is browned and pulled away from the edges of the pan.

Insert a knife around the edges of the pan to loosen the cake. Carefully tap the pan and invert on to a plate. Whisk together the water and peach preserves until blended. Pour over the cake. Let stand 5 minutes before serving. Serve warm or at room temperature. Sprinkle the remaining tablespoon of almonds over the top.

YIELD: 8 servings

CALORIES	CARBOHYDRATES: 36.7 GM	TOTAL FAT: 3.9 GM
Per serving: 198	PROTEIN: 5.6 GM	Saturated fat: .4 GM
Fat: 17%	DIETARY FIBER: 1.6 GM	Monounsaturated fat: 2.3 GM
Carbohydrates: 72%	SODIUM: 102 MG	
Protein: 11%	CHOLESTEROL: 0 MG	

Pyramid equivalencies: ½ grain, 1 extra

Passover Almond Cake

Matzo meal easily transforms the cake into a Passover dessert.

In the Almond Cake recipe, replace the bread crumbs and oatmeal with ¾ cup coarse matzo meal. Increase the almonds to ½ cup.

YIELD: 8 servings

CALORIES	CARBOHYDRATES: 42.0 GM	TOTAL FAT: 4.8 GM
Per serving: 230	PROTEIN: 6.1 GM	Saturated fat: .4 GM
Fat: 18%	DIETARY FIBER: 1.2 GM	Monounsaturated fat: 3.0 GM
Carbohydrates: 72%	SODIUM: 58 MG	
Protein: 10%	CHOLESTEROL: 0 MG	

Pyramid equivalencies: ½ grain, 1 extra

Golden Fruit Mélange

This blaze of golden fruit is a marvelous accompaniment to Almond Cake, frozen yogurt or pancakes. It is also delicious by itself. As a topping, the recipe serves 8. As a compote by itself, consider the recipe 4 servings.

⅓ cup fruit-sweetened apricot or peach preserves

3 tablespoons water

1 tablespoon fresh lemon juice

½ teaspoon ground ginger

1 tablespoon apricot or peach brandy, optional

2 fresh peaches, sliced and pitted

2 fresh nectarines, sliced and pitted

6 apricots, sliced and pitted

In a large bowl, whisk together the preserves, water, lemon juice, ginger and brandy. Add the fruit and toss until well coated. Refrigerate until ready to serve. Do not prepare the fruit more than 6 hours before serving time.

YIELD: 8 servings

CALORIES
Per serving: 58
Fat: 4%
Carbohydrates: 90%
Protein: 6%

CARBOHYDRATES: 15.4 GM
PROTEIN: .9 GM
DIETARY FIBER: .6 GM
SODIUM: 1 MG
CHOLESTEROL: 0 MG

TOTAL FAT: .3 GM
Saturated fat: trace
Monounsaturated fat: trace

Pyramid equivalencies: 1 fruit

23

Soup Kitchen Buffet

A BUFFET of warm, earthy soups is a celebration of "comfort" foods. Today, a younger generation of diners likely thinks a smorgasbord of soups would be a really weird dinner party. I grew up in a time when soup suppers were part of the annual fund-raising events for schools, churches and other civic groups. At the risk of sounding like an old fogy, I would like to bring the soup supper back into fashionable dining. Soup is a nineties thing. It is, I just declared it so! Soup is ideal for our current lifestyle. Soup can be prepared easily, be made in advance and stored, can offer a whole meal in one pot, provide a lot of nutrients, satisfy the appetite of dieters, furnish extra calories to the nondieter and gladden the palate of the gourmand. Enjoy a Soup Kitchen Buffet!

SOUP KITCHEN BUFFET (MENU FOR 4)

Green and Gold Vegetable Soup
Black Bean and Shiitake Mushroom Soup
Peruvian Chicken Soup
Rainbow Crudités
Cheese and Herb Scones with Yogurt Cheese Dollops
Melba Ice

268

Additional Recipes:
Green and White Vegetable Soup
White Bean and Mushroom Soup
Mexican Chicken Soup

Soup has a way of satisfying unlike any other dish. We think of soup as a simple dish, but it can be quite complex. Because the broth that goes into soup is simmered for a long time, it develops a deeper, more complex flavor than most foods that are cooked quickly. Diverse ingredients that end up being cooked together also contribute to the intricate flavor mosaic that makes soups so delicious. If all you have ever eaten is canned soup, this may not make much sense. For me, soup has an appeal that transcends flavor. It's the "idea" of soup—the suggestion of warmth and comfort and appreciation for the simple things of life. A buffet of homemade soups only magnifies that appeal.

Just because it's soup doesn't mean that a buffet of three soups is any easier to prepare than a traditional three-course menu. Soup Kitchen Buffet takes as long as most other menus in this book. However, the greater part of the work can be done several hours before.

If you have three soup tureens, it's easy to serve the soups buffet-style. I usually just bring three pots to the table and serve the guests their choices. Of course, most guests want to sample all three soups! To create the sense of a buffet, I prefer using three soups. What the three soups are doesn't matter a whole lot except that they should offer variety. I wouldn't feature more than one bean soup or more than one milk- or dairy-based soup. I like to offer at least one soup that has a lot of vegetables. If I don't know the preferences of my guests, I would make sure at least one of the soups is suitable for vegetarians.

For this Soup Kitchen Buffet, I chose three soups that seem familiar, yet offer something a little different. An ordinary vegetable soup becomes special when it's devoted to two colors of vegetables, a thick bean soup is given Asian seasonings and basic chicken soup is enriched with an Andean grain. Each of the soups is richly flavored. Your guests will never know you didn't use any refined fat.

Green and gold in Green and Gold Vegetable Soup offer a lot more than just a vibrant display of color. Green and gold also represent a spectrum of valuable nutrients. Deep-green vegetables are rich in a variety of vitamins and minerals that often includes calcium and iron.

Yellow, orange and red vegetables are prime suppliers of beta-carotene. With all of these antioxidants, Green and Gold Vegetable Soup is a delight to the immune system. Green and gold also represent important flavor contributions. Gold vegetables when cooked produce a sweetness that mellows and synthesizes the herbal flavor of deep-green vegetables. To get a balance of nutrients requires eating a variety of products. Alternating the color of vegetables covers a lot of nutritional bases. Green and White Vegetable Soup is a variation that offers other possibilities for good nutrition and good taste.

Black Bean and Shiitake Mushroom Soup reflects a mix of cultures. Soy and ginger are seldom used in Latin American cooking, but are extremely popular in Asian cuisine. Thick bean soups are customary everywhere in Latin America but are foreign to most Asian countries. Black beans are commonly used in Asia, but generally not in thick bean soups. When a thick black bean soup is seasoned with soy and ginger, do you have an Asian or a Latin American dish? Regardless of ethnic origins, this inky black soup has a deep flavor that will satisfy hearty appetites. Although most diners know beans are a valuable source of protein, they may not realize beans also contain vital minerals and vitamins. For a slightly different flavor, try making the soup with white beans. White Bean and Mushroom Soup has an equally pleasing flavor but lacks the dramatic appearance of the black bean version. As beans go, both the black beans and small white beans are relatively quick cooking. Even without soaking, the beans should be tender within 60 to 90 minutes.

Peruvian Chicken Soup is my re-creation of a soup that I had in a restaurant outside of Ollantaytambo, Peru. Instead of noodles or rice, this chicken soup has quinoa, an ancient Incan grain. The grain can be purchased in most health food stores and in some gourmet markets. If you can't find quinoa, try the Mexican Chicken Soup, which has a very different flavor but has all the rustic earthiness of its Peruvian counterpart. Either soup requires a base of full-bodied chicken broth.

Also included in this menu is a simple plate of pear wedges and raw vegetable sticks. Although Rainbow Crudités hardly requires a recipe, it is presented here to show the importance of offering contrasting textures. The firm crispness of raw vegetables complements the softer texture of the soups. The sweetness of the pears helps refresh the palate between soup courses.

Bread is essential with soup. Usually, I prefer a plain, crusty whole wheat bread for sopping up the last morsel of soup. I've incorporated Cheese and Herb Scones into this menu because it's one of the few breads that can be made at the last minute. From the time you first begin mixing ingredients to the time it's out of the oven is about 35 minutes. I like the bread plain, but I realize a lot of people are not going to agree. One of the questions I'm most frequently asked is "If you don't use butter or margarine, what do you put on bread?" Yogurt Cheese Dollops make a splendid topping for bread. The dollops have an elegant appearance that helps turn soup and bread into a grand dining experience!

In keeping with the casual spirit of the menu, I suggest a simple dessert such as fresh fruit, fruit compote or a frozen fruit sorbet. Many supermarkets offer a wide variety of fruit sorbets. Some of these sorbets seem a little too sweet for my taste. Melba Ice is a colorful sorbet with an appealing tartness.

This menu was created for 4 persons, although each soup recipe has 8 servings. I did this so guests can have more than 1 serving of a particular soup. Whenever I prepare soup, I make extra for the next day's lunch. The bean and chicken soups freeze well for later use.

NUTRIENT ANALYSIS FOR SOUP KITCHEN BUFFET

The nutrient analysis for the complete menu includes 1 serving each of Green and Gold Vegetable Soup, Black Bean and Shiitake Mushroom Soup, Peruvian Chicken Soup, Rainbow Crudités, Yogurt Cheese Dollops and Melba Ice. The analysis accounts for 2 servings of Cheese and Herb Scones. This is a very hearty meal. Some diners may want to forgo one of the soups or have only 1 serving of scones.

CALORIES	CARBOHYDRATES: 208.0 GM	TOTAL FAT: 10.4 GM
For total meal: 1,076	PROTEIN: 50.7 GM	Saturated fat: 2.3 GM
Fat: 8%	DIETARY FIBER: 16.7 GM	Monounsaturated fat: 3.9 GM
Carbohydrates: 74%	SODIUM: 1,261 MG	
Protein: 18%	CHOLESTEROL: 55 MG	

Pyramid equivalencies: 4¼ grains, 5 vegetables, 2½ fruits, 1⅔ proteins, ¾ dairy

Green and Gold Vegetable Soup

This colorful soup has a delightful mix of textures, soft and tender to sprightly crisp.

6 cups defatted, unsalted chicken broth or water
1 large leek
4 garlic cloves
1 tablespoon freshly grated lemon peel
2 teaspoons low-sodium soy sauce
½ teaspoon dried red chile flakes
½ teaspoon dry oregano
1 sweet potato, peeled and cubed
1 large carrot, peeled and sliced in ¼-inch rounds

1 cup cooked garbanzo beans
1 cup frozen lima beans
1 cup cooked brown rice
1 cup frozen green peas
1 small green bell pepper, seeded and diced
1 cup fresh or frozen broccoli florets
2 cups chopped fresh spinach (or 1 cup frozen)
2 tablespoons finely chopped parsley or other fresh herb

In a large pot, bring the broth to a low boil. Meanwhile, cut away the upper green part of the leek. Finely chop the rest and wash in a colander. Finely mince the garlic. Add the leek, garlic, lemon peel, low-sodium soy sauce, chile flakes and oregano to the broth. Cover and simmer for 5 minutes.

Add the sweet potato and carrot; cover and simmer for 15 minutes. Add the garbanzo beans and lima beans and cook for 5 minutes. If necessary, add more liquid. At this point, the soup can be prepared and set aside for later use. Do not add the rice and remaining green vegetables until just before serving time.

Combine all of the ingredients and cook for 3 to 5 minutes or until completely heated through. The green products should remain bright and crisp.

YIELD: 8 servings

CALORIES   CARBOHYDRATES: 29.2 GM   TOTAL FAT: .9 GM
Per serving: 150   PROTEIN: 7.4 GM   Saturated fat: .1 GM
Fat: 5%   DIETARY FIBER: 3.5 GM   Monounsaturated fat: .1 GM
Carbohydrates: 76%   SODIUM: 98 MG
Protein: 19%   CHOLESTEROL: 0 MG

Pyramid equivalencies: ¼ grain, 2 vegetables, ½ protein

Green and White
Vegetable Soup

This variation on the previous recipe replaces the yellow vegetables with white ones, creating a totally different flavor.

In the previous recipe, Green and Gold Vegetable Soup, replace the sweet potato with a large white potato. Replace the carrot with 2 parsnips. Replace the rice and garbanzo beans with 2 cups cooked macaroni or other small pasta. Proceed as directed in the previous recipe.

YIELD: 8 servings

CALORIES   CARBOHYDRATES: 34.3 GM   TOTAL FAT: .7 GM
Per serving: 169   PROTEIN: 8.0 GM   Saturated fat: .1 GM
Fat: 3%   DIETARY FIBER: 5.1 GM   Monounsaturated fat: .1 GM
Carbohydrates: 78%   SODIUM: 97 MG
Protein: 19%   CHOLESTEROL: 0 MG

Pyramid equivalencies: ½ grain, 2 vegetables, ⅛ protein

Black Bean and
Shiitake Mushroom Soup

Other mushrooms can be substituted for the shiitakes. In fact, a mix of mushrooms is superb.

2½ cups dry black beans
8 cups water or unsalted, defatted chicken broth
1 large yellow onion, coarsely chopped
8 cloves garlic, finely minced
1 tablespoon fresh ginger, finely minced
½ pound shiitake mushrooms, coarsely chopped

1 cup dry sherry
2 tablespoons low-sodium soy sauce
2 green onions, finely diced (including green top)
½ cup finely diced red or yellow bell pepper
½ cup coarsely chopped fresh cilantro or parsley

Rinse the beans in cold water and check for any small pebbles or debris. In a soup pot, combine the water or broth, beans, yellow onion, garlic and ginger. Cook covered at a low temperature for 1½ hours or until the beans are tender.

Transfer one-third of the bean mixture to a blender and puree until smooth. Return the puree to the soup pot. Also add the mushrooms, sherry and soy sauce. Continue cooking at low temperature for 40 minutes. If necessary, add more water to the pot.

Serve hot, garnished with green onion, bell pepper and cilantro or parsley.

YIELD: 8 servings

CALORIES	CARBOHYDRATES: 44.4 GM	TOTAL FAT: 1.1 GM
Per serving: 237	PROTEIN: 15.4 GM	Saturated fat: trace
Fat: 4%	DIETARY FIBER: .3 GM	Monounsaturated fat: trace
Carbohydrates: 71%	SODIUM: 146 MG	
Protein: 25%	CHOLESTEROL: 0 MG	

Pyramid equivalencies: 1 vegetable, ⅔ protein

White Bean and Mushroom Soup

What are typically labeled "small white beans" in supermarkets can be substituted for the black beans in the previous recipe. This bean is similar in size to black beans and generally takes about the same length of time to cook. Sometimes, the mushrooms will cause the white beans to have an unappealing gray color. If this happens, add 1 to 2 table-spoons of unsalted tomato paste to improve the color.

Nutrient information is nearly identical to recipe for Black Bean and Shiitake Mushroom Soup.

Peruvian Chicken Soup

Richly flavored chicken soup depends on using a full-bodied chicken broth (see page 49).

6 cups defatted, unsalted chicken broth (do not use water)
1 cup finely chopped red onion
3 cloves garlic, finely minced
2 teaspoons low-sodium soy sauce
¼ cup uncooked quinoa
1 large potato, diced
2 medium carrots, sliced
2 large chicken breast halves, bone, skin and fat removed
Freshly ground pepper
2 tablespoons finely minced fresh oregano

Combine the broth, red onion, garlic and soy sauce and bring to a boil. Reduce the heat and add the quinoa, potato and carrots and simmer covered 30 minutes or until the vegetables are nearly tender.

Meanwhile, dice the chicken breast. Add to pot and continue cook-ing covered for 10 minutes. Serve hot with a little black pepper ground over each bowl. Complete with a sprinkling of fresh oregano.

YIELD: 8 servings

CALORIES   CARBOHYDRATES: 13.8 GM   TOTAL FAT: 1.1 GM
Per serving: 106   PROTEIN: 10.0 GM   Saturated fat: .3 GM
Fat: 9%   DIETARY FIBER: .4 GM   Monounsaturated fat: .5 GM
Carbohydrates: 53%   SODIUM: 72.3 MG
Protein: 38%   CHOLESTEROL: 22 MG

Pyramid equivalencies: 1 vegetable, ⅓ protein

Mexican Chicken Soup

There are so many variations on chicken soup that someday I'm tempted to devote a whole book to it. For instance, in the previous recipe, for a taste variation substitute yams for the potato and rice for the quinoa. My favorite variation is this one that I call Mexican Chicken Soup, based on a "caldo" (broth) that I used to have at one of my neighborhood restaurants in Los Angeles.

In the previous recipe, Peruvian Chicken Soup, replace the potato with a sweet potato. Omit the quinoa. Remove the husk and silk from 2 ears of white corn. Cut the corn into 1-inch-thick rounds. After the chicken has cooked for 8 minutes, add the corn and cook another 5 minutes. Serve the soup with a variety of fresh condiments on the side. These may include wedges of lime or lemon, freshly chopped cilantro, finely minced jalapeño or serrano chiles and freshly chopped tomato.

YIELD: 8 servings

CALORIES   CARBOHYDRATES: 18.5 GM   TOTAL FAT: 1.2 GM
Per serving: 123   PROTEIN: 10.4 GM   Saturated fat: .3 GM
Fat: 8%   DIETARY FIBER: 2.8 GM   Monounsaturated fat: .4 GM
Carbohydrates: 59%   SODIUM: 75 MG
Protein: 33%   CHOLESTEROL: 22 MG

Pyramid equivalencies: ¼ grain, 1 vegetable, ⅓ protein

Rainbow Crudités

Simple, unadorned raw vegetables offer a pleasing contrast in color and texture to other dishes on the menu.

2 celery stalks, cut into 2- to 3-inch sticks
1 large carrot, cut into 2- to 3-inch sticks
1 yellow crookneck squash, cut into 2- to 3-inch sticks
1 bunch radishes, washed and trimmed
2 large pears
2 tablespoons fresh lemon juice
¼ cup water
3 large red cabbage leaves

Prepare all of the vegetable crudités and rinse in cold water. Tightly wrap the vegetables in plastic and refrigerate. Core the pears and cut in thin wedges. Mix together the lemon juice and water and immediately toss the pear wedges in the mixture and refrigerate.

When ready to serve, place the cabbage leaves on a platter and attractively arrange the vegetables and pear wedges on top.

YIELD: 4 servings

CALORIES
Per serving: 59
Fat: 6%
Carbohydrates: 88%
Protein: 6%

CARBOHYDRATES: 14.5 GM
PROTEIN: 1.0 GM
DIETARY FIBER: 3.4 GM
SODIUM: 27 MG
CHOLESTEROL: 0 MG

TOTAL FAT: .4 GM
Saturated fat: trace
Monounsaturated fat: .1 GM

Pyramid equivalencies: 1 vegetable, ½ fruit

Cheese and Herb Scones

This is a heavy scone that is a delicious accompaniment to soups and salads.

1½ *cups whole wheat flour*
¼ *cup cornstarch*
1½ *teaspoons baking powder*
½ *teaspoon baking soda*
½ *cup oatmeal*
1 *cup plain nonfat yogurt*
3 *tablespoons freshly grated Parmesan cheese*

1 *tablespoon extra-virgin olive oil*
1 *tablespoon honey*
1 *tablespoon water*
2 *tablespoons finely minced fresh parsley*
1 *tablespoon finely minced fresh rosemary*

Preheat oven to 375°F. Sift together the flour, cornstarch, baking powder and soda. Stir in the oatmeal and set aside.

Stir together the yogurt, cheese, oil, honey and water. Add the dry mixture and fresh herbs. Mix well and knead for 2 or 3 minutes on a floured surface. If dough is too sticky, add more flour. Shape the dough into a flat circle, about the size of a pie pan.

Spray a baking sheet with nonstick cooking spray. Cut the dough into 8 pie-shaped pieces. Transfer the scones to the baking sheet. Bake at 375°F. for 20 to 25 minutes or until lightly browned.

YIELD: 8 servings

CALORIES
Per serving: 152
Fat: 18%
Carbohydrates: 65%
Protein: 17%

CARBOHYDRATES: 25.6 GM
PROTEIN: 6.5 GM
DIETARY FIBER: 3.2 GM
SODIUM: 118 MG
CHOLESTEROL: 0 MG

TOTAL FAT: 3.1 GM
Saturated fat: .9 GM
Monounsaturated fat: 1.6 GM

Pyramid equivalencies: 2 grains, ¼ dairy

Yogurt Cheese Dollops

This is kind of a do-it-yourself spread for bread. Each dollop has 3 separate flavors: slightly tart, richly pungent and very sweet. The presentation of the dollop allows the diner to keep the flavors separate or to mix them together.

Basic Yogurt Cheese (recipe
on page 255) (about
2 tablespoons per portion)
Grainy Dijon-style mustard
(1 teaspoon per portion)
Honey in a squeeze bottle
container (1 to 3 teaspoons
per portion)

Finely minced fresh parsley or
other fresh herb (¼ to ½
teaspoon per portion),
optional

(NOTE: one recipe Basic Yogurt Cheese will yield 10 to 12 dollops.)

Yogurt Cheese Dollops are to be prepared as individual portions for each diner. I like to use little flat dishes like the ones that are used in Asian restaurants for dipping sauce.

Using a 1-ounce ice cream scoop, large melon baller or soup spoon, place a dollop of Yogurt Cheese on small individual serving plates. Using the backside of a teaspoon, press on the dollop, creating a small crater and slightly flattening the dollop.

Gently spoon a teaspoon of mustard into the center of the dollop. You may need a small spatula or another spoon to slide the mustard into place. If you don't care for mustard, spoon the fresh herb into the center of the dollop. Even if you use the mustard, you may want to sprinkle a little parsley over the dollop after the honey has been applied.

Carefully squeeze a thin ring of honey around the dollop of Yogurt Cheese. The Yogurt Cheese Dollops can be prepared up to 2 hours before dining. Refrigerate until ready for use. Any leftover dollops can be mixed together and used as a dressing for salads or sandwiches.

YIELD: 1 serving

CALORIES	CARBOHYDRATES: 11.7 GM	TOTAL FAT: .4 GM
Per serving: 61	PROTEIN: 3.0 GM	Saturated fat: .1 GM
Fat: 5%	DIETARY FIBER: trace	Monounsaturated fat: trace
Carbohydrates: 76%	SODIUM: 30 MG	
Protein: 19%	CHOLESTEROL: 1 MG	

Pyramid equivalencies: ¼ dairy

Melba Ice

This sorbet was created for quick and easy preparation in a food processor.

2 cups frozen, unsweetened peach slices

½ cup fruit-sweetened peach preserves

1 cup frozen, unsweetened raspberries

2 tablespoons fruit-sweetened raspberry preserves

1 tablespoon raspberry-flavored liqueur

4 sprigs fresh mint for garnish, optional

Additional thawed peach slices or raspberries for garnish, optional

This recipe begins with frozen fruit. Do not thaw the fruit. Combine the frozen peach slices and peach preserves in a food processor. Process until smooth and creamy. If necessary, add a little water to process. Transfer to a suitable bowl and place in the freezer.

Combine the frozen raspberries, raspberry preserves and liqueur in the food processor and puree until smooth and creamy. If necessary, add a little water to process. Remove the peach puree from the freezer. Swirl the raspberry mixture into the peach puree. Return to the freezer.

Before serving, let stand at room temperature for a few minutes to soften. Serve in goblets garnished with fresh mint or thawed peach slices or raspberries.

YIELD: 4 servings

CALORIES
Per serving: 159
Fat: 1%
Carbohydrates: 97%
Protein: 2%

CARBOHYDRATES: 43.2 GM
PROTEIN: .9 GM
DIETARY FIBER: 2.7 GM
SODIUM: 1 MG
CHOLESTEROL: 0 MG

TOTAL FAT: .3 GM
Saturated fat: trace
Monounsaturated fat: trace

Pyramid equivalencies: 2 fruits

24

Sicilian Three Pasta Supper

LONG, LEISURELY meals that take 3 or 4 hours to eat are becoming a rarity in the United States. Fortunately, the tradition is alive and well in Italy. Three pastas with three sauces is generally served as a first course at a long meal. The pasta trio is usually served at room temperature and may be part of a large table of appetizers. The sauces commonly include one or more vegetarian sauces, an anchovy or fish-flavored sauce and possibly a sauce seasoned with ham or sausage. For this menu, I've made the three pastas the main focus of the meal. This is not a 3-hour dinner; on the other hand, it isn't intended to be eaten in 30 minutes, either.

SICILIAN THREE PASTA SUPPER (MENU FOR 4)

Whole Wheat Spaghetti with Broccoli and Tomatoes
Fusilli with Anchovy and Red Pepper Sauce
Penne with Mushrooms, Artichoke Hearts and Dried Tomatoes
Fennel Salad with Lemon-Garlic Dressing
Whole Wheat Bread Sticks
Strawberries Balsamic

This is a Sicilian meal adapted for the American table. I use much less oil than is traditional for preparing sauces and dressings. I reduced the amount of pasta in each dish because of serving three pastas at once. If you were serving these dishes separately, I would plan on two ounces of dry pasta per serving instead of the 1½ ounces you find in these recipes. Because the entire meal uses a lot of flour, I feel we should include whole grain flour as well as the refined product. Whole wheat pasta is probably more popular in the United States than Italy. However, whole grain breads, including bread sticks, are common on the Italian table.

Part of the fun of the Sicilian Three Pasta Supper is to offer pastas with a variety of shapes and textures. The pasta identified with each sauce is just one possibility. Feel free to experiment with a variety of fresh or dry pastas. Whole Wheat Spaghetti with Broccoli and Tomatoes has pasta with a slightly nutty flavor and texture. Fusilli with Anchovy and Red Pepper Sauce captures the sauce in the folds of the pasta. Penne with Mushrooms, Artichoke Hearts and Dried Tomatoes draws the brothy sauce into the tubular pasta. All of the pastas are topped with sauces redolent of flavorful vegetables. The meal hardly requires any other vegetable dish, but Fennel Salad with Lemon-Garlic Dressing offers a pleasant contrast in texture and aromatic flavor. Crispy Whole Wheat Bread Sticks also offer a delightful contrast to the soft texture of the pasta. A simple dessert is the best answer to this hearty meal. Strawberries Balsamic is a satisfying choice. A full-bodied red or white wine, mineral water and espresso would serve well as beverages.

NUTRIENT ANALYSIS FOR SICILIAN THREE PASTA SUPPER

This is a family-style, help-yourself menu. The way I serve the dishes is to prepare them all at once, place them on the table and let everyone serve themselves. The nutrient analysis for the whole meal is based upon a full serving of each pasta dish. Apart from growing teenagers and athletes, I doubt that most diners would eat full servings of each. Realizing that the figures for the total meal are for more food than you would likely consume, don't feel guilty about a glass of Chianti or an extra bread stick!

The nutrient analysis for the complete meal includes 1 serving each of Whole Wheat Spaghetti with Broccoli and Tomatoes, Fusilli with Anchovy and Red Pepper Sauce, Penne with Mushrooms, Artichoke Hearts and Dried Tomatoes, Fennel Salad with Lemon-Garlic Dressing and Strawberries Balsamic. The analysis also includes 2 Whole Wheat Bread Sticks.

CALORIES

For total meal: 1,192

Fat: 21%

Carbohydrates: 64%

Protein: 15%

CARBOHYDRATES: 210.8 GM

PROTEIN: 48.0 GM

DIETARY FIBER: 24.2 GM

SODIUM: 935 MG

CHOLESTEROL: 5 MG

TOTAL FAT: 31.3 GM

Saturated fat: 4.3 GM

Monounsaturated fat: 16.0 GM

Pyramid equivalencies: 6½ grains, 6 vegetables, 1⅛ fruits, ¼ dairy

Whole Wheat Spaghetti with Broccoli and Tomatoes

Whole wheat pasta requires an assertive sauce to match the nutty, robust flavor of the pasta.

½ cup dry sherry

¼ cup fresh orange juice

2 tablespoons balsamic vinegar

2 tablespoons fresh lemon juice

½ teaspoon low-sodium soy sauce

½ cup finely diced red onion

4 cloves garlic, finely minced

1 red or yellow bell pepper, seeded and diced

1 tablespoon unsalted tomato paste

1 tablespoon extra-virgin olive oil

8 Roma tomatoes, quartered

1 tablespoon finely minced fresh rosemary

6 ounces whole wheat spaghetti

4 quarts boiling water

4 cups fresh broccoli florets, broken into small pieces and blanched in hot water

¼ cup finely grated Parmesan cheese

In a saucepan, mix together the sherry, orange juice, vinegar, lemon juice and soy sauce. Bring the liquid to a boil, reduce the heat to low and add the onion and garlic. Cover the pot and simmer for 10 minutes. Add the bell pepper and simmer 2 minutes. Stir in the tomato paste and olive oil and cook for 2 minutes. Add the tomato quarters and rosemary and heat through.

Meanwhile, drop the whole wheat pasta in the boiling water. Two minutes before the end of the cooking time listed on the package, check the pasta for doneness. Whole wheat pasta usually takes about 10 minutes to cook. Drain pasta when done. The hot pasta water may be used to blanch the broccoli. Rinse the pasta under warm tap water. If using the pasta water to blanch the broccoli, also rinse the broccoli under warm tap water.

Toss the pasta with the sauce. Spoon the broccoli over the pasta. Sprinkle the broccoli with the cheese. Serve the dish warm or at room temperature.

YIELD: 4 servings

CALORIES	CARBOHYDRATES: 49.6 GM	TOTAL FAT: 7.4 GM
Per serving: 310	PROTEIN: 15.8 GM	Saturated fat: 1.9 GM
Fat: 21%	DIETARY FIBER: 10.9 GM	Monounsaturated fat: 3.1 GM
Carbohydrates: 60%	SODIUM: 230 MG	
Protein: 19%	CHOLESTEROL: 5 MG	

Pyramid equivalencies: 1½ grains, 2¼ vegetables, ¼ dairy

Fusilli with Anchovy and Red Pepper Sauce

The sauce is suitable for a variety of pastas. I like to use "twisted" pastas such as fusilli, rotelle or even farfalle (butterfly, bow-tie shapes).

½ cup extra-dry vermouth
1 large red onion, finely chopped
8 cloves garlic
1 tablespoon finely grated lemon peel
1 tablespoon fresh lemon juice
¼ teaspoon ground black pepper
2 red bell peppers, seeded and diced
4 Roma tomatoes, finely chopped

4 canned anchovy fillets, rinsed and finely minced
2 teaspoons unsalted tomato paste, optional
6 ounces dry "twisted" semolina pasta (fusilli, rotelle, farfalle)
4 quarts boiling water
¼ cup finely minced fresh basil
3 tablespoons pine nuts

Combine the vermouth, red onion, garlic, lemon peel, lemon juice and black pepper in a saucepan. Simmer covered at low temperature for 5 minutes. Add the red peppers and tomatoes, cover and continue cooking at low temperature for 30 minutes. Stir in the anchovies and heat through. If desired, stir in the tomato paste to thicken.

Meanwhile, drop the pasta into the boiling water. Two minutes before the end of the cooking time listed on the package, check the pasta for doneness. When the pasta is cooked, drain it and rinse in warm water. Immediately toss the pasta with the sauce. Sprinkle the fresh basil over the top followed by the pine nuts. Serve immediately.

YIELD: 4 servings

CALORIES	CARBOHYDRATES: 46.6 GM	TOTAL FAT: 4.6 GM
Per serving: 256	PROTEIN: 10.1 GM	Saturated fat: .8 GM
Fat: 15%	DIETARY FIBER: 3.9 GM	Monounsaturated fat: 2.0 GM
Carbohydrates: 70%	SODIUM: 161 MG	
Protein: 15%	CHOLESTEROL: trace	

Pyramid equivalencies: 1½ grains, 1½ vegetables

Penne with Mushrooms, Artichoke Hearts and Dried Tomatoes

Any tubular pasta will serve well in this dish.

½ cup extra-dry vermouth
½ pound sliced mushrooms
2 ounces dried tomatoes
¼ cup minced shallots
4 cloves garlic, finely minced
¼ teaspoon black pepper
9 ounces frozen artichoke hearts
6 ounces canned unsalted vegetable juice cocktail

12 olives, sliced
2 tablespoons rinsed capers
6 ounces dry penne or other tubular pasta
4 quarts boiling water
2 tablespoons finely minced fresh basil
2 tablespoons finely minced fresh Italian parsley

Combine the vermouth, mushrooms, dried tomatoes, shallots, garlic and black pepper in a saucepan. Simmer covered at low temperature for 30 minutes. Remove the lid, add the artichoke hearts and vegetable juice cocktail. Simmer uncovered for 15 minutes. Add the olives and capers and cook for 5 minutes.

Meanwhile, drop the pasta into the boiling water. Two minutes before the end of the cooking time listed on the package, check the pasta for doneness. When the pasta is cooked, drain it and rinse with warm water. Immediately toss the pasta with the artichoke sauce. Sprinkle the fresh herbs over each serving.

YIELD: 4 servings

CALORIES	CARBOHYDRATES: 57.5 GM	TOTAL FAT: 7.9 GM
Per serving: 292	PROTEIN: 12.3 GM	Saturated fat: .3 GM
Fat: 11%	DIETARY FIBER: 3.2 GM	Monounsaturated fat: 5.0 GM
Carbohydrates: 73%	SODIUM: 489 MG	
Protein: 16%	CHOLESTEROL: 0 MG	

Pyramid equivalencies: 1½ grains, 1 vegetable

Fennel Salad with Lemon-Garlic Dressing

Fennel Salad is often served as a first course in Sicily. I also like to serve it as a condiment or side dish to a main course.

2 bulbs of fennel, sliced thinly   4 cups shredded romaine lettuce
1 recipe Lemon-Garlic
   Dressing (recipe follows)

After slicing the fennel, immediately toss with the Lemon-Garlic Dressing. Refrigerate and marinate 1 to 4 hours in the dressing. Serve over shredded lettuce.

YIELD: 4 servings

CALORIES
Per serving: 72
Fat: 34%
Carbohydrates: 52%
Protein: 14%

CARBOHYDRATES: 8.4 GM
PROTEIN: 3.5 GM
DIETARY FIBER: 1.1 GM
SODIUM: 5 MG
CHOLESTEROL: 0 MG

TOTAL FAT: 5.6 GM
Saturated fat: .5 GM
Monounsaturated fat: 2.5 GM

Pyramid equivalencies: 1 vegetable, ⅛ fruit

Lemon-Garlic Dressing

In addition to salads, use this dressing as a sauce for steamed vegetables. It is excellent either hot or cold. If desired, add a tablespoon of minced fresh herbs. If you wish to reduce your fat intake even further, omit the olive oil and substitute 1 tablespoon tomato puree.

3 tablespoons fresh lemon
juice
3 tablespoons fresh orange
juice
1 tablespoon extra-virgin olive
oil

1 teaspoon low-sodium Dijon-
style mustard
2 cloves garlic

Place all of the ingredients in a blender and process for 15 seconds. Let stand 1 hour before using. Stir before using. Will keep 4 or 5 days in the refrigerator.

YIELD: 4 servings

CALORIES
Per serving: 41
Fat: 72%
Carbohydrates: 26%
Protein: 2%

CARBOHYDRATES: 2.8 GM
PROTEIN: .3 GM
DIETARY FIBER: .2 GM
SODIUM: 1 MG
CHOLESTEROL: 0 MG

TOTAL FAT: 3.5 GM
Saturated fat: .5 GM
Monounsaturated fat: 2.5 GM

Pyramid equivalencies: ⅛ fruit

Whole Wheat Bread Sticks

This recipe was designed for the quick preparation of bread sticks, taking about half the time of more traditional recipes. To make the recipe, you must use rapid-rise yeast. This is available in most super-markets and is usually next to the envelopes of standard yeast.

2 cups whole wheat flour	¼ cup extra-virgin olive oil
2 cups all-purpose flour	2 tablespoons honey
1 envelope quick-rise yeast	1 tablespoon low-sodium soy
2 teaspoons granulated garlic powder	sauce
½ teaspoon ground black pepper	1 egg white, slightly beaten with 2 tablespoons water
1¼ cups water	2 tablespoons sesame seeds

In a large bowl, sift together the flours, yeast, garlic powder and pepper. Mix well and set aside.

Bring the water to a boil. Remove from the heat and immediately stir in the oil, honey and soy sauce. Mix until the honey is completely dissolved. Let stand 1 minute.

When the liquid is cool enough to touch, but still warmer than luke-warm, add to bowl with the flour. Mix until completely blended. Transfer the mixture to a clean, floured surface. Knead for about 5 minutes or until the mixture is smooth and elastic, but not sticky. If necessary, incorporate more flour into the dough. Transfer the mound of dough to an oiled bowl. Cover with a cloth, place in draft-free, slightly warm area. Let stand 10 minutes.

Transfer the dough to a floured work surface. Pat the dough into a 16-by-4-inch rectangle. Cut the dough into 4 equal rectangles. Cut each section into 8 strips. Lift each strip and pull, creating a long strip. Do not make any longer than the width of the baking sheet. Place the strips on a baking sheet sprayed with nonstick cooking spray, allowing about ½ inch between strips. Brush each strip with the egg white and sprinkle sesame seeds over the top. Return to a warm, draft-free area and let rise for 1 hour.

After preheating an oven to 425°F., bake for 10 to 15 minutes or until the sticks are browned.

Serve immediately or allow to cool and store in a dry, covered container. Do not refrigerate. Will keep several days.

YIELD: 32 sticks

CALORIES	CARBOHYDRATES: 16.7 GM	TOTAL FAT: 2.9 GM
Per stick: 103	PROTEIN: 2.9 GM	Saturated fat: .4 GM
Fat: 25%	DIETARY FIBER: 1.6 GM	Monounsaturated fat: 1.7 GM
Carbohydrates: 64%	SODIUM: 24 MG	
Protein: 11%	CHOLESTEROL: 0 MG	

Pyramid equivalencies: 1 grain

Strawberries Balsamic

The combination of balsamic vinegar and strawberry preserves gives the berries a rich, tangy flavor.

¼ cup balsamic vinegar
3 tablespoons fruit-sweetened
   strawberry preserves
2 tablespoons water

1 pint strawberries, stemmed
   and halved
5 small sprigs fresh mint

Whisk together the balsamic vinegar, preserves and water. Toss with the strawberries. Let stand 10 minutes in the refrigerator.

Just before serving, coarsely chop the leaves of 1 sprig of mint and toss with the strawberries. Garnish with the remaining sprigs of mint.

YIELD: 4 servings

CALORIES	CARBOHYDRATES: 15.3 GM	TOTAL FAT: 0 GM
Per serving: 56	PROTEIN: .5 GM	Saturated fat: 0 GM
Fat: 0%	DIETARY FIBER: 1.9 GM	Monounsaturated fat: 0 GM
Carbohydrates: 93%	SODIUM: 2 MG	
Protein: 7%	CHOLESTEROL: 0 MG	

Pyramid equivalencies: 1 fruit

25

Simple
Pleasures

A LOAF of bread, a bowl of soup, a little cheese, a bottle of wine and thou—what could be better? The nutritional bonuses and delicious rustic flavors of simple European fare can be a sensational choice for the health-conscious gourmet. When freshly made with the best ingredients, ordinary dishes become a festival of culinary pleasures. Inviting someone over for a bowl of soup sounds awfully basic, but often that's just what our guests would like. The honesty of fresh ingredients, homemade dishes and your warm company may in the long run be better than any extravagant meal. This is a menu that proves simple pleasures are often our greatest treasure.

SIMPLE PLEASURES (MENU FOR 4)

Smoky Pea Soup
Hearty Whole Wheat Rolls with Roasted Garlic
Spicy Greens with Citrus Vinaigrette
Apples and Cheese

Additional Recipes:
Herb Garden Rolls
Light Blue Cheese Spread

I like food, just about any food you can name. I like all sorts of elaborate, complex creations, both to eat and prepare. But I also like plain, ordinary dishes as well. Unfortunately, a lot of so-called "plain food" is often dependent on butter or oil for flavor. In this menu, my goal has been to offer honest, homey flavors without refined fats or meat. Although this is a vegetarian meal, I tried to create a menu that would appeal to meat eaters as well.

There's no ham in the Pea Soup, but there is a faint smoky flavor. This earthy taste of the Smoky Pea Soup is complemented by Hearty Whole Wheat Rolls, a heavy, rustic bread. Besides flavor, the two dishes also complement each other nutritionally, with split peas and the whole wheat flour mixing to form a complete protein. A lot of cooks avoid bread baking because they don't think they have the time. Using rapid-rise yeast, you can complete the rolls by the time the soup is done. Herb Garden Rolls demonstrate how a little seasoning creates a bread with a totally different flavor. If you are looking for a fat-free spread for the bread, Roasted Garlic is ideal.

Spicy Greens with Citrus Vinaigrette is a lively salad. We don't usually picture salad greens as being piquant, but raw mustard greens and watercress can definitely add a little heat to the palate. They also add a rich dose of vital nutrients. Because the greens have a lot of flavor before you ever add the dressing, you can get by with a less assertive dressing.

Apples and Cheese is a simple dessert reflective of a European life-style. In this menu, the cheese, made with a blend of yogurt and blue cheese, proves you can have low-fat dishes without giving up richness. "Delicate" is not usually a word we associate with blue cheese, but you may change your culinary vocabulary after tasting the Light Blue Cheese Spread.

NUTRIENT INFORMATION FOR SIMPLE PLEASURES

Total nutrient information for the meal is based on each diner having 1 serving of Smoky Pea Soup, Spicy Greens with Citrus Vinaigrette and Apples and Cheese and 2 servings of Hearty Whole Wheat Rolls with Roasted Garlic. For a heartier meal, you may elect to have a second bowl of soup, another roll or additional fruit. If you are wanting to lose weight, you may elect to omit the oil in the salad dressing.

CALORIES	CARBOHYDRATES: 139.6 GM	TOTAL FAT: 14.2 GM
For total meal: 781	PROTEIN: 31.5 GM	Saturated fat: 3.3 GM
Fat: 16%	DIETARY FIBER: 14.7 GM	Monounsaturated fat: 8.5 GM
Carbohydrates: 68%	SODIUM: 180 MG	
Protein: 16%	CHOLESTEROL: 7 MG	

Pyramid equivalencies: 4 grains, 3 vegetables, 1 fruit, ½ protein, 1¼ dairy

Smoky Pea Soup

Pea soup with the flavor of smoked ham has long been a European country favorite. This is a meat-free version of that classic.

1½ cups yellow or green split peas
1 medium potato, peeled and diced
6 cloves garlic
3 leeks, trimmed and diced
1 teaspoon ground sage
½ teaspoon thyme
½ teaspoon black pepper
4 cups water

4 cups unsalted, defatted broth
3 large carrots, diced
3 parsnips, diced
2 tablespoons low-sodium soy sauce
¼ teaspoon liquid smoke
1 cup dry sherry
¼ cup finely minced fresh parsley

Combine the peas, potato, garlic, leeks, sage, thyme, pepper and water in a pot. Simmer at low temperature for 1½ hours, stirring occasionally.

Add the broth, carrots, parsnips, soy sauce and liquid smoke. Stirring regularly, cook at low temperature for 1 hour or until the vegetables are tender. Taste the soup to determine if you want to add more smoke flavoring.

Transfer 3 cups of the soup mixture to a blender and puree until smooth. Return the puree to the soup pot with the sherry and simmer for 20 minutes.

Serve hot with fresh parsley sprinkled over each bowl.

YIELD: 8 servings

CALORIES
Per serving: 234
Fat: 3%
Carbohydrates: 78%
Protein: 19%

CARBOHYDRATES: 48.9 GM
PROTEIN: 11.8 GM
DIETARY FIBER: 5.9 GM
SODIUM: 180 MG
CHOLESTEROL: 0 MG

TOTAL FAT: .8 GM
Saturated fat: .1 GM
Monounsaturated fat: .3 GM

Pyramid equivalencies: 2 vegetables, ½ protein

Hearty Whole Wheat Rolls

This recipe was designed for the quick preparation of bread, taking about half the time of more traditional recipes. To make the recipe, you must use rapid-rise yeast. This is available in most supermarkets and is usually next to the envelopes of standard yeast.

2 cups whole wheat flour
2 cups all-purpose flour
½ cup nonfat dry milk powder
1 envelope rapid-rise yeast
1 tablespoon dry dill
2 teaspoons granulated garlic powder

½ teaspoon ground black pepper
1¼ cups water
¼ cup extra-virgin olive oil
¼ cup honey
1 tablespoon low-sodium soy sauce

In a large bowl, sift together the flours, milk powder, yeast, dill, garlic powder and pepper. Mix well and set aside.

Bring the water to a boil. Remove from the heat and immediately stir in the oil, honey and soy sauce. Mix until the honey is completely dissolved. Let stand 1 minute.

When the liquid is cool enough to touch, but still warmer than luke-warm, add to bowl with the flour. Mix until completely blended. Transfer the mixture to a clean, floured surface. Knead for about 5 minutes or until the mixture is smooth and elastic, but not sticky. If necessary, incorporate more flour into the dough. Transfer the mound of dough to an oiled bowl. Cover with a cloth, place in draft-free, slightly warm area. Let stand 10 minutes.

Divide the dough into 4 equal parts. Roll the dough between your hands to create 4 short, thick strands. Cut each strand into 4 portions. Place the rolls on a baking sheet sprayed with nonstick cooking spray. Return to a warm, draft-free area and let rise for 1½ hours.

After preheating oven to 375°F., bake for 10 to 15 minutes or until the rolls are browned.

As with most breads, these rolls are best right out of the oven. You can, however, wrap the rolls in plastic and serve the following day. Keep in a cool place but do not refrigerate.

YIELD: 16 rolls

CALORIES   CARBOHYDRATES: 28.1 GM   TOTAL FAT: 3.7 GM
Per roll: 163   PROTEIN: 4.7 GM   Saturated fat: .6 GM
Fat: 21%   DIETARY FIBER: 2.5 GM   Monounsaturated fat: 2.5 GM
Carbohydrates: 68%   SODIUM: 45 MG
Protein: 11%   CHOLESTEROL: 0 MG

Pyramid equivalencies: 1½ grains

Herb Garden Rolls

The addition of a few herbs produces a bread with a completely different flavor. This roll is also excellent with soups and salads.

To the preceding recipe, add with the other spices 1 tablespoon finely crushed dry rosemary, 1 tablespoon dry leaf oregano (not ground oregano) and 1 tablespoon finely grated fresh lemon peel.

Nutrient values are the same as for Hearty Whole Wheat Rolls.

Roasted Garlic

Slow, lengthy cooking produces garlic with a rich, sweet flavor. Use as spread for bread or add to soups or sauces.

2 whole bulbs garlic

Do not peel the garlic; leave the entire bulb intact. Place the garlic on a baking sheet and bake at 300°F. for 45 minutes or until the garlic is tender.

Remove from the oven. Let stand 5 minutes. Carefully slice the bulb crosswise in half. To serve, each diner separates a clove from the bulb and squeezes the tender garlic from the dry skin onto a piece of bread or roll. With a knife, the garlic can be spread as easily as butter.

YIELD: 16 servings (2 cloves per serving)

CALORIES	CARBOHYDRATES: 2.0 GM	TOTAL FAT: trace
Per serving: 9	PROTEIN: .4 GM	Saturated fat: trace
Fat: 1%	DIETARY FIBER: 0 GM	Monounsaturated fat: trace
Carbohydrates: 83%	SODIUM: 2 MG	
Protein: 16%	CHOLESTEROL: 0 MG	

Pyramid equivalencies: no equivalencies

Spicy Greens with Citrus Vinaigrette

If the mustard greens seem too hot for you, use a lesser amount, but do keep some to enliven the salad. The nectarines offer a pleasing contrast to the spicy greens. Peach or apricot slices also work well.

4 cups green leaf lettuce, torn in bite-size pieces	1 recipe Citrus Vinaigrette (recipe follows)
1½ cups fresh mustard greens, torn in bite-size pieces	2 green onions, chopped
	1 large ripe nectarine, sliced
1½ cups fresh watercress, torn in bite-size pieces	

After the greens have been washed, drained and torn in bite-size pieces, toss with the Citrus Vinaigrette.

Transfer the dressed greens to individual salad plates. Sprinkle the green onions over each serving and garnish with the nectarine slices.

YIELD: 4 servings

Nutrient information also includes the salad dressing.

CALORIES	CARBOHYDRATES: 9.7 GM	TOTAL FAT: 3.4 GM
Per serving: 74	PROTEIN: 2.0 GM	Saturated fat: .5 GM
Fat: 42%	DIETARY FIBER: 2.0 GM	Monounsaturated fat: 2.5 GM
Carbohydrates: 48%	SODIUM: 15 MG	
Protein: 10%	CHOLESTEROL: 0 MG	

Pyramid equivalencies: 1 vegetable, ⅓ fruit

Citrus Vinaigrette

In addition to salads, use this dressing as a sauce for steamed vegetables. It is excellent either hot or cold. If desired, add a tablespoon of minced fresh herbs. If you wish to reduce your fat intake even further, omit the olive oil and substitute 1 tablespoon tomato puree.

⅓ cup fresh orange juice
2 tablespoons fresh lemon juice
1 tablespoon extra-virgin olive oil

1 teaspoon low-sodium, Dijon-style mustard
1 clove garlic, finely minced

Whisk together all of the ingredients, stirring until completely blended. Use immediately or store in a refrigerator for up to 4 days.

YIELD: 4 servings

CALORIES	CARBOHYDRATES: 3.1 GM	TOTAL FAT: 3.5 GM
Per serving: 43	PROTEIN: .3 GM	Saturated fat: .5 GM
Fat: 70%	DIETARY FIBER: .2 GM	Monounsaturated fat: 2.5 GM
Carbohydrates: 28%	SODIUM: 1 MG	
Protein: 2%	CHOLESTEROL: 0 MG	

Pyramid equivalencies: ⅛ fruit

Apples and Cheese

This dish is most attractive when made with both red and green apples. Red and green pears also make a lovely presentation.

1 red apple or pear
1 green apple or pear
¼ cup frozen lemonade
 concentrate

¼ cup water
1 recipe Light Blue Cheese
 Spread (recipe follows)

Do not prepare the apples more than 6 hours before serving. To prepare, core the apples and cut in thin slices. Mix the lemonade concentrate and water. Toss the apple slices with the mixture and refrigerate.

Mound the Light Blue Cheese Spread in the center of a plate. Arrange the apple slices, alternating colors, around the cheese. Serve immediately.

YIELD: 4 servings

CALORIES
Per serving: 147
Fat: 15%
Carbohydrates: 63%
Protein: 22%

CARBOHYDRATES: 24.8 GM
PROTEIN: 8.3 GM
DIETARY FIBER: 1.8 GM
SODIUM: 188 MG
CHOLESTEROL: 7 MG

TOTAL FAT: 2.6 GM
Saturated fat: 1.5 GM
Monounsaturated fat: .7 GM

Pyramid equivalencies: ½ fruit, 1¼ dairy

Light Blue Cheese Spread

In addition to fruit, this spread is delicious with crackers, Belgian endive and vegetable crudités.

1 ounce blue cheese
2 teaspoons unsalted Dijon-style mustard
2 cups nonfat yogurt

2 teaspoons finely grated lemon peel
½ teaspoon dry dill

Take the blue cheese, mustard and a small amount of the yogurt (about ⅓ cup) and mash together until smooth and creamy. This can be easily done in a blender, but use only a small amount of the yogurt because blending the entire amount would whip too much air into the mixture. Use a whisk or spoon to mix the blended blue cheese mixture with the remaining yogurt. Stir in the lemon peel and dill.

Line a strainer with a paper coffee filter or with cheesecloth. Pour the yogurt mixture into the strainer. Place the strainer over a bowl, allowing plenty of room for the whey to drain out of the mixture. Refrigerate and let drain overnight. Transfer to an airtight container and refrigerate until ready to serve. Will keep 5 to 6 days in the refrigerator.

YIELD: 4 servings

CALORIES
Per serving: 103
Fat: 20%
Carbohydrates: 50%
Protein: 30%

CARBOHYDRATES: 13.3 GM
PROTEIN: 8.1 GM
DIETARY FIBER: .1 GM
SODIUM: 186 MG
CHOLESTEROL: 7 MG

TOTAL FAT: 2.3 GM
Saturated fat: 1.4 GM
Monounsaturated fat: .7 GM

Pyramid equivalencies: 1¼ dairy

26

Winter Cheers

A ROARING fire, baked apples and steaming cups of hot spiced wine—
What better way is there to ward off a winter chill? Entertaining with
food can feature a banquet of dishes or a simple snack. Most of the
menus in this book are for complete meals; however, I thought it
important to demonstrate how healthy dining can also include those
occasions when we may entertain with only appetizers or desserts.
Rustic desserts and hot beverages offer a special warmth and comfort
that is certain to cheer all your guests during the winter months.

WINTER CHEERS (MENU FOR 8)

Wassail Spiced Tea
Traditional Wassail
Wassail Spiced Wine
Wassail Spiced Cider
Baked Apples
Date Nut Bread
Marsala Creme
Cranberry-Almond Balls

Additional Recipes:
Wassail Syrup
Fancy Baked Apples

Many Christmases ago, fresh out of college, living alone and distant from my family, I began to create my own Christmas traditions. It was also the beginning of my interest in cooking. My brothers had just traced our family tree. Our family had very little sense of tradition and certainly nothing that made me aware of our English roots. That Christmas, I decided to create an English celebration. Wassail was the first dish I made, and it's something I've been doing every Christmas since.

Wassail is a kind of hot punch. Early versions consisted of mixing ale and brandy with sweet spices and serving the drink hot over baked apples and toast. It is from this tradition that we get the expression "to toast." At Christmas, to go wassailing referred to a custom in which the poor could sing carols door-to-door in exchange for food and money and a cup of hot beverage. In contemporary times, wassailing is more likely to refer to going to your neighbor's house and getting a little sloshed on hot punch! When you drink wassail, be prepared "to toast" your holiday guests. If words escape you, simply quote the chorus of an old carol:

> "Love and joy come to you,
> And to you your wassail too,
> And God bless you, and send you a happy new year!"

My Wassail recipe was created for easy entertaining. The recipe starts with a syrup that can be prepared several days ahead and used for a bowl of punch or individual servings. During the winter months, I keep Wassail Syrup on hand to create a variety of beverages. Traditional Wassail is made with the syrup, dark beer and brandy. A much less alcoholic beverage is Wassail Spiced Wine. I also enjoy creating an alcohol-free Wassail Spiced Cider or Wassail Spiced Tea.

Our Wassail party includes Baked Apples and Date Nut Bread. If you want to be traditional, place slices of bread in soup bowls, top with a baked apple and pour hot Wassail over it. This is a dessert you can eat and drink. Frankly, I rarely serve it this way. I prefer to present the hot punch, bread and apples as separate dishes. I also like to serve Marsala Creme on the side as a topping for the Baked Apples or Date Nut Bread. A more elegant recipe, Fancy Baked Apples, is also included.

For the party, I've added Cranberry-Almond Nut Balls, a marvelous little candy that you don't have to feel guilty eating. It's not often that you have a delicious candy that is also good for you! Dried cranberries are the secret of the wonderful flavor.

A final note, remember warm alcoholic beverages affect you more rapidly than cold ones. Don't forget your guests who do not drink alcohol. The Wassail Syrup enables you to quickly prepare alcoholic or nonalcoholic versions of Wassail. Hot apple cider or even hot tea is delicious when sweetened with Wassail Syrup.

NUTRIENT INFORMATION FOR WINTER CHEERS

Nutrient data for the complete menu include 1 serving of the Date Nut Bread, 1 Baked Apple, 1 cup of the Wassail Spiced Wine and 3 Cranberry-Almond Nut Balls.

CALORIES	CARBOHYDRATES: 98.3 GM	TOTAL FAT: 11.7 GM
For total meal: 544	PROTEIN: 10.5 GM	Saturated fat: 1.2 GM
Fat: 18%	DIETARY FIBER: 6.8 GM	Monounsaturated fat: 6.0 GM
Carbohydrates: 68%	SODIUM: 234 MG	
Protein: 7%	CHOLESTEROL: 1 MG	
Alcohol: 7%		

Pyramid equivalencies: 1¼ grains, 4 fruits, ¼ dairy, 1 extra

Wassail Syrup

Although ground spices may be used, the texture and flavor are superior with whole spices. The Syrup is also excellent for sweetening a cup of hot herbal tea. If you are doing a lot of entertaining, make a double recipe. The Syrup can be stored 2 or 3 weeks in the refrigerator.

12 *cinnamon sticks
(3 tablespoons ground
cinnamon)*

2 *teaspoons allspice berries
(1 teaspoon ground allspice)*

2 *teaspoons whole coriander
seeds (1 teaspoon ground
coriander)*

1 *whole nutmeg (³/₄ teaspoon
ground nutmeg)*

1 *tablespoon whole cloves
(1 teaspoon ground cloves)*

3 *cups water*

2 *cups frozen, unsweetened
apple juice concentrate*

¼ *cup frozen orange juice
concentrate*

Simmer all of the spices in the water for 1 hour. Strain the spiced water, discard the whole spices and any concentrated sediment. Pour the spiced water into a large measuring pitcher with the juice concentrates. Add more water to make a total of 4½ cups syrup.

YIELD: 36 servings (1 ounce each)

CALORIES	CARBOHYDRATES: 6.9 GM	TOTAL FAT: .1 GM
Per serving: 28	PROTEIN: .1 GM	Saturated fat: trace
Fat: 2%	DIETARY FIBER: trace	Monounsaturated fat: trace
Carbohydrates: 96%	SODIUM: 4 MG	
Protein: 2%	CHOLESTEROL: 0 MG	

Pyramid equivalencies: ½ fruit

Wassail Spiced Tea
(For 1 Serving)

For a soothing cup of hot tea, brew your favorite tea and add 1 ounce of the Wassail Syrup. The nutrient information is essentially the same as a 1-ounce serving of the Wassail Syrup (previous recipe).

Traditional Wassail
(For 1 Serving)

This hot toddy will definitely warm the cockles! Some people will want to forgo tradition and mix in a little apple juice and use less of the alcohol.

1 ounce Wassail Syrup (recipe page 301)	3 ounces ale or dark beer
1 ounce (2 tablespoons) water	1 ounce brandy
	Lemon or orange wedge

Combine syrup and water and heat to just below the boiling point. Add the ale and brandy and heat through. Serve with a lemon or orange wedge.

YIELD: 1 serving (6 ounces)

CALORIES	CARBOHYDRATES: 10.8 GM	TOTAL FAT: .1 GM
Per serving: 137	PROTEIN: .4 GM	Saturated fat: trace
Fat: 0	ALCOHOL: 13.2 GM	Monounsaturated fat: trace
Carbohydrates: 32%	DIETARY FIBER: trace	
Protein: 1%	SODIUM: 10 MG	
Alcohol: 67%	CHOLESTEROL: 0 MG	

Pyramid equivalencies: ½ fruit, 1 extra

Wassail Spiced Wine (For 1 Serving)

Wine is used to make this lighter version of Wassail.

> 1 ounce Wassail Syrup (recipe page 301)
> 1 ounce (2 tablespoons) water
>
> ¼ cup dry red wine
> Lemon or orange wedge

Combine syrup and water and heat to just below the boiling point. Add the wine and heat through. Serve with a lemon or orange wedge.

YIELD: 1 serving (6 ounces)

CALORIES	CARBOHYDRATES: 7.9 GM	TOTAL FAT: .1 GM
Per serving: 69	PROTEIN: .3 GM	Saturated fat: trace
Fat: 1%	ALCOHOL: 5.8 GM	Monounsaturated fat: trace
Carbohydrates: 44%	DIETARY FIBER: trace	
Protein: 2%	SODIUM: 4 MG	
Alcohol: 53%	CHOLESTEROL: 0 MG	

Pyramid equivalencies: ½ fruit, 1 extra

Wassail Spiced Cider
(For 1 Serving)

Cider is a wonderful base for creating a nonalcoholic Wassail.

1 ounce (2 tablespoons) water   *¼ cup apple cider*
1 ounce Wassail Syrup (recipe   *Lemon or orange wedge*
   page 301)

   Combine the first 3 ingredients and heat to just below the boiling point. Serve with a lemon or orange wedge.

YIELD: 1 serving (6 ounces)

CALORIES	CARBOHYDRATES: 14.1 GM	TOTAL FAT: .1 GM
Per serving: 57	PROTEIN: .2 GM	Saturated fat: trace
Fat: 2%	DIETARY FIBER: .1 GM	Monounsaturated fat: trace
Carbohydrates: 97%	SODIUM: 6 MG	
Protein: 1%	CHOLESTEROL: 0 MG	

Pyramid equivalencies: 1 fruit

Baked Apples

Simple and homey, baked apples are old-fashioned cooking at its best.

8 cinnamon sticks   *1 cup Wassail Syrup*
8 large Delicious apples, cored

   Wedge a cinnamon stick into the core of each apple. Place the apples in a baking dish, closely fitting but not touching.
   Pour the Wassail Syrup into the dish. Add enough water to create a

depth of ½ inch. Cover the pan and bake at 350°F. for 30 minutes. Remove the cover and continue baking for another 15 minutes or until the apples are tender.

Serve hot or cold with some of the baking liquid poured over each serving. The apples are also excellent with the Marsala Creme (recipe this chapter).

YIELD: 8 servings

CALORIES	CARBOHYDRATES: 28.0 GM	TOTAL FAT: .6 GM
Per serving: 109	PROTEIN: .4 GM	Saturated fat: .1 GM
Fat: 4%	DIETARY FIBER: 3.0 GM	Monounsaturated fat: .2 GM
Carbohydrates: 95%	SODIUM: 5 MG	
Protein: 1%	CHOLESTEROL: 0 MG	

Pyramid equivalencies: 1½ fruits

Fancy Baked Apples

This is a slightly more elaborate version of the previous recipe.

In the previous recipe, omit the cinnamon stick in the core of the apple. Instead, pack into the core of each apple raisins, dried apricots and walnuts. Use 1 cup raisins, ½ cup diced dried apricots and ¼ cup crushed walnuts. Spoon some of the poaching liquid into the core of each apple. Bake as directed in the previous recipe.

YIELD: 8 servings

CALORIES	CARBOHYDRATES: 46.0 GM	TOTAL FAT: 2.7 GM
Per serving: 197	PROTEIN: 2.0 GM	Saturated fat: .3 GM
Fat: 11%	DIETARY FIBER: 7.0 GM	Monounsaturated fat: .1 GM
Carbohydrates: 85%	SODIUM: 8 MG	
Protein: 4%	CHOLESTEROL: 0 MG	

Pyramid equivalencies: 2 fruits

Date Nut Bread

This sweet, dense bread is delicious as a dessert, breakfast bread or accompaniment to soup or salad.

1 cup whole wheat flour
⅓ cup cornstarch
2 teaspoons baking soda
1 teaspoon ground cinnamon
½ teaspoon ground ginger
¼ cup oatmeal (do not use instant or one-minute oatmeal)
¼ cup chopped walnuts

1 cup unsweetened applesauce
⅔ cup frozen, unsweetened apple juice concentrate
2 egg whites
3 tablespoons canola oil
½ teaspoon walnut extract
⅔ cup chopped and pitted dates
1 tablespoon finely grated orange peel

Preheat oven to 350°F. Sift together the whole wheat flour, cornstarch, baking soda, cinnamon and ginger. Stir in the oatmeal and walnuts and set aside.

Using a mixer, or by hand, beat together the applesauce, juice concentrate, egg whites, oil and walnut extract. Beat for 2 or 3 minutes. Mix in the dates and orange peel and stir until evenly blended.

Stir in the dry ingredients and mix until well incorporated. Pour into a loaf pan sprayed with nonstick cooking spray. Bake at 350°F. for 40 minutes or until inserted toothpick comes out clean.

Let the bread stand 20 minutes before removing from the pan. Serve warm or at room temperature. Excellent plain or with Marsala Creme (recipe follows).

YIELD: 10 servings

CALORIES
Per serving: 168
Fat: 32%
Carbohydrates: 60%
Protein: 8%

CARBOHYDRATES: 26.4 GM
PROTEIN: 3.7 GM
DIETARY FIBER: 3.2 GM
SODIUM: 177 MG
CHOLESTEROL: 0 MG

TOTAL FAT: 6.4 GM
Saturated fat: .5 GM
Monounsaturated fat: 3.1 GM

Pyramid equivalencies: 1 grain, 1 fruit

Marsala Creme

This is a perfect topping for Baked Apples or Date Nut Bread.

¼ cup fluid nonfat milk   *¼ cup honey or ¼ cup brown*
¼ cup dry nonfat milk powder   *sugar, tightly packed*
2 tablespoons cornstarch   *¼ cup Marsala*
1 cup plain nonfat yogurt   *2 egg whites*

In the top of a double boiler, whisk together the fluid milk, dry milk powder and cornstarch. Add the yogurt, honey, Marsala and egg whites. Stir until thoroughly blended.

Cook in the double boiler, stirring regularly until thickened, about 10 minutes. Nonfat milk products curdle easily. If that should happen, transfer the mixture to a blender and puree until smooth. Return the mixture to the double boiler and continue cooking until the sauce is thickened. Serve immediately or refrigerate for later use. May be served cold or reheated.

YIELD: 1¾ cups, about 14 servings

CALORIES   CARBOHYDRATES: 8.4 GM   TOTAL FAT: .1 GM
Per serving: 42   PROTEIN: 2.2 GM   Saturated fat: trace
Fat: 2%   DIETARY FIBER: trace   Monounsaturated fat: trace
Carbohydrates: 78%   SODIUM: 32 MG
Protein: 20%   CHOLESTEROL: 1 MG

Pyramid equivalencies: ¼ dairy

Cranberry-Almond Balls

If you love cranberries as I do, this candy was meant for you! Dried cranberries are found in health food stores and specialty gourmet markets.

¾ cup sliced almonds
1 cup dried cranberries
½ cup pitted and chopped dates
1¾ cups raw oatmeal (do not use instant or one-minute oatmeal)

¾ cup frozen cranberry juice concentrate
2 tablespoons finely grated orange peel
1 teaspoon almond extract

With steel blade of food processor, grind the almonds to a fine meal. Transfer to a plate and set aside.

Combine cranberries, dates, oatmeal, juice concentrate, peel and almond extract in a food processor. Process until completely chopped and well mixed. If the mixture is quite sticky, add more oatmeal.

Form the mixture into ½-inch balls. Set the balls on a sheet of waxed paper. Spread the ground almonds on a plate, roll the balls in the almonds until coated. Cover and refrigerate. Will keep several days in the refrigerator.

YIELD: 36 balls

CALORIES
Per ball: 52
Fat: 25%
Carbohydrates: 66%
Protein: 9%

CARBOHYDRATES: 9.2 GM
PROTEIN: 1.3 GM
DIETARY FIBER: .2 GM
SODIUM: 1.9 MG
CHOLESTEROL: 0 MG

TOTAL FAT: 1.5 GM
Saturated fat: .2 GM
Monounsaturated fat: .9 GM

Pyramid equivalencies (for 3 candies) ¼ grain, 1 fruit

27

Royal Pancake Breakfast

HIGH-FIBER grains, nonfat dairy products and egg whites may be healthy but do not project much glamour as gourmet food. This menu proves that humble, nutritious products can become royal delights!

ROYAL PANCAKE BREAKFAST (MENU FOR 4)

Healthy Gourmet Hot Chocolate
Royal Pancakes with Spiced Pear Topping
Lemon-Yogurt Cheese and Glazed Strawberries

Healthy Gourmet Hot Chocolate has a fraction of the fat of traditional hot chocolate, yet has an incredibly rich flavor. The fat has been replaced with other ingredients that help give the beverage body and a deeper flavor. Brown sugar instead of white sugar, coffee and cinnamon added to the cocoa, and skim milk enhanced with dry milk all combine to enrich the flavor.

Royal Pancakes are decadent tasting, yet have no butter, oil or egg yolks. Yogurt gives the pancakes a sourdough flavor. Almonds and dates provide richness, while oatmeal offers an interesting texture. With the

Spiced Pear Topping, you won't miss the butter and syrup usually served with pancakes.

Aside from being a strong source of calcium and fat free, Lemon-Yogurt Cheese is a delicious accompaniment to fresh fruit and a tantalizing spread for raisin and cinnamon bagels. Yogurt cheese should always be made a day or more before serving. It will keep several days and only seems to get better with age.

The Glazed Strawberries are an excellent example of how fruit preserves can be used as an effective sweetener for fresh fruit. On a hot day, I might forgo making the Spiced Pear Topping for the Royal Pancakes and just serve them topped with Lemon-Yogurt Cheese and Glazed Strawberries.

NUTRIENT INFORMATION FOR ROYAL PANCAKE BREAKFAST

Diners wanting a smaller breakfast, or fewer calories, may omit the Hot Chocolate or Lemon-Yogurt Cheese. Those who want a heartier meal may elect to have additional pancakes.

Nutrient information is for 1 serving of each recipe.

CALORIES	CARBOHYDRATES: 170.4 GM	TOTAL FAT: 7.6 GM
For total meal: 783	PROTEIN: 34.3 GM	Saturated fat: 1.3 GM
Fat: 8%	DIETARY FIBER: 12.0 GM	Monounsaturated fat: 3.1 GM
Carbohydrates: 76%	SODIUM: 516 MG	
Protein: 15%	CHOLESTEROL: 8.9 MG	
Alcohol: 1%		

Pyramid equivalencies: 2 grains, 2½ fruits, 2½ dairy

Healthy Gourmet Hot Chocolate

This recipe is for a quick cup of hot chocolate made in the microwave.

2 *tablespoons dry nonfat milk powder*	½ *teaspoon instant coffee granules*
1 *tablespoon and 1½ teaspoons brown sugar*	⅛ *teaspoon cinnamon*
	¾ *cup fluid nonfat milk*
1 *tablespoon cocoa powder*	⅛ *teaspoon vanilla extract*

Whisk together the milk powder, brown sugar, cocoa, instant coffee and cinnamon. Add the fluid milk and vanilla extract. Stir until completely blended. Heat in a microwave or double boiler until hot but not boiling.

YIELD: 1 cup

CALORIES	CARBOHYDRATES: 50.4 GM	TOTAL FAT: .9 GM
Per cup: 175	PROTEIN: 10.5 GM	Saturated fat: .3 GM
Fat: 2%	DIETARY FIBER: 0 GM	Monounsaturated fat: .1 GM
Carbohydrates: 70%	SODIUM: 186 MG	
Protein: 28%	CHOLESTEROL: 5 MG	

Pyramid equivalencies: 1 dairy

Royal Pancakes

For this recipe, do not use instant or one-minute oatmeal. Other varieties of oatmeal are fine.

½ cup whole wheat flour	¾ cup plain nonfat yogurt
1 teaspoon low-sodium baking powder	¾ cup fluid nonfat milk
½ teaspoon baking soda	¼ cup fruit-sweetened apricot or peach preserves
½ teaspoon ground cinnamon	½ teaspoon almond extract
1 cup uncooked oatmeal (see note above)	¼ cup sliced almonds
¾ cup egg whites	½ cup chopped dates

Sift together the flour, baking powder, baking soda and cinnamon. Stir in the oatmeal and set aside.

Combine the egg whites, yogurt, nonfat milk, preserves and almond extract. Mix until evenly blended. Add the flour mixture and stir until smooth.

Lightly spray a nonstick griddle or skillet with nonstick cooking spray. Heat to medium temperature. It should be hot enough so that a few drops of water will sizzle when dropped on the pan. Pour the batter in

4-inch rounds. Sprinkle a few almond slices and bits of chopped dates over each pancake. When the pancakes begin to bubble, turn over with a spatula to cook on the other side, 1 to 2 minutes.

Serve immediately with warm maple syrup, fresh fruit and yogurt or Spiced Pear Topping (recipe follows).

YIELD: 4 servings, 8 pancakes

CALORIES	CARBOHYDRATES: 49.3 GM	TOTAL FAT: 5.6 GM
Per serving: 297	PROTEIN: 15.6 GM	Saturated fat: .8 GM
Fat: 16%	DIETARY FIBER: 5.6 GM	Monounsaturated fat: 2.9 GM
Carbohydrates: 64%	SODIUM: 231 MG	
Protein: 20%	CHOLESTEROL: 2 MG	

Pyramid equivalencies: 2 grains, ½ dairy

Spiced Pear Topping

This topping is also delicious with the Pumpkin Gingerbread (page 187) or as a topping for nonfat frozen yogurt.

> 3 pears, ripe but firm
> ⅓ cup raisins
> 1 teaspoon cinnamon
> ½ teaspoon ground ginger
>
> ¼ teaspoon ground cloves
> ½ cup frozen, unsweetened apple juice concentrate
> ½ cup water

Core and slice the pears. Combine with all the remaining ingredients in a skillet. Cook uncovered at medium to high temperature. Stir regularly and cook until the pears are tender and the liquid has thickened slightly.

Serve warm as a topping for pancakes, hot cereal, frozen desserts or cake.

YIELD: 4 servings

CALORIES   CARBOHYDRATES: 39.3 GM   TOTAL FAT: .6 GM
Per serving: 154   PROTEIN: 1.0 GM   Saturated fat: .1 GM
Fat: 3%   DIETARY FIBER: 3.4 GM   Monounsaturated fat: .1 GM
Carbohydrates: 95%   SODIUM: 11 MG
Protein: 2%   CHOLESTEROL: 0 MG

Pyramid equivalencies: 1½ fruits

Lemon-Yogurt Cheese

To make Lemon-Yogurt Cheese, do not use a yogurt that has been thickened with gelatin. I especially like to serve the cheese surrounded by Glazed Strawberries (recipe follows) or other fresh fruit.

2 cups plain nonfat yogurt   1 tablespoon finely grated lemon
2 tablespoons frozen,   peel
  unsweetened orange juice   ¼ teaspoon pure lemon extract
  concentrate

Whisk together all the ingredients. Refrigerate for 2 hours. Place a paper coffee filter or cheesecloth in a strainer. Pour the yogurt mixture into the strainer. Set the strainer in a bowl, cover with plastic wrap and refrigerate overnight.

The whey will drain out, leaving a thickened yogurt, similar to the texture of cream cheese. The longer it sits, the denser it will get. To serve, remove from the strainer and mound on a plate. For a fancy presentation, line a mold with plastic wrap and press the cheese into the mold. Invert the mold on a serving plate and pull away the mold and plastic wrap.

Serve with bagels, English muffins or fresh fruit.

YIELD: 4 servings

CALORIES   CARBOHYDRATES: 12.3 GM   TOTAL FAT: .2 GM
Per serving: 78   PROTEIN: 6.7 GM   Saturated fat: .1 GM
Fat: 3%   DIETARY FIBER: .1 GM   Monounsaturated fat: trace
Carbohydrates: 63%   SODIUM: 87 MG
Protein: 34%   CHOLESTEROL: 2 MG

Pyramid equivalencies: 1 dairy

Glazed Strawberries

These strawberries are delicious by themselves, in addition to being served with the Lemon-Yogurt Cheese.

¼ cup fruit-sweetened
   strawberry preserves
2 tablespoons fresh orange
   juice

1 tablespoon orange-flavored
   liqueur
¼ teaspoon ground cinnamon
1 pint fresh whole strawberries

Whisk together the preserves, orange juice, liqueur and cinnamon. If the preserves are lumpy, you may want to use a blender or force the mixture through a sieve. Transfer the mixture to a saucer.

Carefully wash the strawberries, leaving the stems intact. Grasp each berry at the stem and gently roll back and forth in the glaze mixture. Place the berries on a serving platter. Do not prepare the strawberries more than 2 hours before serving. Serve the berries plain or with the Lemon-Yogurt Cheese (preceding recipe).

You may also elect to slice the berries and simply toss with the glaze mixture. This makes an excellent topping for frozen desserts or cakes.

YIELD: 4 servings

CALORIES
Per serving: 79
Fat: 3%
Carbohydrates: 86%
Protein: 2%
Alcohol: 9%

CARBOHYDRATES: 19.1 GM
PROTEIN: .5 GM
ALCOHOL: 1.0 GM
DIETARY FIBER: 2.0 GM
SODIUM: 1 MG
CHOLESTEROL: 0 MG

TOTAL FAT: .3 GM
Saturated fat: trace
Monounsaturated fat: trace

Pyramid equivalencies: 1 fruit

28

Office Brunch

YOU vow that you are going to eat more healthfully. You start the day with a strong resolve, then you go off to that morning business meeting. Placed on the conference table are platters of Danish pastry, doughnuts and bagels with assorted flavors of cream cheese. How is your resolve holding up? It was that kind of situation that led me to create this menu for an Office Brunch.

Business persons are starting to ask for healthier choices. Most people realize that what they eat affects long-range health. Additionally, people are beginning to see that food choices may actually affect how one feels during the workday. This Office Brunch is an energy-enhancing meal that also satisfies the palate.

OFFICE BRUNCH (MENU FOR 8)

Apple Pie Muffins
Date Cheese
Eye Opener Fruit Compote
Muesli
Breakfast "Creme"

Additional Recipe:
Royal Porridge

315

Even a fast-food version of the office brunch can offer healthy alternatives. The easy answer is a stop at the market for fresh fruit, nonfat yogurt, bagels and nonfat cream cheese. But if you want something a little special, this Office Brunch offers some creative alternatives.

The Apple Pie Muffins may not look anything like an apple pie, but they do have a flavor reminiscent of that fabulous dessert. The muffins are oil free but still have some fat from the almonds. If you want a lower-fat product, omit the nuts. Because the fat in almonds is primarily monounsaturated, and the nuts contain other vital nutrients, almonds certainly have a place in a healthy diet.

Bagels are a delicious, low-fat breakfast choice. But what do you use as a spread instead of cream cheese? Date Cheese, made from nonfat cottage cheese, is excellent for cinnamon bagels and other plain or sweet bagels.

Breakfast cereal is a good habit. It may not seem like very exciting fare for a business brunch, but I find more and more business persons have an appreciation for healthy fare. In fact, Muesli has a sort of glamorous appeal. Our homemade version has no refined fat. Muesli can be made ahead and stored for several days. You don't have to have a business meeting to enjoy Muesli.

Fruit juice is synonymous with breakfast. Although I do not condemn juice, fresh whole fruit, with all of the fiber, is still a better bet. Whole fruit fills us up with fewer calories. Enjoy your morning juice, but don't forget that fresh fruit can be satisfying, too. Eye Opener Fruit Compote is a salad for impressing your colleagues.

You know that nonfat milk is the healthiest choice for cereal or coffee, but you just have not learned to like its lighter flavor. So how bad is it if you don't switch to nonfat milk?. One-half cup of nonfat milk has 45 calories and has less than half a gram of fat. The same amount of low-fat (also called 2%) milk has 60 calories and 2.3 grams of fat. This means that so-called low-fat milk derives 35% of its calories from fat. Whole milk has 75 calories and 4 grams of fat per half cup. Forty-nine percent of the calories come from fat. This menu features two ways of enriching the flavor of nonfat milk without adding fat. I'm sure you will find one of the Breakfast "Cremes" that will appeal to your palate.

NUTRIENT INFORMATION FOR OFFICE BRUNCH

Nutrient information includes 1 serving each of Apple Pie Muffins, Date Cheese, Muesli, Breakfast "Creme" and Eye Opener Fruit Compote.

CALORIES	CARBOHYDRATES: 114.5 GM	TOTAL FAT: 7.9 GM
For total meal: 588	PROTEIN: 22.2 GM	Saturated fat: 1.1 GM
Fat: 12%	DIETARY FIBER: 8.1 GM	Monounsaturated fat: 3.5 GM
Carbohydrates: 74%	SODIUM: 319 MG	
Protein: 19%	CHOLESTEROL: 5 MG	

Pyramid equivalencies: 2 grains, 3 fruits, 1 dairy

Apple Pie Muffins

You can make these muffins the night before. Shortly after removing from the oven, wrap each muffin in plastic to retain freshness.

1¼ cups whole wheat flour	¼ cup sliced almonds
¼ cup cornstarch	1 cup apple sauce
2 teaspoons baking soda	⅓ cup egg whites
2 teaspoons cinnamon	1 cup frozen, unsweetened apple
¼ teaspoon cloves	juice concentrate
¼ teaspoon nutmeg	1 teaspoon almond extract
½ cup oatmeal	1 large apple, cored and diced

Preheat oven to 400°F. Sift together the flour, cornstarch, baking soda and spices. Stir in the oatmeal and almonds. Set aside.

Mix together the apple sauce, egg whites, juice concentrate and almond extract until smooth and thoroughly blended. Combine the two mixtures and blend well. Stir in the diced apple and mix until evenly distributed.

Spray a muffin pan with nonstick cooking spray. Pour the mixture into the cups. Bake at 400°F. for 20 to 25 minutes, or until an inserted toothpick comes out clean.

If not serving immediately, wrap each muffin individually in plastic wrap before the muffins are completely cool. Serve muffins warm with apple butter or Date Cheese.

YIELD: 12 muffins

CALORIES	CARBOHYDRATES: 27.2 GM	TOTAL FAT: 1.8 GM
Per serving: 131	PROTEIN: 2.9 GM	Saturated fat: .2 GM
Fat: 12%	DIETARY FIBER: 2.6 GM	Monounsaturated fat: .9 GM
Carbohydrates: 80%	SODIUM: 144 MG	
Protein: 8%	CHOLESTEROL: 0 MG	

Pyramid equivalencies: 1 grain, ½ fruit

Date Cheese

This is an excellent spread for bagels, English muffins or even the Apple Pie Muffins.

> 1 pint nonfat cottage cheese   ¼ teaspoon ground cinnamon
> 1 cup pitted, chopped dates

Place the cottage cheese in food processor and puree until smooth and creamy. Add the dates and cinnamon and continue processing until well blended. Chill before serving.

YIELD: 24 servings

CALORIES	CARBOHYDRATES: 8.4 GM	TOTAL FAT: .1 GM
Per serving: 42	PROTEIN: 2.6 GM	Saturated fat: trace
Fat: 2%	DIETARY FIBER: 1.0 GM	Monounsaturated fat: trace
Carbohydrates: 75%	SODIUM: 50 MG	
Protein: 23%	CHOLESTEROL: 1.0 MG	

Pyramid equivalencies: ⅛ fruit, ⅛ dairy

Eye Opener Fruit Compote

This compote can easily be made the night before. Fresh fruit compote is one of those dishes people find so appealing that you could leave out all the spices (the orange peel, ginger and cinnamon), and guests would be just as appreciative. I like the spicing just because it gives the fruit an extra zip.

1 *medium-sized cantaloupe,*
   peeled, seeded and cubed
1 *medium-sized pineapple,*
   peeled and cubed
4 *large navel oranges, peeled*
   and sectioned
1½ *tablespoons finely grated*
   orange peel

2 *teaspoons finely minced fresh*
   ginger or ½ teaspoon dry
   ginger powder
¼ *teaspoon ground cinnamon*
¾ *cup unsweetened pineapple or*
   orange juice

Combine all of the ingredients in a bowl. Marinate 2 hours or overnight in the refrigerator. Stir two or three times during the marinating process. Other fruits can also be used. The ones I included happen to hold well when made the night before. Grapes, mango, papaya and other melons also do well prepared in advance. If using berries, peaches, nectarines, kiwi, plums or apricots, do not add until just before serving.

YIELD: 8 servings

CALORIES
Per serving: 94
Fat: 4%
Carbohydrates: 90%
Protein: 6%

CARBOHYDRATES: 23.2 GM
PROTEIN: 1.4 GM
DIETARY FIBER: .8 GM
SODIUM: 6 MG
CHOLESTEROL: 0 MG

TOTAL FAT: .5 GM
Saturated fat: trace
Monounsaturated fat: trace

Pyramid equivalencies: 1½ fruits

Muesli

This homemade breakfast cereal also makes an appealing afternoon snack.

4 *cups raw oatmeal (don't use*
   instant or one-minute
   oatmeal)
⅓ *cup sliced almonds*
2 *teaspoons ground*
   cinnamon
¼ *teaspoon ground cloves*

½ *cup frozen, unsweetened apple*
   juice concentrate
½ *teaspoon almond extract*
⅓ *cup raisins*
⅓ *cup chopped dates or other*
   dried fruit

Preheat oven to 375°F. In a large bowl, stir together the oatmeal, almonds, cinnamon and cloves. Set aside.

In a small cup, stir together the juice concentrate and almond extract. Slowly drizzle the juice and extract over the oatmeal mixture, stirring constantly. Rub the mixture between your fingers to distribute evenly. Pour the mixture onto a baking sheet. Toast for 5 to 10 minutes until the oatmeal is dry and lightly browned.

Combine the roasted oatmeal mixture with the dried fruit. Store in a dry, well-sealed container until ready to use. Serve with nonfat milk or Breakfast "Creme" (recipes on following page).

YIELD: 8 servings

CALORIES	CARBOHYDRATES: 45.1 GM	TOTAL FAT: 5.1 GM
Per serving: 245	PROTEIN: 7.9 GM	Saturated fat: .7 GM
Fat: 18%	DIETARY FIBER: 3.7 GM	Monounsaturated fat: 2.5 GM
Carbohydrates: 70%	SODIUM: 7 MG	
Protein: 12%	CHOLESTEROL: 0 MG	

Pyramid equivalencies: 1 grain, 1 fruit

Royal Porridge

If hot cereal is more to your liking, try this version of cooked Muesli. Cooking the Muesli in hot milk completely changes the flavor and creates a custardlike texture.

Pour 4 cups of nonfat milk into a double boiler. When the milk is hot, add 1¼ cups of Muesli (previous recipe) and continue cooking, stirring regularly. After a short time, the oatmeal and milk will bind, producing a creamy texture. Serve immediately.

YIELD: 4 servings

CALORIES	CARBOHYDRATES: 34.5 GM	TOTAL FAT: 3.0 GM
Per serving: 209	PROTEIN: 12.3 GM	Saturated fat: .6 GM
Fat: 13%	DIETARY FIBER: 1.9 GM	Monounsaturated fat: 1.4 GM
Carbohydrates: 64%	SODIUM: 130 MG	
Protein: 23%	CHOLESTEROL: 4 MG	

Pyramid equivalencies: ½ grain, ½ fruit, 1 dairy

Breakfast Creme #1
(Enriched Nonfat Milk)

Adding dry skim milk powder to liquid nonfat milk creates a sweeter, richer-tasting milk.

4 cups fluid nonfat milk   *1 cup dry nonfat milk powder*

Whisk together the ingredients until the dry milk is dissolved. Chill well before serving.

YIELD: 8 servings (½ cup per serving)

CALORIES	CARBOHYDRATES: 10.6 GM	TOTAL FAT: .4 GM
Per serving: 76	PROTEIN: 7.4 GM	Saturated fat: .2 GM
Fat: 4%	DIETARY FIBER: 0 GM	Monounsaturated fat: .1 GM
Carbohydrates: 56%	SODIUM: 112 MG	
Protein: 40%	CHOLESTEROL: 4.0 MG	

Pyramid equivalencies: 1 dairy

Breakfast Creme #2
(Enriched Nonfat Milk)

This is another way of making richer-tasting milk from nonfat products.

2½ cups fluid nonfat milk   *1½ cups evaporated nonfat milk*

Whisk together the ingredients and chill before serving.

YIELD: 8 servings (½ cup per serving)

CALORIES	CARBOHYDRATES: 9.3 GM	TOTAL FAT: .3 GM
Per serving: 65	PROTEIN: 6.4 GM	Saturated fat: .2 GM
Fat: 4%	DIETARY FIBER: 0 GM	Monounsaturated fat: .1 GM
Carbohydrates: 57%	SODIUM: 96 MG	
Protein: 39%	CHOLESTEROL: 3.5 MG	

Pyramid equivalencies: ¾ dairy

Recipes by Category

CHICKEN (*See also* SOUPS)

TURKEY (*See also* SOUPS)

BEEF, LAMB AND PORK

FISH AND SEAFOOD (*See also* SOUPS)

VEGETABLES AND LEGUMES

VEGETARIAN ENTREES

GRAIN DISHES (*See also* PASTAS AND BREADS)

PASTA DISHES

SALADS

SALAD DRESSINGS

BREADS

SPREADS

Index

Entries for recipes by categories are found on pages 323–333.

Acorn squash
  Festive Squash Soup, 68, 69–70
  Two-Squash Soup, 151, 153
After Dinner Treats, 204, 221
Almonds
  After Dinner Treats, 204, 221
  Cake, 257, 265–66
  Cranberry-Almond Balls, 300, 308
  Millet-Almond Pilaf, 4, 7
  Passover Almond Cake, 257, 266
Alternative Green Apple Tabouli, 121,
  124
Anchovies
  Fusilli with Anchovy and Red Pepper
    Sauce, 282, 284–85
  Roasted Pepper and Anchovy Spread,
    104, 109–10
Apple Cheese, 27, 33
Apple cider, Wassail spiced, 300, 304
Apple Pie Muffins, 316, 317–18
Apple(s)
  Apple Pie Muffins, 316, 317–18
  Autumn Vegetable Medley, 78, 87–88
  Baked, 300, 304–5
  Borrego Springs Cranberry Salsa, 78,
    84–85
  California Waldorf Salad, 85–86
  Cheese, 27, 33
  and Cheese, 291, 297
  Cucumber Raita, 204, 217
  Fancy Baked, 300, 305
  Garden Bread, 27, 32–33
  Green Apple Tabouli, 121, 123–24
  Orange Roughy with Tarragon and
    Green Apples, 142–43, 146–47
  Pork Tenderloin with Apple-Vegetable
    Mélange, 182, 184–85

Apple(s) (*continued*)
  Red Fruit Compote, 173, 180
  Salsa Succotash with Hearts of Palm,
    68, 70–71
  Turkey Medallions with Apple-
    Vegetable Mélange, 182, 186
Apricot(s)
  Glaze, 92, 96
  Golden Fruit Mélange, 257, 267
  Jeweled Apricot Chicken, 4, 6–7
  Marsala-Poached Pears with, 192, 199–
    200
  Papaya Salsa, 132, 137
  Salsa Succotash with Hearts of Palm,
    68, 70–71
Artichokes
  Garlicky Artichokes with Lemon-Herb
    Dipping Sauce, 121, 125
  Open-Face Artichoke Sandwich with
    Roasted Vegetable Spread, 257,
    260
  Penne with Mushrooms, Artichoke
    Hearts and Dried Tomatoes, 282,
    285–86
Asian fare, 189–201
  Indian, 201–21
  Pacific Rim, 121, 122–23, 159–70
  Southeast, 233–45
Asian Poached Salmon, 160, 166
Asian Poaching Broth, 234, 240–41
Asparagus
  Herbed, 104, 117
  with Orange-Sesame Marinade, 234,
    235
  Turkey with Penne and, 58, 63–64
Autumn Vegetable Medley, 78, 87–
  88

335